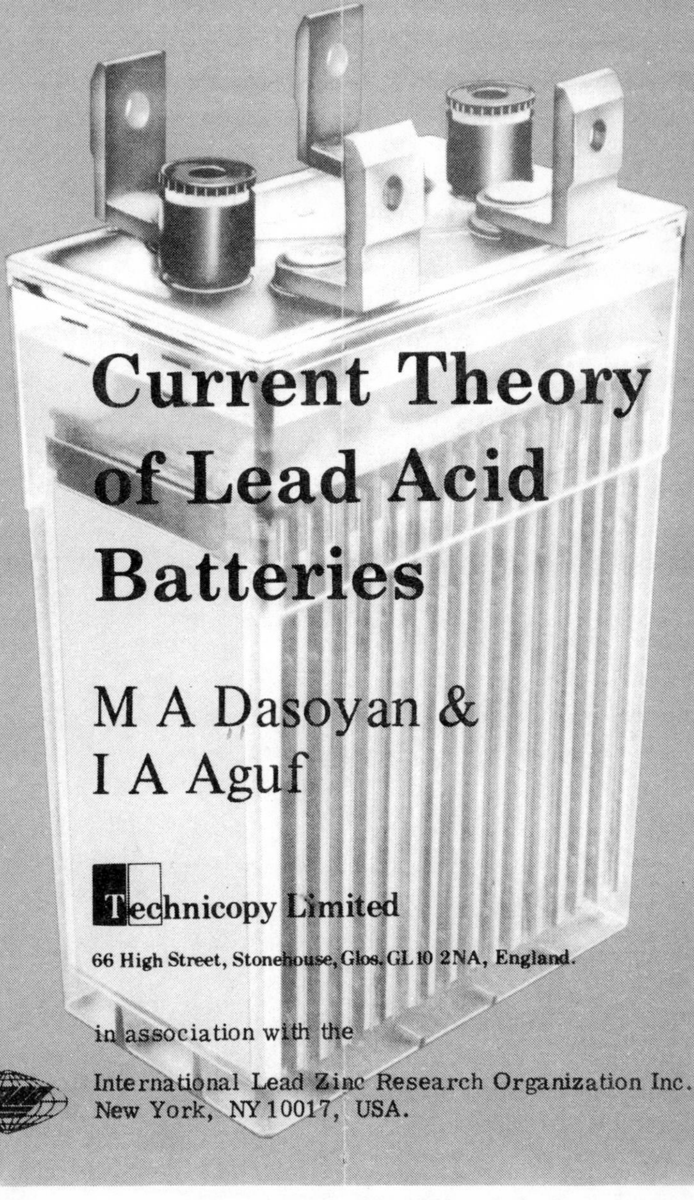

Current Theory of Lead Acid Batteries

M A Dasoyan &
I A Aguf

Technicopy Limited

66 High Street, Stonehouse, Glos. GL10 2NA, England.

in association with the

International Lead Zinc Research Organization Inc.,
New York, NY 10017, USA.

ISBN No. 0 905228 11 1

Printed and published by Technicopy Limited, Stonehouse, Glos.

Abstract

This book provides an up-to-date exposition of the thermodynamics of the operation of lead acid batteries and fundamental ideas about the phenomena of polarisation of the surface of the battery electrodes. A detailed examination is made of the processes occurring on the positive and negative electrodes, the alloy composition, design of grids and other factors influencing the operational characteristics of the battery.

The book is intended particularly for specialists working in the field of research, design and production of lead acid batteries. It will also be useful for students specialising in the field of chemical sources of current, as well as to electro-chemists, since it covers the basic thermodynamics and kinetics of the electro-chemical processes involved.

UDC 621.355.2

Acknowledgements:

The helpful co-operation and support of the International Lead Zinc Research Organisation in the publication of this book is gratefully acknowledged, as is the expertise shown by Mr L R Prout B.Sc., F.I.M., in checking the final text.

Editorial Note

In the text we have adhered to Russian symbols and mathematical usage as far as practicable. Thus, where the expression lg is used it represents $\log_{10}$ and ln is equivalent to $\log_e$.

Foreword

The lead acid battery has now been in existence for over 100 years. During this period its specific electrical characteristics and its service life have been improved by many times, and the field of its application has widened quite considerably. At the present day the lead acid battery, judging from production figures, is firmly established in first place ahead of all other kinds of chemical sources of current and it is continuing to develop at a rapid pace.

An improvement of the characteristics of current lead acid batteries can be achieved both by means of further improvement of their design and by means of using new constructional materials, and as a result of an increase in energy output also, inasmuch as the coeffficient of utilisation of battery electrodes barely reaches 50-60%, even with long-term discharge regimes and with short-term regimes it amounts altogether to 5-10%. An improvement of the electrical characteristics of the lead acid battery by means of electrochemically active materials requires examination in depth and further development of the theory of the lead acid battery.

The processes taking place on the electrodes of a lead acid battery are distinguished by considerable complexity. Therefore a number of questions of the theory of the lead acid battery remain insufficiently studied to this day. On many questions there is no consensus of opinion among researchers.

The results of research devoted to numerous aspects of the lead acid battery are widely discussed in current technical literature. However, in spite of the abundance of scientific publications on the lead acid battery, in the literature a monograph is lacking containing a critical analysis of the articles published and an examination of the perspectives of further development of this source of current. The only work of this kind is Dolecalek's book "The theory of the lead acid battery", which came out more than 70 years ago, has, of course, become very outdated and cannot to any extent be of use in the tasks set.

Wishing to fill the gap which has been pointed out in our country's technical literature the authors took upon themselves the labour of writing this book, in which there are set forth on the basis of current data the thermodynamic theory of the lead acid battery, fundamental ideas about the distribution of polarisation over the surface of battery electrodes, and also a detailed examination is made of the processes taking place on the positive and negative electrodes and of factors influencing the operational characteristics of the electrodes. In the exposition of the material the authors paid fundamental attention to the electrochemical aspect of the problems being examined.

A fundamental difficulty which the authors encountered in the writing of this book consisted of the abundance of published sources and in the complexity of selection of the most valuable works. Clearly understanding the impossibility of including even a tenth of all the publications devoted to the lead acid battery, the authors gave preference to works published during the last 15-20 years. Of pre-war works only the most fundamental research is reflected in this book. The results obtained in the work of the authors and their collaborators are set out with a fair degree of detail.

We should like to emphasise that the theory of the lead acid battery must not be considered as completed. What has been said refers also to the material of the monograph. So thus, the views set out by the authors on many questions cannot in any way be considered as something indisputable and final.

This book, which is clearly the first attempt at making generally available on the basis of current theoretical views a large amount of experimental material in the field of the lead acid battery, is of course not devoid of shortcomings. Therefore the authors would be quite grateful to all readers pointing out any deficiencies observed.

The authors express sincere acknowledgement to all collaborators whose work is reflected in the present book. The authors are also grateful to B B Brustina for the help given in the formulation of the bibliography.

Please send all requests and observations c/o Leningradskoye otdyeleniye izdatelstva "Energiya", Marsovo Pole, 1, 192401 Leningrad.

Contents

Chapter 4: The positive electrode of a lead acid battery 115

Chapter 1: Introduction

The basic stages of the origin and development of the lead acid battery

The work that paved the way for the finding of ways of storing electrical energy dates back to the initial period of development of electrochemistry. In 1800 Volta created the first chemical source of current (the Voltaic pile), opening wide possibilities for the study of electric current, and, in particular of its electrolytic action. The Voltaic pile must rightly be considered the ancestor not only of the Galvanic cells, but also of batteries. Subsequent work on the study of the properties of and on the use of the Voltaic pile led to the creation of the electric battery, capable of storing up and of giving out electrical energy without great losses.

In 1801 Gottereau established the phenomenon of secondary polarisation current between platinum or silver electrodes used for the decomposition of acidified water, and Ritter with the aid of this polarisation current resolved the water into its component parts. The first secondary cell constructed by Ritter was called a charge pile. This cell consisted of 50 copper discs separated from each other by cloth spacers, soaked in a solution of sodium chloride or sal ammoniac. On its own this element was not active, but after charging it acquired in a short time the ability to give out a powerful current. Besides copper, Ritter also investigated a number of other metals.

In 1826 in the anodic polarisation of a lead plate by the primary source of current, Nobile first observed the formation on it of lead dioxide. However, these experiments, which later gave brilliant results, at that time passed unnoticed.

Taking earlier work as a basis, Grove in 1824 constructed his well known gas cell, in which the secondary current was obtained by means of the reunification of hydrogen and oxygen obtained in the decomposition of acidified water. Grove's cell possessed all the properties of a battery, but it did not find any practical application as a result of its very low capacity and the necessity of using expensive platinum as electrodes. The efficiency of the gas storage battery was later considerably increased by the use of cellular electrodes of platinum and palladium.

The origin of the lead acid battery is linked with the name of the French scientist Gaston Planté (1834-1889). The objective originally being pursued in the scientist's research was the strengthening of the polarisation effect occurring in electrolysis to such values that it would be possible to use it for practical needs.

In 1850, even before Planté, Zinstedten showed that in the electrolysis of dilute sulphuric acid between two lead electrodes PbO_2 is formed on the positive electrode and spongy lead on the negative one and that after switching off the current a difference of potential equal to ~2 V is found on the electrodes. Zinstedten, however, did not draw any practical conclusions from these observations. The inference about the possibility of creating an electrochemical instrument capable of storing up electrical energy for subsequent use of it was made in 1859 by Planté. That year is considered the date of the invention of the lead acid battery.

Planté's first storage battery (fig. 1.1), presented by him to the French Academy of Sciences in 1860, was exceptional for that time in the size of the charge current and in this respect it surpassed all existing primary current source batteries[1]). Suffice it to say that the total active surface of the electrodes of this first lead acid battery amounted to $10m^2$. The storage units of Planté's first battery consisted of two lead plates placed one upon the other with a coarse cloth spacer. These plates were coiled in a spiral and to each of them was soldered a lead strip for current supply. The name of Planté is immortalised in the batteries with so-called surface plates, on which the active mass is formed electrochemically from the lead of the plate itself.

Fig. 1. 1. The first lead acid storage battery, presented by G Planté to the Paris Acadamy of Sciences.

The batteries constructed by Planté worked for a very short time, since the cloth separator was quickly destroyed in the acid and the plates short circuited. Later on Planté improved the design, using flat plates with rubber rings placed over them for insulation or coiling them in a spiral but with a rubber tape separator. To increase the capacity of the battery Planté subjected it to repeated charges and discharges, periodically changing the polarity of the electrodes during this. This process, called by him forming, lasted several months, and in some cases even up to two years.

This defect was eliminated by Planté's pupil Faure (1841-1898), who in 1880 took out a patent for the preparation of electrodes of a lead acid battery by means of the application to the lead plates of lead oxides in the form of a paste prepared with sulphuric acid. The first battery of this type was produced by Faure in 1882. It consisted of 35 cells with a capacity of 168Ah and a mass of ~43 kg each. The main disadvantages of Faure's battery were short separator life, with felt being used for this, and also weak connection of the active mass with the current-carrying base of the electrode.

Further development of the lead acid battery was based on the improving of the batteries of Planté and Faure. Improvement of Planté's battery occurred mainly in the direction of simplification of the methods of forming and of increasing the capacity by means of the extension of the active surface of the electrodes. The first of these tasks was solved by Lucas, who in 1896 proposed to carry out the forming of the plates not in sulphuric acid, but in solutions of chlorates and perchlorates, and achieved a shortening of the duration of the forming process from several months to several days. This forming process is used in the preparation of plates of the surface type to the present day.

For the solution of the second task - the possibility of further developing the electrode surface - a host of methods was proposed, the essence of which came to the use of laminations of thin plates, sometimes corrugated, or of whole plates with a ribbed surface. The latter was obtained by the method of stamping or rifling on special machines, or by casting the plates in special moulds.

The casting method is at the present time predominantly used in Europe. In Britain and in the USA they prefer the Manchester type of plates (first lead strips are extruded; these are cut and rolled mechanically and pressed or stamped into circular holes in a lead matrix to form a plate). The improvements enumerated made it possible to produce batteries of the Planté type with a specific energy of 15-20Wh/kg and resulted in the use of such batteries, possessing a long service life, not only in stationary installations, but also for the lighting of railway carriages, and for traction in electric vans and electric locomotives. In stationary installations the capacity of batteries of the Planté type attains 50-100 000 Ah.

Work on the improvement of Faure's battery pursued the aims on the one hand of improving the adhesion of the lead oxides to the base and on the other hand of improving as far as possible the quality of the active material.

The problem of keeping the active masses on the current-carrying bases was solved thanks to the use of bases of grid construction instead of solid lead plates. The first patent for a battery plate with grid base was taken out in 1881 by Volckmar (1847-1884). Later Sellon took out a patent for a battery in which the lead of the base of the plates was replaced by an alloy of lead and antimony, which considerably increased the mechanical strength of the electrodes. Examples of grids of those times are shown in fig. 1.2. Such grids have now not been used for a long time. However, some principles used in their construction were used in the production of contemporary current-carrying bases (fig. 1.3).

Improvement of the methods of preparation of the electrode materials went in parallel with the study of the battery itself. According to Faure's method, the paste was prepared by mixing minium with a sulphuric acid solution, which gave a mixture of lead oxide and lead sulphate. This original technique has basically been retained to the present day. From the time of Faure's invention an enormous quantity of patents have been issued for paste formulae and for the method of preparing them, but very few of them have found any practical application.

A British firm - The Electrical Storage Battery Company - on the basis of Faure, Volckmar and Sellon's patents, produced successful examples of lead acid batteries with paste filled plate, suitable for practical use. These batteries were extremely widely used and under the name of Faure-Sellon-Volckmar batteries were produced in various constructional forms.

The technical properties of batteries with pasted plates have been materially improved from the time of Faure, both in relation to specific electrical characteristics and to service life. Thus, if the better versions of batteries of those times had a specific energy equal to 7-8Wh/kg and lasted ~100 charge-discharge cycles for contemporary versions of batteries these values attain 35-40Wh/kg and 400-500 cycles, while for batteries with tubular (armoured) electrodes a service life equal to 1200-1800 cycles appears normal. The field of application of lead acid batteries has quite considerably widened.

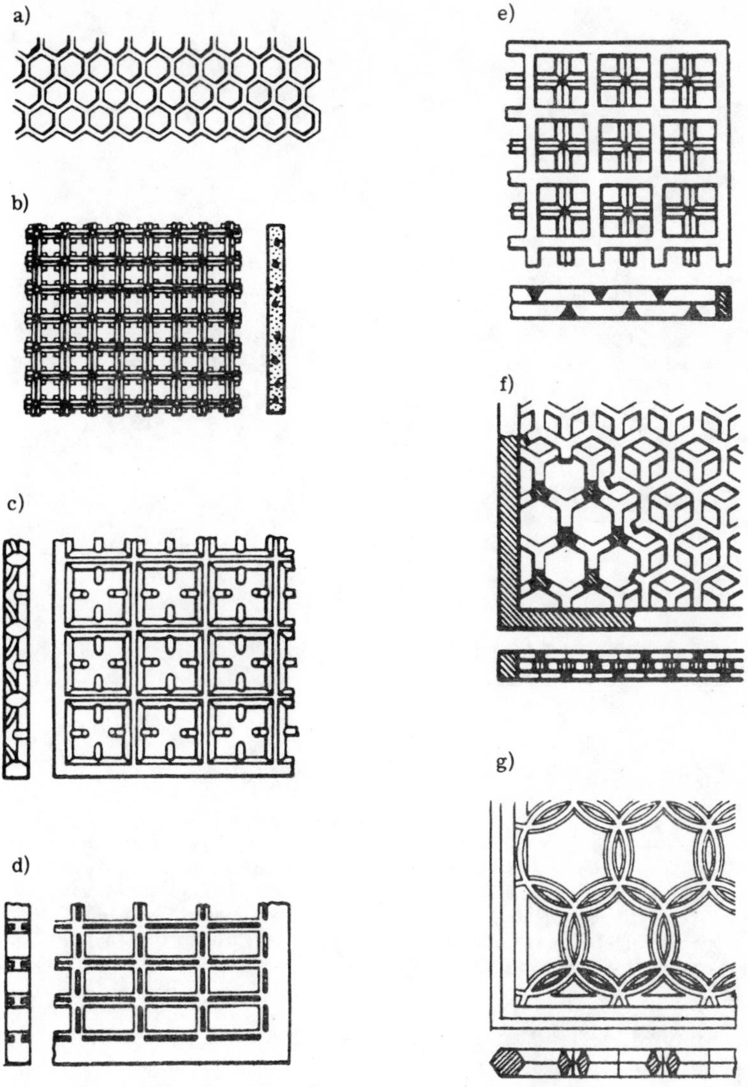

Fig. 1. 2 The construction of battery grids, created in the period from 1881-1892: a) Swan's grid (1881); b) Sellon's double grid (1889); c) King and Clarke's grid; d) Hailey's grid (1889); e) Corren's grid (1889) f) Beyer and Hagen's grid with double lattice (1889); g) Ferberka and Sheneko's grid (1886).

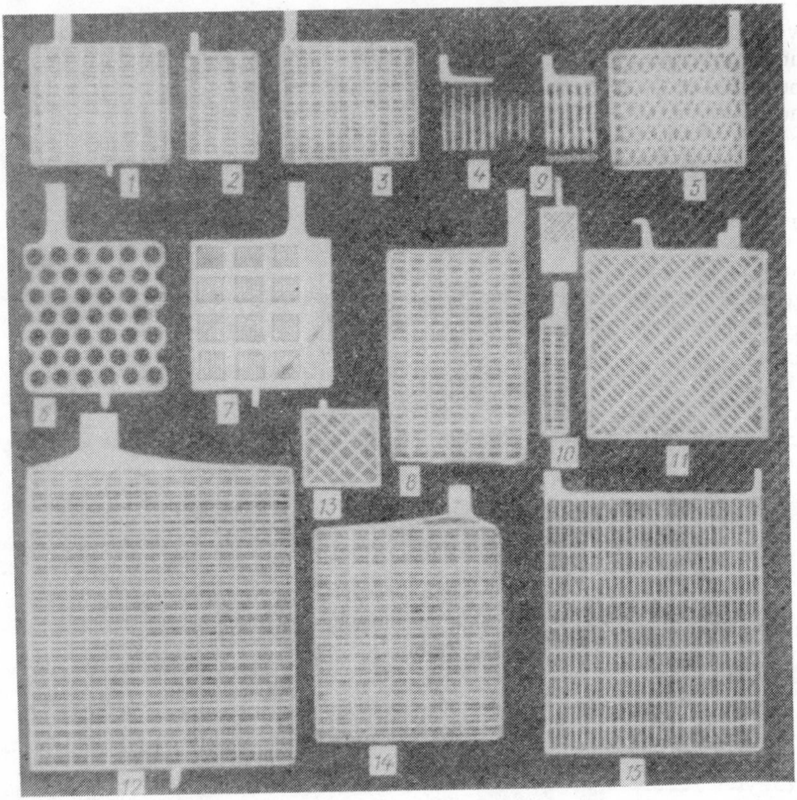

Fig. 1. 3 1, 2 and 5 grids for small batteries in glass tanks; 3 grid of a propulsion battery; 4 grid of an armoured plate, assembled and dismantled; 6 grid of a Manchester positive plate; 7 grid of a negative box plate; 8 grid of a propulsion battery; 9 and 10 grids of small experimental batteries; 11 and 13 reinforced grids for stationary batteries; 12 and 14 reinforced grids for stationary batteries of Taytex type; 15 lead calcium grid for stationary batteries.

If the birth of the lead acid battery, having its origins in Planté's pioneering experiments, is dated as 1859, the appearance of industrial production of batteries must be dated back only to the beginning of the 80's of the last century, since the whole period preceding this was only a period of constant laboratory attempts to find the optimum types of battery construction and ways of cheapening both the process of preparation of the battery itself and of charging it. Starting only from 1881, when this research work reached a successful conclusion and relatively cheap dynamos for battery charging appeared, did industrial production of lead acid batteries take place almost simultaneously in such countries as France, Britain, the USA and Russia, where, as will be shown below, the development of battery technology followed completely original lines without any borrowing from abroad.

Origin of the lead acid battery in Russia

With the appearance of the first reports about Volckmar's batteries already at the end of 1881 experiments began at the Mining Officers' School of the town of Kronstadt on the creation of a lead acid battery for using in the detonation of mines and for deck lighting. These experiments were begun under the direction of the well-known Russian electrical engineer I F Iordansky who, already in 1882, was taking an active part in the testing of the first form of battery afloat. After the death of I F Iordansky (1882) direction of the work on the creation and testing of lead acid batteries was taken over by his colleague, later also to become a well-known Russian electrical engineer E P Tveritinov [2]) under whose direction batteries of the MOK type were created, which not only were as good as the best types from foreign firms of that time in their electrical and utilisation characteristics, but even surpassed them.

It must be emphasised that the design and technology of manufacture of Volckmar's batteries were certainly never described, and nothing about them was known to E P Tveritinov, except the information that such batteries existed. Therefore in the MOK type and Volckmar's batteries it can be reckoned that only the employment of grids is a common feature[3]).

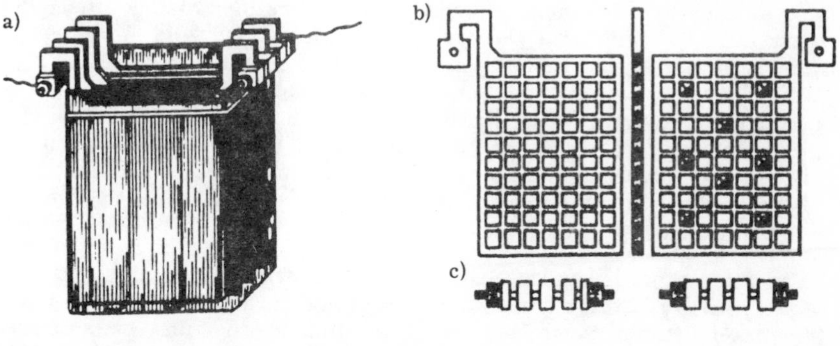

Fig. 1.4 MOK type battery of open type: a) general view; b) battery grids; c) rods for suspension of the plates.

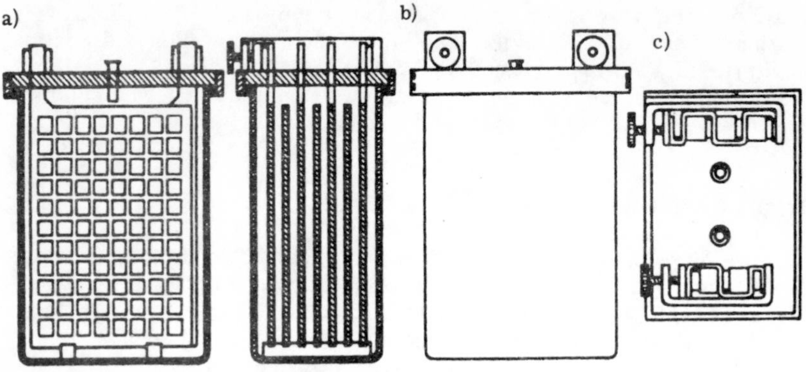

Fig. 1.5 MOK type battery of closed type: a) cross sections; b) side view; c) top view

MOK batteries were put into production for stationary (fig. 1.4) and mobile (fig. 1.5) installations. The first of these batteries consisted of three positive and four negative plates, uniform in their construction. The grids for these plates with 70 straight-through openings were cast from lead in copper moulds. The horizontal bars and vertical ribs of the grids had a uniform hexahedral section. The smearing of the plates with a paste of litharge or minium was carried out on two sides. The plates were first wrapped in calico and subjected to a high pressure, then they were set and kept in an acid solution with a density of 1.035. The forming of the negative plates was carried out separately together with the uncharged electrodes and lasted 70-80 hours. Three formed plates were assembled with four unformed ones in glass tanks. For the fixation of the plates of opposite signs at the determined distance from each other the paste was removed from some of the cells in the unformed plates, and rubber plugs were then inserted into these cells. The assembled batteries were subjected to a supplementary 80 hour forming, in the process of which the lead of the three middle plates turned into lead dioxide and the paste of the four other plates was reduced to spongy lead. In order to prevent splashing of the acid solution the surface of the electrolyte was covered with a 5-6 mm layer of liquid paraffin.

The facts quoted about the batteries of the MOK system show the originality of their design and technology of manufacture. In the construction of these batteries, the following are, for example, clearly original - the form of the lugs of the plates and the manner of suspension of them, the size of the cells, the covering of the electrolyte with paraffin etc. Particularly important innovations were made in the process of manufacturing of MOK batteries. These refer to: litharge paste of the consistency of grout, thick smearing of it on to the grids from two sides, high pressure on the plates, setting of the plates unlimited in time after the pressing, forming on the negative with the low density current of positive plates with uncharged electrodes, assembly of the elements with unformed negative plates and forming of the latter simultaneously with the positive plates and the first charging of the battery directly in the battery tank, etc.

Batteries of MOK type, besides the uses mentioned above, were also used igniting mine fuses, in diving lights, for an electric motor for a boat, in signalling balloons etc. The testing of the first electrically propelled boat in the world, powered by MOK batteries, was carried out in 1884 under the direction of E P Tveritinov. This electric boat developed a speed of 4.56 knots. The capacity of the batteries ensured a cruising speed range of more than 30 miles. In the opinion of E P Tveritinov, the superiority of electric propulsion consisted in the safety from explosion, cleanness of the installation, absence of smoke and sparks, complete absence of noise etc.

In the same year MOK batteries were used to feed the lamps of a signalling apparatus which rose to a height of 90-100 m by means of a balloon of capacity 17.5 m^3, and the light from its lamps could be seen at a great distance.

Scientists of the Mining Officers' School - the cradle of Russian battery technology - besides the purely applied work also carried out important theoretical research aimed at elucidating the nature of the electrode processes occurring in a lead acid battery. Among this work there stands out the research into measurement of the temperature of formation of lead dioxide carried out by M N Beklemeshev and V A Kanin, under the direction of I M Cheltsov. The results obtained by them made it possible to calculate the temperature of the reaction taking place in the battery while it is working, and in this way to calculate the electromotive force of the battery. The research of G Tsivinsky into the measurement of the electromotive force and of the internal resistance of Planté's battery also had an important significance for the theory of the lead acid battery, as did that of P Levitsky into the determination of the performance coefficient of the lead acid batteries and the dependence of capacity on discharge current, and that of A G Lozinsky on the verification of the role of sulphuric acid in the overall current-forming reaction of the lead acid battery etc.

Concluding the review of the work on batteries carried out at the Mining Officers' School, the remarkable work of E P Tveritinov "Electric Batteries" [3]), which played an important role in the training of cadres in work on batteries for a number of generations cannot be omitted. Tveritinov's book contained an explanation of the theory and properties of lead acid batteries, and practical information about their manufacture and use. It was indeed the first Russian original work in the field of electric batteries, many of the basic assumptions of which retain their value even in our own day. The appearance of this book brought a very complimentary mention from the author of the world famous physics course O D Khvolson. The monograph of V N Chikolev[4]) also must also be included among the first important publications on the lead acid battery.

The material described here shows convincingly that the beginning of Russian battery construction must be reckoned as 1881, i. e. battery production started in Russia at the same time as its appearance in the West. The honour of creating an original battery technology in Russia belongs to the workers of the Naval Department. A study of historic documents also convinces us of the fact that the laboratories of the Mining Officers' School at Kronstadt were the first scientific research centre in the field of battery technology in Russia, and two of its scientists - I M Cheltsov and E P Tveritinov - by their classic work on the theory and production of batteries, have earned a permanent place in the history of our native electrical engineers.

The development of the production of lead acid batteries in the USSR

Industrial production of batteries of the MOK type was carried out by the Naval Department in the town of Kronstadt. This independently designed type of battery was for a long time installed in ships of the navy. About the same time the inventor of the electric lamp P N Yablochkov organised small-scale production of such batteries at Nizhny Novgorod (now the town of Gorki), supplied the Volga steamers with batteries. In St. Petersburg itself, lead acid batteries were produced at the Gernet factory, and later at the Baltic shipyard.

In this period the production of batteries took place on a very small scale and only in 1897 when the German battery firm of Tudor bought the Gernet factory and expanded its production did it begin to take on industrial significance. In later years (1911-1912) two more battery factories were opened at St. Petersburg - the French Thème and the Russian Rex, but these young and not yet established factories had little importance in the battery market, which continued for the most part to use the Tudor factory[5]).

The pre-revolutionary battery industry in Russia, for the most part finding itself dependent on foreign capital, developed very little. In the factories listed manual labour universally prevailed; the foundation-laying work of the Mining Officers' School was practically forgotten. The factory owners, understanding the instability of social conditions in pre-revolutionary Russia, did not think of developing work on the battery and satisfied themselves with only exploiting the already existing means of production technology.

After the Great October Socialist Revolution the battery factories were nationalised. The creation of a battery industry, in truth began again, and a scientific centre was organised for it at the end of 1924 in Leningrad - the Central Battery Laboratory (Centralnaya Akkumulatornaya Laboratoriya - CAL), which in 1946 was reorganised into the Scientific Research Institute for Batteries (Nauchno-Issledovatelsky Akkumulatorny Institut - NIAI). The CAL and NIAI, the head of which for a period of more than 20 years was V F Federov, played an exclusive role in the establishment and development of a native battery industry.

The existence of a number of brilliant reviews[6-8]) of the activity of the CAL and NIAI frees us from the necessity of a detailed exposition of all the fields of activity of these scientific centres, and we shall limit ourselves only to a short mention of a few items of work on the theory and production of lead acid batteries carried out in these institutions in pre-war and post-war years.

The work on lead acid batteries in the subjects studied by the CAL began to take a dominating place from 1932 onwards. The first work of the period under consideration was the search for home sources of battery raw materials and a refusal to import lead and antimony. Technological processes were worked out to obtain battery minium, litharge and lead powder. At the existing and newly founded battery factories new recipes were used for litharge-minium and powder pastes. This and other technological work to a considerable extent eliminated the gap then existing between home and foreign technique of production of lead acid batteries and paved the way for further massive development of work on the battery at the country's factories. The carrying out of this work is linked with the names of S A Rosenweg, N A Kirmalova, E I Krepakova, A P Semenov, N G Kuznetsova and S I Galperin, working under the direction of B A Kosobryukhov.

New types of batteries were created (short-discharge batteries for the needs of the Navy, powerful lead acid batteries for submarines, armoured batteries for electrically driven trucks, radio anode and radio filament batteries, starter batteries for cars, etc.). In the creation of new products a great contribution was made by G V Bolkunov, A N Mokeyev, A K Lorenz and others; the person in charge of this work was G O Okun.

The necessity for further improvement of native lead acid batteries and for improving their efficiency in the complicated conditions of utilisation resulted in the initiation of a wide range of theoretical work on the lead acid battery, which was carried out at the CAL with the co-operation of a number of academic institutions of our country, including the Institute of Physical Chemistry of the Academy of Sciences of the USSR. Here, mention must be made of the brilliant research of A K Lorenz and B N Kabanov on the thermodynamics of the lead acid battery and many other related problems, and of the work of V S Lyzlov on methods of calculation of the battery characteristics, and of V P Mashovets on battery alloys etc.

Already at the beginning of 1940 the Soviet battery industry formed itself into an independent branch of production, combining a number of factories and having at its disposal a large detachment of qualified cadres and its own scientific research organization. In the years of the Great Patriotic War (1941-1945) these cadres successfully dealt with the organisation of production in factories evacuated to the eastern regions of the country.

In the post-war period a great deal of work was carried out on the establishment and reconstruction of battery factories and conversion of the industry to the production of articles of civilian use. This work lead to a considerable increase in the production of lead acid batteries (in comparison with 1940): 258% (starter type), 772% (motorcycle type), 488% (electric truck type).

If in the development of the production of lead acid batteries (1946-1950) may be called the period of liquidation of the consequences of the war, the following years (1951-1955) must be regarded as the period of technical reconstruction of lead acid battery factories. The latter were equipped with plant mechanising the basic, heaviest and harmful processes of production, for example, by automatic foundry plant, chipping presses for removal of excess material from grids, paste-coating machines etc.

An extraordinarily important stage of development of the Soviet battery industry was the working out of a plan of complex mechanisation and automation of the production of lead acid batteries (1956), undertaken on the initiative of and under the direction of V G Prelkov and I I Koval. The idea put forward in this plan consisted in the combination of machines and mechanisms that were separate from each other in the production and processing of parts and plates into one mechanised production line which included all the operations of production, beginning from the preparation of the lead powder and ending with the assembly of the batteries. Such lines were laid down at almost all factories of this branch of industry. To-day they include automatic mills for obtaining lead powder, automatic foundry plant for casting grids and small parts, machines for coating the plates and conveyors for drying and forming of the plates. The question of mechanisation of the assembly of cells and batteries is solved.

The execution of the above-mentioned plan made it possible already in 1960 to increase the production of batteries in our country 1. 8 times in comparison with the 1955 production and to increase the productivity of labour in the whole industry by over 45%.

The production of starter batteries in the last 30 years has increased in relation to 1940: 2.54 times by 1950, 6.9 times by 1955, 11 times by 1960, 14.8 times by 1965 and 45 times by 1970. This increase was to a considerable extent ensured by the execution of the plan of complex mechanisation and automation of the production of batteries and of a scientific organisation of labour in factories of this branch of industry.

Considerable interest in the work of the institutes and factories is being devoted to the problem of increasing the quality of home produced lead acid batteries, and particularly to the problem of further increasing the specific characteristics and service life. At the present time the task of bring the specific energy of the batteries up to 35-38 Wh/kg and the service life to 400-500 cycles is being set. For this such measures as more widespread use of arsenic alloys and a going over to thin plates are contemplated, a change-over to the linking of the elements through partitions of the monobloc, the use of polypropylene monoblocs, the use of fluorinated plastics and polyvinyl chloride fibre for eliminating the swelling of the active mass of the positive electrode, the introduction of more effective expanders, separators, etc.

Thus the production of lead acid batteries in our country during the years of Soviet government has turned into a highly organised branch of industry with its own scientific research institutions and experienced cadres, within whose power are new, more complex tasks of further technical development.

An important part in the improvement of the characteristics of lead acid batteries was played by the work of Ya. I Kasparov, P B Zhivotinsky, V A Orakht, L D Pustovoyt, I A Selitsky, G M Basotov, E A Alekseyev, D A Kozlov etc. A considerable contribution to the theory of the lead acid battery was made by Soviet scientists: B N Kabanov,

N A Balashova, D I Leykis, L I Antropov, M F Skalozubov, A I Levin, V P Mashovets etc[9]). Mention should also be made of foreign scientists of the pre-war period (Harned, Hamer, Weinel, Dolecalek etc) and of the post-war period (Lander, Burbank, Ruetschi, Bode, Pavlov, Icari, Yeshizawa, Wynne-Jones, etc) whose work has importance in principle in the establishment of the current theory of the lead acid battery.

At the present time the quality of home series-built batteries according to some parameters does not correspond to the level achieved in the world. This is emphasised by comparative data concerning the main characteristics of batteries in series production and the best foreign batteries (table 1.1)

Table 1.1: Main characteristics of starter batteries

Index of comparison	Batteries in series Production	Batteries of other types
Nominal capacity guaranteed	for 10 cycles	
Duration of discharge at 30°C min	5 (for 6 cycles)	7 (for 4 cycles)
Duration of discharge at -18°C min	3 (for 8 cycles)	4 (for 4 cycles)
Voltage of 12V battery at start V	8.8	9.4
Speed of bringing into operation of dry-charged battery	with 5-hour boosting charge	without boosting charge
Capacity for 1 cycle in percentage of nominal	80 80	90
PbO_2 content in (+) electrode %	75	92
Spongy lead content in (-) electrode %	85	95

The basic reason for the lower efficiency of the batteries produced in series in the initial cycles consists in the decreased content of active masses in the electrodes. The specific characteristics and service life of home and foreign batteries are close in practice. Our starter batteries have thinner plates, which is necessitated by the more complex conditions of their utilisation. This somewhat lowers their specific characteristics, but on the other hand considerably increases the service life of the batteries. Insofar as specific characteristics and service life are mutually connected values, it would be more correct to compare home and foreign batteries according to output of energy throughout the service life. The results of comparative tests on domestically produced batteries and those of foreign manufacture irrefutably testify in favour of the former. Together with this and independently of these results a further increase of the specific energy of our batteries must be considered the most important task, since this opens real possibilities of savings in scarce metals and manpower, the insufficiency of which becomes each year more and more noticeable.

For the carrying out of this task it is necessary to give up the obsolete monoblocs, which lower the characteristics 20-25% and shorten the service life of the batteries through insufficient resistance to frost and heat. In the selection of materials for the tanks and monoblocs preference should be given to polythene, polypropylene and other current polymers. For the organisation of production of current stationary batteries the production of moulded glass tanks must be set in motion.

It is essential to carry out work on the creation of new, more economical types of separators for the different types of lead acid batteries. New types of separators are being produced abroad (composed of powdered mica and glass, eumicron etc.) which have better characteristics than micaplast and similar materials. There are interesting solutions being worked out in our country too (powdered PVC, asbestos board etc.). However, at the present time our industry uses, basically, only micaplast which does not satisfy the new increased requirements. It is vitally important in the very near future to replace micaplast by new, more modern separators.

The use of grids made of new, lighter, mechanically robust and chemically stable materials promises considerable advantage. The special working conditions of the positive electrode strongly limit the chances of using new materials. Thus, for example, it has been shown that lead-plated duralumin, copper, stainless steel and many other metals are not suitable for the current-carrying bases of this electrode. At the same time it is possible to use grids made of titanium covered with lead dioxide, or perforated vinyl plastic reinforced with lead alloy for the positive plates.

It is far simpler to make a selection of materials for the current-carrying bases of the negative electrode. For this electrode, current-carrying bases made of lead-plated aluminium, copper, titanium are suitable, as well as reinforced vinyl plastic. The use of such electrodes makes it possible to increase markedly the specific energy of the plates without significantly raising their cost.

The suggested combinations of lighter, mechanically robust and corrosion-resistant grids need first to be produced in batteries intended for the electric car. As the calculations show, this makes it possible to increase substantially the specific energy and to create a lead variant of the battery for an electric car with an energy equal, approximately, to 70Wh/kg.

Greater reserves for the improvement of the quality of the battery are to be found in the active masses of the electrodes themselves. As has already been said, the utilisation coefficient of the active masses of lead acid batteries at the present time is very low; under the starter discharge regime it constitutes 10% for positive temperatures, and at negative temperatures it falls to 4%. With lengthy regimes only half of the active masses is used.

The low coefficient of utilisation is due, in particular, to the poor role of the deep-down strata of the active masses in the current forming process, particularly at low temperature. The elimination of the defect mentioned by means of the creation of highly porous electrodes of the skeletal type, containing different fibrous materials of organic and inorganic origin, can make it possible to increase noticeably the coefficient of utilisation of the active masses and on that basis to increase the specific energy of the batteries.

Along with the solution of tasks of purely electrochemical character, we are confronted with the task of carrying out a number of substantial measures for the improvement of the construction of batteries. What we have in mind is the creation of batteries with a common cover and with centralised filling of the electrolyte and with gas vent; the realisation of a method of linking the elements through the monobloc bulkheads etc. We need to solve the question of the design and realisation of new batteries with armoured plates, the service life of which reaches 1200-1800 cycles. Finally, the necessity has become imminent for creating fully mechanised production units for the manufacture of the mass-produced types of batteries, and for this the existing technological processes of the present day must first of all be improved and unified.

In connection with the fact that a frequent reason for complaints and for short service life of the batteries is the breaking of the rules for utilisation, we need to strengthen the interest in questions of the utilisation of batteries shown by the user. Thus, in order to achieve a new higher level in the development of the lead acid battery it is necessary to study a wide range of questions, which concerns the improvement of literally all components of the battery, and also methods of their production and utilisation.

The significance of the lead acid battery in current technology

At the present time industry is producing batteries of different electrochemical systems. In general use they are known under the name of lead acid, nickel-cadmium (Ni-Cd), iron-nickel (Fe-Ni), silver-zinc (Ag-Zn), silver-cadmium (Ag-Cd), and nickel-zinc (Ni-Zn) types. Batteries of some of the systems enumerated in their turn are divided into different types depending on their construction. For example, a differentiation is made between lead acid batteries with Planté's plates, with pasted plates and with tubular (armoured) electrodes. Batteries with pasted plates are made in the normal or in the hermetically sealed version. There are also quite a few differences among batteries of other systems.

The most important parameters for comparing batteries of different systems and construction are: specific energy, calculated per unit of mass or capacity; service life, defined by the number of cycles or the utilisation time; shelf life (with electrolyte and without electrolyte); rapidity of self-discharge; range of working temperatures; complexity of maintenance and utilisation; cost and several other characteristics.

It must be mentioned that not one of the known batteries satisfies all the above-mentioned parameters equally. Thus Ag-Zn and Ag-Cd batteries, possessing the highest specific discharge characteristics, are at the same time also the most expensive. Besides, these batteries need complicated maintenance. Lead acid batteries give way to Ag-Zn and Ag-Cd batteries in specific energy, but they have the cheapest cost and, thanks to this, find an incomparably wider application.

The actual conditions of utilisation of the batteries are obviously vitally important. For example for stationary conditions of service, where characteristics of capacity and weight are not very important, it is predominantly the cheapest and most readily available lead acid batteries that admit of no doubt as to their use, but in those conditions of utilisation where specific characteristics have decisive importance preference must be given of Ag-Zn and Ag-Cd batteries in spite of their expense. In other words, in the selection of a battery it is necessary to give very careful consideration to the concrete conditions in which it will be working, since there does not exist, indeed there cannot possibly be any universal source of current, uniformly suitable for all instances of use.

Up to the present time a definite practice of selection of the type of battery has been traditionally established. This practice takes account of both the application requirements and the battery characteristics. Lead acid batteries are traditionally used in many fields of technology. These sources of current supply radio, telephone and telegraph, they are used for car lighting and for that of railway carriages, as auxiliary batteries at electric power stations and sub-stations, and also in installations for lighting of public buildings and dwelling houses with emergency light. Lead acid batteries are exclusively used for ignition of internal combustion engines in cars, tractors and other motor vehicles; they areused for propulsion in electric trucks, electric loading installations etc. Hermetically sealed low-capacity lead acid batteries, along with Ni-Cd batteries, have found wide use in recent years in domestic electrical engineering and in portable equipment.

In this far from complete list, there are fields where the selection of the lead acid battery is perfectly indisputable, as it is in the aggregate of its qualities and especially on cost the best of all the batteries.

There are, however, fields of application where the supremacy of lead acid batteries is not so obvious and must be analysed more closely. To these fields belong mine and field transport, where sufficiently widespread use is made of both lead acid and Fe-Ni batteries[10]), and also the field of domestic electrical engineering, where along with lead acid batteries Ni-Cd ones are widely used.

Propulsion batteries of lead acid and Fe-Ni type have approximately uniform specific weight characteristics (~30Wh/kg), but in a more important parameter - specific capacity energy - the lead acid battery is preferable, as it possesses a specific energy of ~85Wh/kg and the Fe-Ni battery ~70Wh/kg.

The service life of the Fe-Ni battery with tubular electrodes made by the firm of Saft is ~3000 cycles. The lead acid battery with armoured electrodes possesses a service life of 1200-1800 cycles (with an average of 1500 cycles). However, taking into account the fact that according to many reliable data the cost of the Fe-Ni battery exceeds the cost of lead acid batteries 3-4 times, it can be stated that in service life also the superiority is on the side of lead acid batteries, as the user for the same sum can purchase instead of one alkaline battery 3-4 lead acid batteries, i. e. instead of 3000 cycles obtain 4500-6000 cycles.

For the charging of lead acid batteries noticeably less finance is expended than for the charging of alkaline batteries, as can be seen from table 1.2. In order to obtain 1kWh of energy one must expend in the discharge of lead acid batteries 1.5kWh, and for alkaline ones 2.1kWh, i.e. 40% more. If in addition to this we take into account the fact that the coefficient of performance of discharge does not exceed 0.8 the difference becomes even greater (table 1.2). This circumstance is, obviously, the main reason giving rise to a wider spread of lead acid batteries for propulsion abroad than of alkaline ones.

Table 1.2: Comparison of the efficiency of the discharge process of lead acid and alkaline propulsion batteries

Type of Battery	Discharge		Charge		Coefficient of Performance
	Voltage V	Capacity %	Voltage V	Capacity %	
Lead acid	1.9	100	2.35	120	0.67
Alkaline	1.2	100	1.7	150	0.47

For propulsion batteries the volt-ampere characteristics have vital significance. The less the voltage drop at starting load, the less the reduction of the energy of the battery at the moment of starting and the faster the acceleration of the machine takes place, which, in its turn, makes its work more efficient. As a comparison of the volt-ampere characteristics shows, the superiority is to be found on the side of the lead acid batteries, which is explained by their lower (2-3 times) internal resistance per unit of energy. For this same reason the voltage drop during the duration of discharge in lead acid batteries is only half that in alkaline ones. The utilisation defects of alkaline batteries in the given instance consist in the fact that the excess voltage at the beginning of work is too high for optimum utilisation of the electromotor and is uselessly dissipated in starting resistances, while the lack of voltage at the end of the discharge lowers the efficiency of the work of the electromotor.

The temperature range of the work of lead acid and alkaline propulsion batteries is: from -30 to +45°C. The utilisation of batteries of both systems at higher temperatures leads to a shortening of their service life, and a lowering of the temperature to a reduction of discharge capacity, with low temperatures showing a particularly strong influence on the performance of Fe-Ni batteries. Lead acid batteries heat up in the discharge process less quickly than alkaline ones, which makes them preferable for use in a hot climate. The charging of lead acid batteries, in contrast to alkaline ones, is accompanied by a sharp rise in voltage, temperature and rate of gassing. A noticeable change in the lead acid battery is also produced by the density of the electrolyte. Therefore any of the parameters mentioned may be used for determination of the end of the charging of lead acid batteries, and, as is already beginning to happen, for automation of the process of charging them.

An important point of superiority of lead acid propulsion batteries over alkaline ones also resides in the possibility of charging them with high currents without excessive overheating or ejection of the electrolyte.

Departures from the charging regimes and discharging ones affect the condition of lead acid and alkaline batteries differently. Undercharging of lead acid batteries leads to sulphation of the plates and overcharging can have a harmful effect on the service life as a result of the speeding up of the corrosion of the grids of the positive electrode. Only systematic underchargings show any harmful influence on Fe-Ni batteries.

Maintenance of propulsion batteries, basically, boils down to topping up the electrolyte. The expenditure of time on this operation in lead acid batteries, thanks to their higher coefficient of performance in respect of capacity and the smaller number of elements in the battery, is several times less than for alkaline ones, however, the electrolyte of alkaline batteries is less corrosive to surrounding materials.

Fe-Ni batteries can be kept for a long time both in the charged and in the discharge state, with electrolyte and without it. In this respect they have some superiority over lead acid ones; which can only be kept without maintenance in the unfilled state, and with the electrolyte, only in the charged state. In the latter case it is necessary to charge it periodically to prevent irreversible sulphation of the battery. The average daily rate of spontaneous reduction of the battery capacity in the process of keeping for a month reaches 3% in Fe-Ni batteries, while in this time it constitutes ~1% in lead acid batteries. Thus in rate of self-discharge during keeping the lead acid batteries have a clear superiority over alkaline Fe-Ni batteries.

The comparison that we have made of the electrical and operational characteristics of propulsion batteries of alkaline and lead acid types makes it possible to draw the conclusion that lead acid batteries are better suited for electric propulsion motors than alkaline ones are. The indisputability of the superior qualities of lead acid propulsion batteries over alkaline ones has been shown in their work [11]. Trying to explain why, in spite of the obviousness of the qualities of the lead acid variant, the propulsion battery production in the USSR is developing along the line of alkaline batteries, the authors [11] refer to the limited amount of lead resources allocated for battery production. However, this motivation seems to us groundless, for the shortage of lead felt at the present time in the battery industry can to a considerable extent be eliminated as a result of the carrying out of work on the further improvement of lead acid batteries and with the appropriate organisation for the return of battery scrap.

Calculations show, for example, that an increase in the main characteristics of starter batteries to the level of the better foreign batteries and the realisation in them of a method of linking the elements through the bulkheads of the monobloc would make it possible to reduce considerably the amount of lead used and to save about 50 000 tons of the metal annually. It would be possible to save approximately the same amount of lead annually if there were organised in practice a complete return of battery scrap. At the present time the latter is used to an insufficient extent. In the USA the re-using of lead raw material reaches 92% [11].

The necessity of periodic topping up with water and greater gassing at the end of the charging of a lead acid battery until recently made this source of current unsuitable for a large number of today's users. However, at the present time, thanks to the use of lead-calcium alloys, a gel type electrolyte and a special charging regime, these defects have been successfully overcome and many foreign firms (USA, German Federal Republic, Japan) are producing a wide variety of hermetically sealed Ni-Cd batteries, which in the last 20 years have won themselves immense popularity throughout the world.

The widespread use of lead acid hermetically sealed batteries abroad in a very short space of time (5-8 years) was due to their considerably lower cost (in comparison with Ni-Cd batteries), lower rate of self-discharge, better rechargeability, more gradual discharge characteristics and higher specific power.

A particular superiority of hermetically sealed lead acid batteries is the comparatively low dependence of their capacity on temperature. The electrolyte, having a gel type structure, endows the battery with frost resistance, and the latter does not lose efficiency even when the electrolyte freeezes. In specific weight and capacity characteristics, small-sized lead acid batteries have a noticeable superiority in comparison with Ni-Cd batteries composed of prismatic storage units. If we add to what has been said the fact that hermetically sealed lead acid batteries, having a service life of 200 cycles, are 3.5 - 4 times as cheap as the comparable Ni-Cd batteries, the tendency observed abroad to replace Ni-Cd batteries in domestic technology by lead acid batteries becomes understandable.

The material set forth in this chapter shows convincingly enough that the lead acid battery has quite an important significance for current technology and is indeed the most widely used chemical source of energy. In spite of the fact that current lead acid batteries are far from perfect, they form the basis of battery production throughout the world. From a large volume of evidence in literature we shall here refer to the well known monograph of Falk and Salkind[12]), in which current data are given about the production of different batteries in the USA, Canada and Western Europe.

According to the data[12]) the annual production of all types of chemical sources of current in the USA in 1967 amounted to (expressed in monetary terms) a billion dollars. The share falling to storage batteries of all systems amount to $700 mn. (or 70%), and the share of primary batteries the remaining $300 mn. (30%). The data on the production of storage batteries of the different systems is of particular interest: lead acid batteries $644 mn. (92%), alkaline batteries of all systems $56 mn. (8%). Of these $56 mn., the figure for production of Ni-Cd batteries was reckoned at $38 mn., $6 mn. for Ni-Fe, $8 mn. for Ag-Zn, and $1 mn. for Ag-Cd. According to the same source, a similar picture is presented by the structure of production on the Canadian market which amounts to approximately 10% of the volume of production of the USA, and also on the European market, which we can roughly compare with the volume of production of the USA.

The low cost of the lead acid battery fills specialists throughout the world with unflagging interest in continuing efforts directed towards further improvement of this source of current.

Chapter 2: Thermodynamic theory of the lead acid battery

Equilibrium in the Pb-H_2SO_4-H_2O system

For an explanation of the nature of the processes taking place on the electrodes of a lead acid battery, and also those taking place in the technological cycle of production of the batteries, considerable interest is presented by a thermodynamic examination of the reactions possible in the system lead-aqueous sulphuric acid solution[1]).

Using the classification of electrochemical processes accepted in the work of Pourbaix and his colaborators[2]), it is possible to divide all the reactions capable of occurring in the given system into reactions connected with the oxidation or reduction of lead, and the oxidation-reduction processes accompanied by the transfer of electrons across the interphase boundaries of the interface. Reactions of the first type are sufficiently fully characterised from the thermodynamic point of view by the standard values of the corresponding increments of Gibbs free energy (ΔG^o cal), linked with the constants of equilibrium of the reactions (K) at a temperature of 25°C by the equation

$$\lg K = -\Delta G^o/2.303\,RT = -\Delta G^o/1364 \qquad (2.1)$$

where R is the universal gas constant, and T the absolute temperature.

Reactions of the second type can be principally characterised by the magnitude of the equilibrium potential, the standard value of which (φ^0V) is also determined by the magnitude of ΔG^o in accordance with the equation

$$\varphi^0 = -\Delta G^o/zF = -\Delta G^o/23060z \qquad (2.2)$$

Here F is the Faraday number, and z the number of electrons taking part in the given oxidation-reduction reaction.

Lead belongs to the group of p-elements with four valency electrons. In its compounds it is in the overwhelming majority of cases characterised by a valency of +2 or +4. The number of lead compounds, the appearance of which is possible in the system under consideration, is quite large. The thermodynamic characteristics of many of these compounds are known with insufficient accuracy, and for a number of compounds they are not described at all in literature. All this often hinders the carrying out of thermodynamic calculations according to the equations quoted above (2.1) and (2.2).

Table 2.1: Thermodynamic characteristics of compounds in the Pb-H_2SO_4-H_2O system

Compound	ΔG^o kcal/mol	ΔH^o kcal/mol	S^o cal (mol-degree)	Refs
Pb (cryst.)	0.0	0.0	15.51	[3]
Pb^{2+} (aq)	-5.73	0.3	4.587	[4]
Pb^{4+} (aq)	-72.3	-	-	[3]
PbO red	-45.25	-52.40	16.2	[3]
PbO yellow	-45.05	52.07	16.6	[3]
$HPbO_2^-$ (aq)	-81.0	-	-	[3]
$Pb(OH)_2$	-100.6	-123.0	21	[3]
α-PbO_2	-51.94	-63. 2	-	[5]
β-PbO_2	-52.34	-66.12	18.3	[5]
Pb_3O_4	-147.6	-175.6	50.5	[3]
$PbSO_4$	-193.89	-219.50	35.2	[3]
$PbSO_4 \cdot PbO$	-243.20	-	-	[6]
$3PbO \cdot PbSO_4 \cdot H_2O$	-397.30	-	-	[6]
$5PbO \cdot 2H_2O$	-336.35	-	-	[6]
Pb_2O_3	-98.42	-	-	[3]
SO_4^{2-} (aq)	-177.34	-216.90	4.1	[3]
HSO_4^- (aq)	-179.94	-211.70	30.32	[3]
H_2SO_4	-177.34	-216.90	4.1	[3]
H_2O (liq)	-56.69	-68.317	16.716	[3]
H^+ (aq)	0.0	0.0	0.0	[3]
H_2 (gas)	0.0	0.0	31.211	[3]

Note: The values of the thermodynamic characteristics of α and β modifications of lead dioxide in calculation of the variable oxidisability of these compounds show the known dependence of the equilibrium on the composition (see table 2.5).

The thermodynamic properties (free energies ΔG^o, enthalpies of formation ΔH^o, and entropies S^o) of a number of compounds which can appear in the Pb-H_2SO_4-H_2O system are shown in table 2.1. These data can be used, in particular, for calculation of the changes of free energy adduced, for calculating of the changes in free energy corresponding to non-electrode (table 2.2) and oxidation-reduction equilibria (table 2.3) and also for calculation of the corresponding equilibrium constants and standard potentials.

Table 2.2: Standard changes of free energy and of equilibrium constants of of non-electrode reactions in the Pb-H_2SO_4-H_2O system

Number of reaction	Reaction	ΔG^o kcal/mol	K	Ref.
1	$HPbO_2^- + 3H^+ \rightleftarrows Pb^{2} + 2H_2O$	- 38.11	$6.3 \cdot 10^{27}$	2)
2	$PbO_3^{2-} + 6H^+ \rightleftarrows Pb^{4+} + 3H_2O$	- 31.55	$1.35 \cdot 10^{23}$	2)
3	$Pb(OH)_2 + 2H^+ \rightleftarrows Pb^{2+} + 2H_2O$	- 18.51	$4.2 \cdot 10^{13}$	2)
4	$HPbO_2^- + H^+ \rightleftarrows Pb(OH)_2$	- 19.6	$2.3 \cdot 10^{14}$	2)
5	$PbO_{yellow} + 2H^+ \rightleftarrows Pb^{2+} + H_2O$	- 17.17	$4.2 \cdot 10^{12}$	2)
6	$PbO_{red} + 2H^+ \rightleftarrows Pb^{2+} + H_2O$	- 17.37	$6.2 \cdot 10^{12}$	2)
7	$HPbO_2^- + H^+ \rightleftarrows PbO_{yellow} + H_2O$	- 20.74	$1.6 \cdot 10^{15}$	2)
8	$HPbO_2^- + H^+ \rightleftarrows PbO_{red} + H_2O$	- 20.94	$2.1 \cdot 10^{15}$	3)
9	$PbO_2 + 4H^+ \rightleftarrows Pb^{4+} + 2H_2O$	+ 10.85	$8.9 \cdot 10^{-8}$	3)
10	$PbO_3^{2-} + 2H^+ \rightleftarrows PbO_2 + H_2O$	- 41.60	$1.7 \cdot 10^{30}$	2)
11	$HSO_4^- \rightleftarrows H^+ + SO_4^{2-}$	+ 2.69	10^{-2}	7)
12	$PbSO_4 + H^+ \rightleftarrows Pb^{2+} + HSO_4^-$	+ 8.22	$1.5 \cdot 10^{-6}$	3)
13	$PbSO_4 \rightleftarrows Pb^{2+} + SO_4^{2-}$	+ 10.82	$1.6 \cdot 10^{-8}$	3)
14	$HPbO_2^- + SO_4^{2-} + 3H^+ \rightleftarrows PbSO_4 + 2H_2O$	- 49.10	$9.1 \cdot 10^{35}$	2)
15	$5HPbO_2^- + 5H^+ \rightleftarrows 5PbO \cdot 2H_2O + 3H_2O$	-105.7	$3.1 \cdot 10^{77}$	6)
16	$5PbO \cdot 2H_2O + 10H^+ \rightleftarrows 5Pb^{2+} + 7H_2O$	- 85.92	10^{63}	6)
17	$2HPbO_2^- + SO_4^{2-} + 4H^+ \rightleftarrows PbO \cdot PbSO_4 \cdot 3H_2O$	- 75.28	$1.6 \cdot 10^{55}$	6)
18	$PbO \cdot PbSO_4 + 2H^+ \rightleftarrows 2Pb^{2+} + SO_4^{2-} + H_2O$	- 2.29	$4.8 \cdot 10$	6)
19	$4HPbO_2^- + 6H^+ + SO_4^{2-} \rightleftarrows 3PbO \cdot PbSO_4 \cdot H_2O \cdot 4H_2O$	-124.4	$1.6 \cdot 10^{91}$	6)
20	$3PbO \cdot PbSO_4 \cdot H_2O + 6H^+ \rightleftarrows 4Pb^{2+} + SO_4^{2-} + 4H_2O$	- 29.72	$5 \cdot 10^{20}$	6)

Table 2.3: Standard potentials of oxidation-reduction equilibria in the $Pb-H_2SO_4-H_2O$ system

Number of reaction	Oxidised product	Reduced product	$\varkappa$	φ^o V	Ref.
1	$PbSO_4$	Pb	2	-0.356	[3]
2	Pb_3O_4	$HPbO_2^-$	2	-0.297	[2]
3	Pb^{2+}	Pb	2	-0.124	[3]
4	$PbO \cdot PbSO_4$	Pb	4	-0.099	[10]
5	H^+	H_2	2	0.000	[3]
6	$3PbO \cdot PbSO_4 \cdot H_2O$	Pb	8	+0.037	[11]
7	$4PbO \cdot PbSO_4$	Pb	10	+0.115	[12]
8	$Pb(OH)_2$	Pb	2	+0.242	[2]
9	PbO	Pb	2	+0.248	[2]
10	$5PbO \cdot 2H_2O$	Pb	10	+0.260	[11]
11	PbO_2	$HPbO_2^-$	2	+0.649	[2]
12	PbO_2	Pb	4	+0.677	[12]
13	$HPbO_2^-$	Pb	2	+0.706	[2]
14	Pb_3O_4	$5PbO \cdot 2H_2O$	10	+0.960	[11]
15	PbO_2	$5PbO \cdot 2H_2O$	10	+1.070	[11]
16	Pb_3O_4	PbO	2	+1.076	[2]
17	PbO_2	Pb_2O_3	2	+1.090	[11]
18	Pb_3O_4	$Pb(OH)_2$	2	+1.101	[2]
19	PbO_2	PbO	2	+1.107	[2]
20	PbO_2	$Pb(OH)_2$	2	+1.113	[2]
21	PbO_2	Pb_3O_4	4	+1.122	[2]
22	PbO_2	$4PbO \cdot PbSO_4$	10	+1.172	[12]
23	O_2	H_2O	4	+1.225	[3]
24	Pb_2O_3	Pb_3O_4	2	+1.230	[11]
25	PbO_2	$3PbO \cdot PbSO_4 \cdot H_2O$	8	+1.285	[11]
26	PbO_2	$PbO \cdot PbSO_4$	4	+1.422	[11]
27	Pb_2O_3	$3PbO \cdot PbSO_4 \cdot H_2O$	4	+1.480	[11]
28	PbO_2	Pb^{2+}	2	+1.482	[2]
29	PbO_3^{2-}	$HPbO_2^-$	2	+1.543	[2]
30	Pb_3O_4	$3PbO \cdot PbSO_4 \cdot H_2O$	8	+1.605	[11]
31	PbO_2	$PbSO_4$	2	+1.690	[13]
32	Pb^{4+}	Pb^{2+}	2	+1.691	[3]
33	Pb_2O_3	$PbO \cdot PbSO_4$	2	+1.750	[11]
34	Pb^{4+}	$PbSO_4$	2	+1.865	[2]
35	PbO_3^{2-}	PbO	2	+2.001	[2]
36	PbO_3^{2-}	$Pb(OH)_2$	2	+2.007	[2]
37	Pb_3O_4	$PbO \cdot PbSO_4$	4	+2.010	[11]
38	Pb_3O_4	Pb^{2+}	2	+2.200	[2]
39	Pb_2O_3	$PbSO_4$	2	+2.270	[11]
40	PbO_3^{2-}	$PbSO_4$	2	+2.344	[2]
41	PbO_3^{2-}	Pb^{2+}	2	+2.375	[2]
42	PbO_3^{2-}	Pb_3O_4	4	+2.463	[2]
43	Pb_3O_4	$PbSO_4$	2	+2.912	[2]

It must be mentioned that in the examination of the thermodynamics of the Pb-H_2SO_4-H_2O system in literature there are definite contradictions connected with the calculation of the dissociation of the sulphuric acid. As is known, this electrolyte is fully dissociated in aqueous solutions only according to the scheme

$$H_2SO_4 \rightleftarrows H^+ + HSO_4^- \qquad (2.3)$$

The dissociation constant of the bisulphate ion $K_{HSO_4^-}$ is quite small [7-9]). The dependence of the magnitude of $K_{HSO_4^-}$ on temperature over a wide interval of its change (from 24 to 350°C), in accordance with the data of precision measurements, is expressed by the equation[8])

$$\lg K_{HSO_4^-} = 56.889 - 19.8858 \lg T - \frac{2307.9}{T} - 0.006473T \qquad (2.4)$$

At 25°C $K_{HSO_4^-} = (1.028 \pm 0.02) \cdot 10^{-2}$.

Recently executed spectrophotometric determination[9]) of the magnitude of $K_{HSO_4^-}$ in the temperature interval +25-+175°C has made it possible to express the temperature dependency of $K_{HSO_4^-}$ by the formula

$$\lg K_{HSO_4^-} = 5.162 - \frac{509.56}{T} - 0.01826\ T \qquad (2.4')$$

in accordance with which at 25°C: $K_{HSO_4^-} = 1.016 \cdot 10^{-2}$.

Therefore, in the oxidation-reduction processes occurring on the electrodes of a lead acid battery the participation of HSO_4^- and not SO_4^{2-} ions is the more probable. According to the equation of reaction (2.3), the activity of sulphuric acid is connected with the activities of the corresponding ions by the relationship

$$\alpha_{H_2SO_4} = \alpha_{H^+}\alpha_{HSO_4^-} = \alpha^2_{H^+}\alpha_{SO_4^{2-}}/K_{HSO_4^-} \qquad (2.5)$$

The method of standardisation of the activity of H_2SO_4 reflected in the equation (2.5) may be considered more justified from the point of view of the principles of the thermodynamics of strong electrolytes than the expressions of the magnitude $\alpha_{H_2SO_4}$ often encountered in literature as products of $\alpha^2_{H^+}\alpha_{SO_4^{2-}}$ (without calculation of the dissociation constant of the HSO_4^- ion).

Standard values of the potential experimentally determined from measurements of the emf of cells with no current flow using hydrogen electrodes in the H_2SO_4, must, as a rule, be related to the equilibria in which the $H_2SO_4^{-2}$ ions participate.

We shall examine in somewhat more detail the non-electrode equilibria shown in table 2.2. The data quoted show above all the essential role of the acidity of the electrolyte, which in many cases determines the direction of the process. Thus, in sufficiently acid solutions plumbite or plumbate ions are practically non-existent, since the values of the corresponding equilibrium constants (reactions No. 1, 2, 4, 7, 8, 14, 15, 17 and 19) are quite large. The equilibria shown are completely shifted in these media in the direction of formation of Pb^{2+} or Pb^{4+} ions.

Considerable interest is presented by the question of the existence of sufficiently acid solutions of ions of quadrivalent lead, the formation of which is possible as a result of the dissociation of PbO_2. The corresponding equilibrium constant (table 2.2, reaction 9) is comparatively small. However, the concentration of ions of Pb^{4+} must increase sharply with the increase in the acidity of the electrolyte, since $\alpha_{Pb^{4+}}$ is proportional to the activity of the H^+ ions to the 4th power.

$$\alpha_{Pb^{4+}} = K\alpha^4_{H^+} / \alpha^2_{H_2O} \qquad (2.6)$$

If we are to accept approximately that in a strong H_2SO_4 solution $\alpha_{H^+} \approx [H^+] \approx 10$ and $\alpha_{H_2O} \approx 1$, then in accordance with (2.6) $\alpha_{Pb^{4+}} \approx 9 \cdot 10^{-4}$. This magnitude coincides in its order with the experimental values of the solubility of quadrivalent lead in H_2SO_4 solutions. According to the data of [14]) the concentration of Pb^{4+} in H_2SO_4 solutions with a concentration changing within the limits m = 1.11-7.87g-equiv/1000g H_2O amounts to $(1.1\text{-}1.8) \cdot 10^{-4}$ g-equiv/l and increases somewhat with an increase in the H_2SO_4 content. According to the results of [14]) quadrivalent lead is found in the solution in the form of ions of $PbO(OH)^+$, forming according to the scheme

$$\left.\begin{aligned} PbO_2 + H_2O &= PbO(OH)_2 \\ PbO(OH)_2 + H^+ &= PbO(OH)^+ + H_2O \end{aligned}\right\} \qquad (2.7)$$

Taking into account the inaccuracy in the value of the constant of the equilibrium under consideration (reaction 9, table 2.2), which was determined on the basis of measurements in a nitric acid solution [3]), we must reckon the coincidence of the experimental and calculation values of the Pb^{4+} concentration fully satisfactory.

From the data quoted in table 2.2 it further follows that in neutral and slightly acid solutions stable existence is possible for a number of basic sulphates of lead. A decrease in the acidity of the solution causes an increase in the probability of formation of these compounds and a rise in the proportion of concentrations of $PbO/PbSO_4$ in them.

Several works have been devoted to an all-round study of the basic sulphates of lead. In[15]) crystallo-chemical characteristics of the basic sulphates are quoted. Interest in these compounds is caused, in particular, by the fact that the basic sulphates are formed in the process of preparation of the electrode paste used in the production of lead acid batteries. In this the basicity of the sulphate, and also the water content in its composition to a large extent determines the characteristics of the battery electrodes. The formation of basic sulphates takes place, obviously, also in the active mass in the process of utilisation of the battery, and also in the process of anode corrosion of the lead alloys.

The majority of the electrode reactions in the Pb-H_2SO_4-H_2O system take place with the participation of hydrogen ions. Therefore a vital influence on the magnitudes of the equilibrium potentials (φ_p) is shown by the acidity (pH) of the solution.

The dependencies of the φ_p on the pH of the solution (Pourbaix diagrams) are widely used in current electrochemical literature for determination of the fields of stable existence of these or other phases, depending on the potential and the composition of the medium. The use of Pourbaix diagrams for explanation of the corrosion behaviour of metals in fairly dilute electrolytes showed itself particularly productive. In a number of items of work these diagrams were used for interpretation of the processes occurring in a lead acid battery.

In fig. 2.1 the φ_p - pH diagram is reproduced, calculated in a condition of equality for the unit of concentration (activity of sulphate ions) *). The φ_p values are expressed in respect of the normal hydrogen electrode (nhe) at $\alpha_{H_2O} = 1$. The dependence on pH of the equilibrium potentials of the hydrogen (a) and the oxygen (b) electrodes is marked by dotted lines. As can be seen from the diagram shown, in the field of negative values of potential, lead may find itself in equilibrium with the normal and with basic sulphates, and at high pH levels with hydrated oxides. In the value interval pH $\approx$ 2-8.5, the equilibrium potential of the $Pb/PbSO_4$ system maintains a constant value equal to the corresponding standard potential. At pH $<$ 2 the equilibrium $Pb \rightleftarrows PbSO_4$ is determined by the reaction taking place with the participa-

*) A more detailed φ_p-pH diagram, constructed for different concentrations of potential determining ions, is given in[16]).

tion of bisulphate ions, which causes the known dependence of φ_p on pH.

At pH > 8.5 oxidation of the lead, as can be seen from fig. 2.1, should occur with the formation of basic sulphates, the basicity of which increases with a decrease in the acidity of the solution.

Finally at pH > 14, lead finds itself in equilibrium with bivalent oxides. The thermodynamic stability of the basic sulphates in a slightly alkaline medium explains the predominant formation of these compounds in the preparation of electrode paste for lead acid batteries.

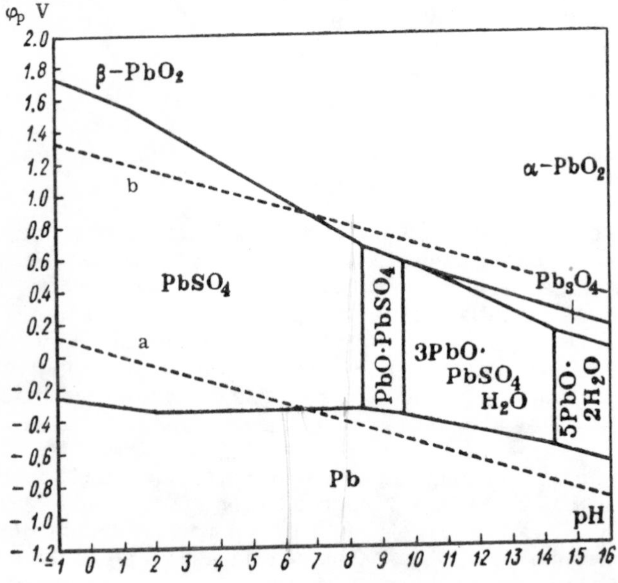

Fig. 2.1 Dependence of equilibrium potentials φ_p on the acidity of the solution pH in the Pb - H_2SO - H_2O (Pourbaix diagram).

From fig. 2.1 it follows that the $Pb/PbSO_4$ system at pH < 6 is thermodynamically unstable, since the graph corresponding to the $Pb \rightleftarrows PbSO_4$ equilibrium lies at potentials more negative than the equilibrium potential $H_2O \rightleftarrows H_2$. In these conditions the lead should reduce the water with the separation of the hydrogen. The circumstance indicated determines the thermodynamic possibility of self-discharge of the negative electrode of the lead acid battery. At the same time the rate of spontaneous solution of pure lead is low thanks to the high value of overvoltage of hydrogen reduction on this metal, which gives the possibility of carrying out experimental measurements of the equilibrium potential of the system under consideration.

In the field of high positive potentials the normal and the basic sulphates and also the hydrated oxides of bivalent lead oxidise into lead dioxide (α or β - PbO_2). A product of the oxidation of tri-basic sulphate, and also of the oxide $5PbO \cdot 2H_2O$ at high pH values is minium, which is stable in a sufficiently narrow interval of potentials, oxidising with the rise in potential into α-PbO_2.

The position of α and β-PbO_2 in the diagram under consideration shows that tetragonal β- modification of the lead dioxide is particularly characteristic for acid media, and rhombic α- modification for alkaline solutions. The graph corresponding to the equilibrium $PbSO_4 \rightleftarrows PbO_2$ at $pH<7.9$ lies above the graph corresponding to the equilibrium $H_2O \rightleftarrows O_2$. As a result of this the lead dioxide can oxidise the water molecules, reducing itself to sulphate of bivalent lead, which determines the possibility of self-discharge of the lead dioxide electrode. The quite high value of the oxygen over-voltage on the lead dioxide (especially on the β- modification of PbO_2 [1]) causes, however, an extraordinarily insignificant rate of this process and the possibility of fairly reliable measurements of the equilibrium potentials $PbO_2 \rightleftarrows PbSO_4$.

The analysis of the Pourbaix diagram for the Pb -H_2SO_4 - H_2O system carried out above gives valuable information with regard to the thermodynamic possibility of occurrence of one set of processes or another on the electrodes of a lead acid battery in the period of its preparation and utilisation. At the same time we must observe the known limitation of the diagram under consideration especially in the event of it being a question of the behaviour of metal in fairly concentrated electrolyte solutions.

First of all, the concept of pH loses in this case its simple physical sense and cannot be directly linked with the concentration of hydrogen ions in the solution. Further, the utilisation of the equilibrium values of the potential, measured in respect of a normal hydrogen electrode, requires to be included in the measurement chain of the diffusion potential jump at the interface boundary; the electrolyte being researched is a standard solution ($\alpha_{H^+} = 1$). The value of the diffusion potentials in strong solutions, as is well known, may be evaluated only approximately. An equation for the calculation of equilibrium potentials, measured in relation to hydrogen zero, includes members which contain the activities of different ions. These last magnitudes are not determinable thermodynamically. The replacement of them by the corresponding concentrations or the average activity of the electrolyte is linked with errors, the exact calculation of which is at the present time not possible. Finally, with the construction of Pourbaix diagrams it is generally accepted that the activity of the water in the solution is $\alpha_{H_2O}=1$. This condition may be utilised without any noticeable error only in quite dilute solutions. In the case of a sulphuric acid electrolyte the magnitude of α_{H_2O} may be accepted as equal to a unit at m<0.1g equiv/1000 g H_2O [7]).

The circumstances noted show that for more accurate thermodynamic analysis of the system under consideration it is necessary, first of all, to use equations of equilibrium potentials which include the activities of the components (H_2SO_4 and H_2O). Such equations can be obtained if the values of the potentials (φ'_p) are expressed in relation to the hydrogen electrode in the same solution. Instead of the hydrogen electrode it is possible to use any other reference electrode convertible in respect of hydrogen or sulphate ions, for example, the mercury-mercurous sulphate reference electrode.

It is appropriate to use the concentration of H_2SO_4 in the solution or any parameter directly connected with the concentration to bring out the argument of the graphical presentation. From such a parameter the density of the electrolyte ($d_{H_2SO_4}$), widely used in battery technology, can be determined. In fig. 2.2 the φ'_p - $d_{H_2SO_4}$ diagram calculated for a number of the most important electrode reactions is shown. The graphs are constructed in the area $d_{H_2SO_4} \leqslant 1.4 g/cm^3$, containing the whole possible gamut of concentrations of sulphuric acid in the electrolyte of lead acid batteries. The values of the coefficients of the activity of the H_2SO_4 and of the activity of the H_2O used in the calculation of φ'_p are obtained by the method of graphic interpolation of data borrowed from [17]) (see fig. 2.3).

The calculation of the potentials was carried out according to formulae (2.8)-(2.19). The lower index in the φ' values corresponds to the number of the oxidation-reduction equilibrium in table 2.3. and the graph in fig. 2. 2.

$$\varphi'_1 = -0.356 - 0.02955 \lg \alpha_{H_2SO_4} \tag{2.8}$$

$$\varphi'_4 = -0.099 - 0.01477 \lg \alpha_{H_2SO_4} \alpha_{H_2O} \tag{2.9}$$

$$\varphi'_6 = +0.037 - 0.00739 \lg \alpha_{H_2SO_4} - 0.02955 \lg \alpha_{H_2O} \tag{2.10}$$

$$\varphi'_7 = +0.115 - 0.00591 \lg \alpha_{H_2SO_4} - 0.02364 \lg \alpha_{H_2O} \tag{2.11}$$

$$\varphi'_{9} \quad +0.248 - 0.02955 \lg \alpha_{H_2O} \qquad (2.12)$$

$$\varphi'_{12} = +0.677 - 0.02955 \lg \alpha_{H_2O} \qquad (2.13)$$

$$\varphi'_{19} = +1.107 - 0.02955 \lg \alpha_{H_2O} \qquad (2.14)$$

$$\varphi'_{22} = +1.172 + 0.00591 \lg \alpha_{H_2SO_4} - 0.03546 \lg \alpha_{H_2O} \qquad (2.15)$$

$$\varphi'_{23} = +1.225 - 0.02955 \lg \alpha_{H_2O} \qquad (2.16)$$

$$\varphi'_{25} = +1.285 + 0.00739 \lg \alpha_{H_2SO_4} - 0.02955 \lg \alpha_{H_2O} \qquad (2.17)$$

$$\varphi'_{26} = +1.422 + 0.01477 \lg \alpha_{H_2SO_4} - 0.04432 \lg \alpha_{H_2O} \qquad (2.18)$$

$$\varphi'_{31} = +1.690 + 0.02955 \lg \alpha_{H_2SO_4} - 0.0591 \lg \alpha_{H_2O} \qquad (2.19)$$

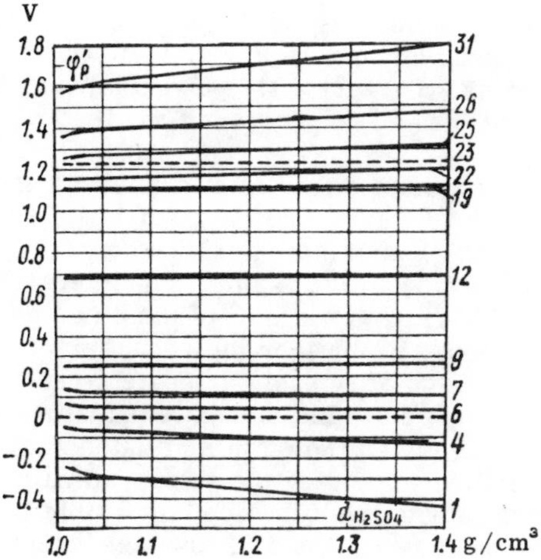

Fig. 2. 2 Dependence of the potentials of electrode equilibria (with reference to the H electrode in the same solution) on the density of the electrolyte. The graph numbers correspond to the oxidation-reduction system numbers in table 2. 3; graphs corresponding to the equilibria $H \rightleftarrows H_2$ (zero line) and $H_2O \rightleftarrows O_2$ (graph 23 are shown by a dotted line).

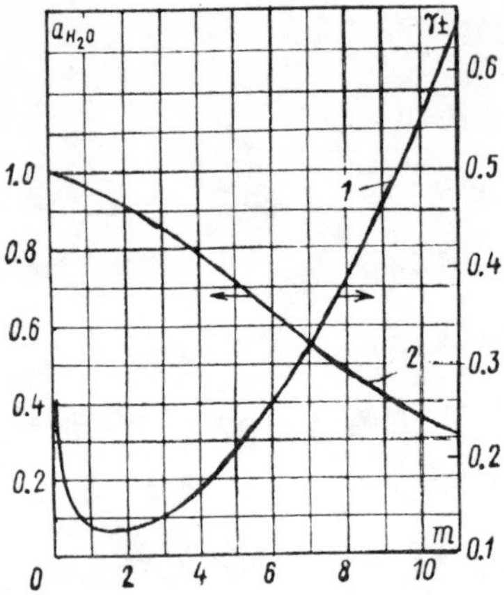

Fig. 2. 3 Graphs of change of mean coefficient of activity of H_2SO_4 (1) and H_2O (2) with the change of molar concentration of the H_2SO_4

Interest is attracted principally by the fact that the graphs of φ_p'-$d_{H_2SO_4}$ over a considerable interval of solution densities show a rectilinear character (fig. 2.2). This circumstance, already mentioned earlier in literature, has so far not found any theoretical explanation.

In fig. 2. 2 it is possible to differentiate spheres respectively of stable existence of lead (the area lying below graph 1), of sulphate of lead (between graphs 1 and 31) and lead dioxide (the area lying above graph 31). From fig. 2. 2 there follows the possibility of intermediate formation of monobasic sulphate of lead as a result of the oxidation of the lead (area of potentials lying above graph 4) or the reduction of PbO_2 (area lying below graph 26), and also of tribasic sulphate (area situated above graph 6 and below graph 25). Intermediate oxidation of the lead into PbO is possible in the area of potentials situated above graph 9, and into PbO_2 (at potentials exceeding the values which correspond to graph 12). Compounds the formation of which is possible in the area of potentials included between graphs 1 and 31 are insufficiently concentrated $H_2SO_4^-$ solutions thermodynamically unstable and must be converted into neutral sulphate of lead.

The conclusions drawn above with reference to the possibility of dissociation of water as a result of the oxidation of lead or the reduction of PbO_2 are confirmed by analysis of the diagram represented in fig. 2. 2. The φ_p'-$d_{H_2SO_4}$ diagram can be used for fairly accurate determination of the equilibrium values of the potentials of the positive and negative electrodes of a lead acid battery at different stages of its work, and also for calculation of the corresponding e. m. f. values of the battery.

Potential-Determining processes at the Electrodes of a Lead Acid Battery

The potential-determining process occurring on the negative electrode of a lead acid battery may be written down in the form

$$Pb + HSO_4^- \rightleftarrows PbSO_4 + H^+ + 2e \qquad (2.20)$$

The potential corresponding to the equilibrium (2.20) is measured with reference to the normal hydrogen electrode.

$$\varphi_p = \varphi^0 + \frac{\nu}{2} \lg \frac{\alpha_{H^+}}{\alpha_{HSO_4^-}} = \varphi_1^0 - \frac{\nu}{2} \lg \alpha_{SO_4^{2-}} \qquad (2.21)$$

where $\varphi_1^0 = \varphi^0 + (\nu/2) \lg K_{HSO_4^-}$, $\nu = 2.3026RT/F$

The value of the equilibrium potential $Pb \rightleftarrows PbSO_4 (H_2SO_4)$ with reference to the hydrogen electrode in the same solution, in accordance with **(2.21)**, is determined at 25°C by the equation **(2.8)**, which can also be written down in a more general form

$$\varphi'_p = \varphi^0 - \frac{\nu}{2} \lg \alpha_{H_2SO_4} \qquad (2.22)$$

According to the equation (2.21) an increase in the concentration (activity) of sulphate ions causes a shift in the equilibrium potential $\varphi_{Pb/PbSO_4}$ to the negative side. At the given concentration (activity) of sulphate ions the value of the potential in practice does not depend on the acidity of the solution.

Thanks to the presence in the system of lead sulphate, the magnitude $\alpha_{SO_4''}$ determines the solubility of this salt. Insofar as the solubility of the $PbSO_4$ does not depend greatly on the concentration of H_2SO_4 over a wide interval of its change *), the equilibrium potential $Pb \rightleftarrows PbSO_4$ measured with reference to the normal hydrogen electrode also changes very little with a change in the concentration of the electrolyte.

The influence of different additives to the electrolyte on the equilibrium potential of a lead sulphate electrode is determined in accordance

---

*) With an increase in concentration of H_2SO_4 from 0.1 to 20N the solubility of the $PbSO_4$ decreases from 2.5 to 1.2mg/l.

with the equation (2.21) by the character of the change of activity of the sulphate ions or, in other words, by the change in solubility of the $PbSO_4$.

The process (2.20), written down in a simplified form, represents the equilibrium of lead with its bivalent ions

$$Pb^{2+} + 2e \rightleftarrows Pb \qquad (2.23)$$

The value of the potential corresponding to equilibrium (2.23) is given by the formula

$$\varphi_p = \varphi^0_{Pb/Pb^{2+}} + \frac{\nu}{2} \lg \alpha_{Pb^{2+}} \qquad (2.24)$$

The standard potential $\varphi^0_{Pb/Pb^{2+}}$ was recently determined in the work[4]) with the aid of measurement of the emf of the two galvanic cells:

$$Pt(H_2)|HClO_4||HClO_4, Pb(ClO_4)_2|Pb, Hg \text{ (sat.)}$$

$$\text{and } Pb, Hg\text{(sat.)}|HClO_4, Pb(ClO_4)_2|Pb \text{ (met.)}$$

according to the data obtained[4])

$$\varphi^0_{Pb/Pb^{2+}} = -(0.1237 \pm 0.0006) \text{ B};$$

the value of the temperature coefficient of $\varphi^0_{Pb/Pb^{2+}}$ at 25°C comprises

$$(\partial\varphi^0/\partial T)_{25} = -(4.38 \pm 0.7) \cdot 10^{-4} \text{ V/degree}$$

The magnitude of the activity of the Pb^{2+} ions may be expressed through the activity of the sulphate ions

$$\alpha_{Pb^{2+}} = L_{PbSO_4} / \alpha_{SO_4^{2-}} \qquad (2.25)$$

where $L_{PbSO_4} = 10^{-8}$ - the solubility product of lead sulphate. Substituting $\alpha_{Pb^{2+}}$ in accordance with (2.25) in formula (2.24), we obtain equation (2.21) the standard potential in which is given by the formula

$$\varphi^0 = \varphi^0_{Pb/Pb^{2+}} + \frac{\nu}{2} \lg L_{PbSO_4} \qquad (2.26)$$

If we substitute in (2.26) the numerical values of $\varphi^0_{Pb/Pb^{2+}}$, ν and L_{PbSO_4} at 25°C, we shall have $\varphi^0 = 0.356$V, i.e. the magnitude which is identical to the one shown in table 2.3 (on the basis of other, earlier research) and used in calculations according to formula (2.8).

Equilibrium at the positive electrode of a lead acid battery, i.e. at the interface boundary of lead dioxide - lead sulphate in a sulphuric acid solution has been the subject of a number of experimental investigations [18][19][20]. The potential-forming process occurring in the given system is generally written down in the form

$$PbO_2 + HSO_4^- + 3H^+ 2e \rightleftarrows PbSO_4 + 2H_2O \qquad (2.27)$$

The equilibrium potential of the lead dioxide electrode (with reference to hydrogen zero), in accordance with equation (2.27), is expressed by the formula

$$\varphi_p = \varphi^0 + \frac{\nu}{2} \lg \frac{\alpha^3_{H^+} \alpha_{HSO_4^-}}{\alpha^2_{H_2O}} = \varphi_2^0 + \frac{\nu}{2} \lg \frac{\alpha^4_{H^+} \alpha_{SO_4^{2-}}}{\alpha^2_{H_2O}} \qquad (2.28)$$

where $\varphi_2^0 = \varphi^0 - (\nu/2) \lg K_{HSO_4^-}$.

The value of the potential with reference to the hydrogen electrode in the same solution (φ'_p), i.e. the emf of the cell $PbO_2/PbSO_4$, H_2SO_4/H_2, can be calculated according to formula (2.19) or

$$\varphi'_p = \varphi_p - \nu \lg \alpha_{H^+} = \varphi^0 + \frac{\nu}{2} \lg \frac{\alpha_{H_2SO_4}}{\alpha^2_{H_2O}} \qquad (2.29)$$

The magnitudes of φ'_p over a wide interval of measurement of the concentration of H_2SO_4 (m = 0. 1-8. 0 mol/kg) are measured in precision conditions for the electrode obtained by electrodeposition of lead dioxide on the plate from the nitric acid electrolyte[7]

The dependence of φ'_p on m at 25°C is expressed according to the exponential series given[7]

$$\varphi'_p = 1629.194 + 73.924 \lg m + 33.020 (\lg m)^2 + 43.220 (\lg m)^3 + 21.567 (\lg m)^4 \text{ mV} \qquad (2.30)$$

A calculation has been made by the authors[7] of the standard value of the potential φ^0 = 1. 6906 V and the mean coefficients of activity of H_2SO_4, which turned out to correspond well to the results quoted in[17].

As a result of a thorough thermodynamic analysis in [21] we quote the most reliable values of standard potential corresponding to the equilibrium $PbO_2 \rightleftarrows PbSO_4(H_2SO_4)$ at different temperatures.

t °C	5	10	20	25	35	45	55
φ^0 B	1.68578	1.68675	1.68935	1.69095	1.69471	1.69894	1.70399

The approximate value of φ^0 at 25°C is also shown in the [13]) $\varphi^0 = (1.68996 \pm 0.00027)$V.

The magnitude of φ^0 depends on the form of crystalline modification of lead dioxide and constitues for the tetragonal modification φ^0_β= 1.6871V[29]), and for the rhombic modification φ^0_α = 1.6971V[30]). The value of φ^0 quoted above is near to the arithmetical mean of the magnitudes of φ^0_α and φ^0_β . This result corresponds to the data of the X-ray phase analysis, according to which lead dioxide electro-deposited from the nitric acid solution represents a mixture of approximately equal quantities of α- and β- PbO_2.

As follows from the data quoted, the difference of the equilibrium potentials of the α- and β- modifications of PbO_2 amounts to ~10mV, which determines the increased stability of β-PbO_2 in sulphuric acid solutions. The phase conversion of α-PbO_2 can occur in a H_2SO_4 solution both by way of electrochemical recrystallisation[23])

$$\alpha\text{-PbO}_2 \rightleftarrows \text{PbSO}_4 \rightleftarrows \beta\text{-PbO}_2 \qquad (2.31)$$

and also by way of direct solution of the dioxide and subsequent deposition of it according to the scheme

$$\alpha\text{ - PbO}_2 \rightleftarrows \text{PbO}_2\text{(solution)} \rightleftarrows \beta\text{ - PbO}_2 \qquad (2.32)$$

The process (2.32) is made possible as a result of the noticeable solubility of the PbO_2 [14]).

In the study of the dependence of the equilibrium potential of the lead dioxide electrode on pH in the solutions with a constant concentration of sulphate ions (0.1 and 1.0M) the values of the potential obtained by Angstadt, Venuto and Ruetschi in the interval pH = -1+03 (fig.2.4)[33]) are easily reproducible. In these solutions the potential of α- and β-PbO_2 measured with reference to a hydrogen electrode in the same solution, decreases with an increase in pH in a straight line at a gradient of $\partial\varphi'_p/\partial pH = -0.063$V/pH. The straight lines (φ'_p, pH) for α and β-PbO_2 go practically parallel at a distance of $\varphi'_\alpha - \varphi'_\beta \approx 10$mV. The situation of these straight lines satisfactorily corresponds to the Pourbaix potential - pH diagram.

At pH>4 experimental values of the potentials of a lead dioxide electrode become difficult to reproduce and do not depend much on the acidity of the solution (in fig. 2.4 the corresponding area is designated by dotted lines). Obviously this is explained by the complication of the potential-determining process, in which at high pH values basic sulphates and oxides of lead may participate. A well defined role in this can be played by an increase in the rate of dissolution of the PbO_2 in neutral and alkaline solutions, also, in connection with which the potential of the electrode noticeably diverges from the equilibrium value. However, it must be noted that, in accordance with the data of the work under consideration[23]), the potential of the rhombic modification of PbO_2 over all the area investigated, viz. pH = 1 - 12, lies at more positive values than the potential of the tetragonal modification (fig. 2.4). Hence it follows that the preferred formation of α-PbO_2 in alkaline solutions cannot be explained by increased thermodynamic stability of this modification and is connected, obviously, exclusively with the kinetic properties of the process.

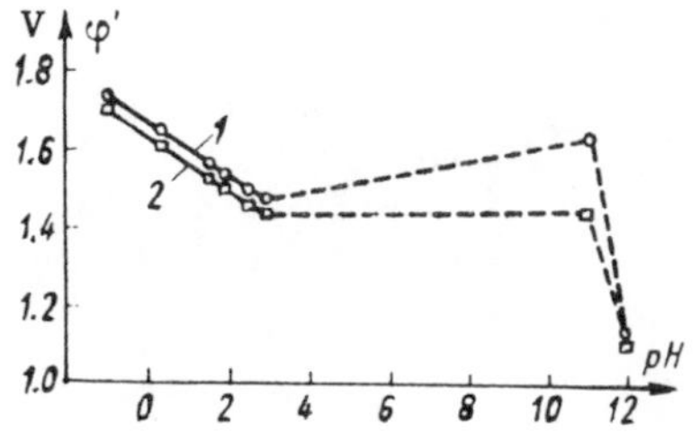

Fig. 2.4 Dependence of the equilibrium potential of $PbO_2 \rightleftarrows PbSO_4$ (1M SO_4^{2-}) pH of the solution 1 - α-PbO_2; 2 - β-PbO_2

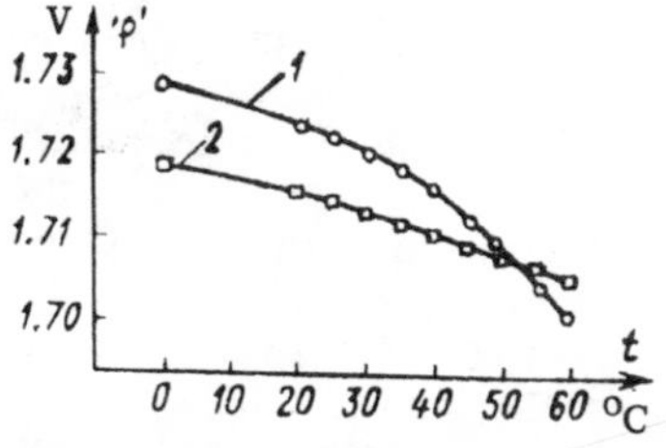

Fig. 2.5 Temperature dependency of the equilibrium potential of $PbO_2 \rightleftarrows PbSO_4$ (3.9M H_2SO_4) 1 - α-PbO_2; 2 - β-PbO_2

A study of the temperature dependency of the equilibrium potentials of α- and β-PbO_2 in 3.9M H_2SO_4 showed[23]) that in the temperature interval from 0 to 60°C the potential of the α-modification decreases more sharply with the rise in temperature. At a temperature $t \approx 50$°C the graphs (φ'_p, t) for α- and β-PbO_2, as can be seen from fig. 2.5, intersect and at $t > 50^{o}C$ $\varphi'_{\alpha} < \varphi'_{\beta}$, i.e. the α-modification becomes, from the thermodynamic point of view, the more stable oxide. In [23]) the following values have been obtained for temperature coefficients of the potentials (at $25^{o}C$ in 4.62M soln. of H_2SO_4):

$$(\partial\varphi'_{\alpha}/\partial T)_p = -0.36mV/degree; \quad (\partial\varphi'_{\beta}/\partial T)_p = -0.20mV/degree$$

Starting out from the values of the equilibrium potentials of α- and β-PbO_2 and the above mentioned temperature coefficients in [23]) a calculation was made of the changes of free energy and of the enthalpy of the process of phase conversion α-$PbO_2 \rightleftarrows \beta$-$PbO_2$ equal respectively to

$$\Delta G_{\alpha-\beta} = -0.4kcal/mol \text{ and } \Delta H_{\alpha-\beta} = -2.6kcal/mol$$

It must be mentioned that in [23]) measurements of the magnitudes of φ'_p and $(\partial\varphi'_p/\partial T)_p$ were carried out in a H_2SO_4 solution of fairly high concentration, where the α-modification of lead dioxide is unstable. Therefore the considerable decrease in φ'_{α} with an increase leading to the magnitudes of φ'_{α} and φ'_{β} coming close to each other caused by a gradual phase transition $\alpha \rightarrow \beta$-PbO_2, the rate of which increases with an increase in temperature [20]). In air the phase conversion $\alpha \rightarrow \beta$-PbO_2 occurs with notable rapidity at $100^{o}C$[24]). At lower and higher temperatures the speed of polymorphic conversion drops sharply. In the literature it is observed that with the keeping of α-PbO_2 at room temperature during a year it was not possible to find in it an admixture of the β-modification[25]). However, the lead dioxide encountered in nature - the mineral Plattnerite - has only the tetragonal structure peculiar to β-PbO_2 [24]).

As will be shown in Chapter 4 the rhombic modification of lead dioxide is characterised by denser packing than the tetragonal modification and by greater specific weight. Therefore at high pressures α-PbO_2 becomes a more stable oxide than β-PbO_2. Conversion of α-PbO_2 to β-PbO_2 according to the data of Ruetschi and Cahan occurs with notable rapidity at a pressure of 8 500 atm. The pressure $p_{\alpha-\beta}$, corresponding to the phase equilibrium α-$PbO_2 \rightleftarrows \beta$-$PbO_2$ at T-const, can be evaluated setting out from the equation

$$\Delta G_{\alpha-\beta} = \int_0^{p_{\alpha-\beta}} (V_{\beta} - V_{\alpha})dp \qquad (2.33)$$

where V_{α} and V_{β} are the molar volumes of the corresponding oxides. Accurate calculation according to formula (2.33) cannot be carried out, since the dependence of the magnitudes of V_{α}

and β pressure is not known. If we allow that the difference $V_\alpha - V_\beta$ is constant (does not depend on p), then at $\Delta G_{\alpha-\beta} = 400$cal/mol ≈ 16.5 atm/mol

$$P_{\alpha-\beta} \approx \frac{\Delta G_{\alpha-\beta}}{V_\beta - V_\alpha} = \frac{16.5}{8 \cdot 10^{-4}} \approx 20\,600 \text{ atm}$$

A comparison of the calculated and the experimental value of $p_{\alpha-\beta}$ shows that the difference of the magnitudes of V_α and V_β should considerably increase with an increase in pressure. This is possible in the event of the molar volume of α-PbO_2 decreasing with increase in pressure to a considerably greater degree than the molar volume of β-PbO_2. This result can be linked with the decreased oxygen content in the crystal lattice of the rhombic modification of lead dioxide.

At ultra-high pressures a cubic modification of PbO_2 was obtained by Japanese researchers [26]) which, however, is unstable and gradually converts into α-PbO_2.

The production of current in a lead acid battery and its thermodynamic basis

Summarising the equations of reaction (2.20) and (2.27) it is not difficult to obtain an equation of the basic current producing process occurring in a lead acid battery at its discharge (→) and charge (←):

$$Pb + PbO_2 + 2H_2SO_4 \rightleftarrows 2PbSO_4 + 2H_2O \qquad (2.34)$$

This equation lies at the base of the so-called "theory of double sulphation" laid down in 1882 by Gladstone and Tribe.

In the formation of the theory, the authors took as their starting point experimental observations according to which the concentration of battery electrolyte falls at discharge and rises in the charging process, the change in the H_2SO_4 content in the solution being proportional to the amount of electricity transmitted. Phase analysis of the initial and final products contained in the active masses, and also subsequent accurate measurements of the changes in the concentration of the electrolyte, fully confirmed the stoichiometry of the reaction (2.34).

An essential role in the foundation of the theory of dual sulphation against which, at various times, numerous objections were raised, was played by the classic research of Harned and Hamer [18-27]). These authors compared experimental values of the emf of a number of galvanic cells including battery electrodes ($Pb/PbSO_4$ and $PbO_2/PbSO_4$). The comparison was carried out in such a way as to exclude possible errors connected with self-dissolution of the lead in sulphuric acid and the corresponding shift to the positive side of the potential of the lead sulphate electrode. This was achieved with the use of amalgam electrodes and a replacement of the acid electrolyte by a saline one.

In [27]) the following galvanic cells were used:

No.	Scheme of cell	Designation of emf
1	$Pb(Hg)/PbSO_4$, Na_2SO_4, Hg_2SO_4/Hg	E_1
2	$Pb/PbSO_4$, Pb^{2+}, $PbSO_4/Pb(Hg)$	E_2
3	$Pb/PbSO_4$, Na_2SO_4, Hg_2SO_4/Hg	E_3
4	$H_2(Pt)/H_2SO_4$, Hg_2SO_4/Hg	E_4
5	$Pb(Hg)/PbSO_4$, $H_2SO_4/H_2(Pt)$	E_5
6	$Pb/PbSO_4$, $H_2SO_4/H_2(Pt)$	E_6
7	$H_2(Pt)/H_2SO_4$, $PbSO_4/PbO_2(Pt)$	E_7
8	$Pb(Hg)/PbSO_4$, H_2SO_4, $PbSO_4/PbO_2(Pt)$	E_8
9	$Pb/PbSO_4$, H_2SO_4, $PbSO_4/PbO_2(Pt)$	E_9

Cell No. 9 represents the lead acid battery. Its emf (E_9) may be represented in the form of an algebraic sum of the emf of the other cells:

$$E_9 = E_7 + E_6 = E_8 - E_5 + E_6 = E_7 + E_3 - E_4 = E_7 + E_1 + E_2 - E_4 \quad (2.35)$$

Accurate observation of the equation (2.35) over a wide interval of change of concentration of H_2SO_4 ($m = 0.05$-7.0g-M/1000g H_2) serves as a direct experimental indication of the presence on the battery electrodes of the equilibria

$$Pb \rightleftarrows PbSO_4 \, (-) \text{ and } PbO_2 \rightleftarrows PbSO_4 \, (+)$$

Harned and Hamer [27]) proposed an empirical formula for the dependency of the emf of a lead acid battery E on temperature t (within the limits 0-60°C) and concentration of the electrolyte m (within the limits 0.05-7.0):

$$E = E_o + at + bt^2 \quad (2.36)$$

The values of the empirical parameters E_o, α and β are quoted in table 2.4.

Table 2.4: Values of the parameters in equation (2.36) depending on the concentration of H_2SO_4

m	E_o	$a \cdot 10^6$	$b \cdot 10^8$
0.05	1.76874	-310	134
0.1	1.80207	-265	129
0.2	1.83495	-181	128
0.5	1.87910	- 45	126
1.0	1.91737	56	108
2.0	1.96637	159	103
3.0	2.00874	178	97
4.0	2.04769	177	91
5.0	2.08502	167	87
6.0	2.11910	162	85
7.0	2.15071	153	80

The theory of sulphation was confirmed by accurate thermodynamic calculations carried out in the pre-war years by B A Kosobryukhov [28]), B N Kabanov [29]), A K Lorenz [30]), and also Craig and Vinal [31]). The thermodynamic basis of theory under consideration may be laid in innumerable ways, which are briefly examined below.

As is well known, the emf of a galvanic cell without transfer, and in particular the emf of a lead acid battery, is determined by the nature and activities of the components participating in the potential-forming processes. The dependency of the emf E on the corresponding activities α_i can be generally expressed by the equation.

$$E = E^0 - \frac{\nu}{z} \lg \prod_i \alpha_i^{\alpha_i \nu_i} \qquad (2.37)$$

where ν_i is the stoichiometric coefficient in the equation of the reaction occurring in the cell, α_i the coefficient, equal to +1 for final and -1 for initial products and E^0 the standard value of emf at $\prod_i \alpha_i^{\alpha_i \nu_i}$.

In conformity with reaction (2.34) occurring in a lead acid battery according to the theory of double sulphation, equation (2.37) takes on the following form

$$E = E^0 + \nu \lg \frac{\alpha_{H_2SO_4}}{\alpha_{H_2O}} \qquad (2.38)$$

Equation (2.38) can be obtained by algebraic summation of formulae (2.21) and (2.28) or (2.22) and (2.29). The value of E^o is determined by the change of free energy in conjunction with equation (2.1). Using values of ΔG^o quoted in table 2.1 it is not difficult to calculate that the change of Gibbs free energy corresponding to reaction (2.34) amounts to 94.14kcal/mol *), whence $E^o = 2.041V$. The value coincides well with the magnitude of emf of the battery at $\alpha_{H_2SO_4}/\alpha_{H_2O} = 1$ (m=3.65)[29]. An approximate value of E^o can be obtained setting out from the above-mentioned standard potentials corresponding to equilibria (2.20) and (2.27); $E^o = +1.690 - (-0.356)$. The values of the emf of the battery calculated from formula (2.38) completely coincide with the experimental values within the limits of error of measurement of the emf[29]. This conformity is observed over a wide interval of change of concentration of H_2SO_4.

Equation (2.38) is used by B N Kabanov[29]) to show the unsoundness of the concepts about oxidation-reduction processes in a lead acid battery which differ from the theory of double sulphation. An analysis of this question showed that the gradient of the graph E, lg $\frac{\alpha_{H_2SO_4}}{\alpha_{H_2O}}$ is obtained as equal to θ only in the event of the process occurring in the battery being described by the equation of the reaction (2.34).

In a number of papers on the thermodynamic basis of a theory of double sulphation, use was made of the calculation of the emf of the battery with the aid of a Gibbs-Helmholtz equation.

$$E = -\frac{4.183\,\Delta H}{zF} + T\left(\frac{\partial E}{\partial T}\right)_p \qquad (2.39)$$

The value of ΔH, representing the change of enthalpy at the reaction (thermal effect), can be calculated from the thermodynamic data, but the temperature coefficient of the emf ($\partial E/\partial T$) is generally determined experimentally. In the calculation of the magnitude of ΔH it is necessary to take into account the changes of enthalpy connected with the effects of dilution.

According to the equation of the reaction (2.34) we may write that

$$\Delta H = \sum_i \alpha_i \nu_i \Delta H_i - 2\Delta H_K + 2\Delta H_B \qquad (2.40)$$

*) In the calculation the value of free energy of the formation of β-PbO_2 was used.

where ΔH_i is the enthalpy of formation of the corresponding compound (see table 2.3), ΔH_K the change of enthalpy on the dissolution of 1 mol of H_2SO_4 in a solution of a given concentration, and ΔH_β the change of enthalpy on the addition of 1 mol of H_2O to the given solution. The calculation carried out with the use of equations (2.30) and (2.40) by A K Lorenz [30] showed that the calculated and measured emf values coincide within the limits of change of acid concentration from 0.488 to 40.707%, with an accuracy down to 0.57%.

B N Kabanov [29] also used calculation of the entropy of the temperature coefficient of the emf of a lead acid battery with the aid of an equation resulting from (2.38) to show the correctness of the equation of the reaction (2.34)

$$\left(\frac{\partial E}{\partial T}\right) = \left(\frac{\partial E^o}{\partial T}\right)_p + \frac{R}{T}\ln\frac{\alpha_{H_2SO_4}}{\alpha_{H_2O}} + \frac{\bar{L}_{H_2O} - \bar{L}_{H_2SO_4}}{FT} \qquad (2.41)$$

where

$$\left(\frac{\partial E^o}{\partial T}\right)_p = \frac{4.183\,\Delta S^o}{zF} \qquad (2.42)$$

$\bar{L}_{H_2O}$ and $\bar{L}_{H_2SO_4}$ are the relative partial molar heat contents of H_2O and H_2SO_4 in the given solution

$$\Delta S^o = \Sigma \nu_i \alpha_i S^o_i \qquad (2.43)$$

S_i is the standard values of entropy of the components of the reaction.

Calculation by formula (2.43) with the use of data quoted in table 1.1 shows that ΔS^o = 61.81cal/mol·degr., whence, according to formula (2.42) $(\partial E^o/\partial T)_p$ = 0.00131V/degr. [1]). The experimental value of $(\partial E^o/\partial T)_p$ = 0.00136V/degr. [29]). The close conformity with the results of the experiment is also given by calculation according to equation (2.41).

In recent years A K Lorenz proposed a new method of verification of the scheme of the current-forming process in a lead acid battery. This method is based on the calculation of the difference of the emf of galvanic cells consisting of a positive or negative battery electrode and a hydrogen electrode:

$PbO_2 | H_2SO_4 | H_2$ and $Pb | H_2SO_4 | H_2$

The current-forming processes occurring in these cells, in conformity with the basic premises of the theory of dual sulphatisation are expressed by the equations of the reactions

$$PbO_2 + H_2 + H_2SO_4 \rightleftarrows PbSO_4 + 2H_2O \tag{2.44}$$

$$Pb + H_2SO_4 \rightleftarrows PbSO_4 + H_2 \tag{2.45}$$

the summation of which leads to equation (2.34).

The difference of the values of the emf of these cells ΔE, in accordance with (2.44) and (2.45) is equal (at 25°C) to:

$$\Delta E = \frac{\Delta G^0_{PbO_2} - 2\Delta G^0_{H_2O}}{46.12} - 0.059 \lg \alpha_{H_2O} \tag{2.46}$$

The calculation by equation (2.46) of the value of ΔE coincides well with the corresponding experimental values. The superiority of this method consists in the fact that for the carrying out of the calculation the knowledge of only two thermodynamic values is required ($\Delta G^0_{H_2O}$ and $\Delta G^0_{PbO_2}$). It must also be mentioned that the values of free energies of the formation of H_2SO_4 and $PbSO_4$, which are essential for the calculation of E^0 by formula (2.38) are known with less accuracy than the corresponding values for PbO_2 and H_2O.

The thermodynamic theory of the lead dioxide electrode with the change of oxidation

The thermodynamic theory of the lead dioxide electrode, based on the use of equations (2.27)-(2.29), lays down that the composition of the oxide corresponds accurately to the stoichiometric formula of PbO_2. However, as is shown by numerous experimental data, the composition of this compound noticeably differs from the stoichiometric and to a considerable extent depends on the form of crystalline modification, the method of obtaining it, the temperature, the composition of the contacting solution, etc. In the literature quite different, and often contradictory, data about the composition of lead dioxide are encountered. In the majority of cases lead dioxide is characterised by stoichiometric deficiencies of the oxygen[32-33]). Numerous attempts to obtain a dioxide corresponding exactly to the formula PbO_2 have not led to success The oxygen content in all forms of lead dioxide which were analysed in[32]) did not exceed 98% of the theoretical value.

The tetragonal modification of the dioxide encountered in nature contains 92% of the theoretical oxygen[32]), i.e. it corresponds to the formula $PbO_{1.84}$ and the composition of the commercial preparation of this oxide may be described by the formula $PbO_{1.85-1.86}$ [34]). The composition of the unformed active mass of the positive electrode of the battery, judging by the data of separate determination of lead and oxygen, corresponds to the formula $PbO_{1.86-1.88}$.

The degree of oxidation of lead oxide can change markedly without a change in the crystallographic structure of the oxide. Thus, if we are to assign to the oxide in its common form the formula PbO_n, then according to the data of Burbank[35]) for α-PbO_n the degree of oxidation is $1.94 < n < 2.02$, and for β-PbO_n $1.87 < n < 2.02$. In the work[36]) a few other values are quoted: for α-PbO_n $1.83 < n < 2.02$, for β-PbO_n $1.95 < n < 2.00$, and in the paper [37]) $1.95 < n < 1.98$ for both crystalline modifications. According to the data obtained in the work of Zaslavsky, Kondrashov and Tolkachev[38]), where the rhombic modification of lead dioxide is first described the degree of oxidation of this oxide lies within the limits $1.94 < n < 2.02$. Judging by the results of the analyses of different forms of PbO_2 quoted, in particular in [33]), the degree of oxidation of the tetragonal modification of the dioxide in the majority of cases exceeds the corresponding value for the rhombic modification ($n_\beta > n_\alpha$). Thus, the thermodynamic theory of the lead dioxide electrode based on the assumption of the constancy of the composition of the oxide and its conformity with the formula PbO_2 is shown to be approximate.

It must be noted that the composition of the oxide under consideration was determined for pure preparations with the absence of contact with lead sulphate and the H_2SO_4 solution, i. e. in conditions that were different from the equilibrium conditions on the lead dioxide electrode. It may be assumed, however, that with equilibrium of the lead dioxide with the $PbSO_4$ in the H_2SO_4 solution, the degree of oxidation of the lead in the dioxide differs somewhat from 2 and is in fact a function of the composition of the equilibrium solution. A similar phenomenon is observed in the case of an electrode made of manganese dioxide, whose electro-chemical properties are known to be similar to those of a lead dioxide electrode.

Taking into account what has been said, it is possible to use for a more accurate description of the equilibrium on a lead dioxide electrode the results of the thermodynamic theory of oxide electrodes of variable composition developed by Vetter[39]). An important result of the thermodynamics of oxides of variable composition is the establishment of the dependency of the degree of oxidation n on the composition of the solution which is in equilibrium with the oxide.

At a constant concentration of the metal ions in the solution the dependence of the equilibrium potential of an oxide electrode on the acidity of the solution is expressed by the formula *[39]).

$$\left(\frac{\partial \varphi_p}{\partial \ln \alpha_{H^+}}\right)_{M^{z+}} = \frac{2n}{2n - z} \frac{RT}{F} \tag{2.47}$$

where z is the change of valency of the metal ions in the transfer from the oxide to the solution.

Expressing the potential of the electrode in relation to a hydrogen electrode in the same solution, it is not difficult to convert the formula (2.47) to apply to a lead dioxide electrode (z = 2):

$$\left(\frac{\partial \varphi'_p}{\partial pH}\right)_{Pb^{2+}} = \frac{\nu}{1 - n} \tag{2.48}$$

whence

$$n = 1 - \frac{\nu}{(\partial \varphi'_p / \partial pH)_{Pb^{2+}}} \tag{2.49}$$

Equation (2.49) makes it possible to calculate the degree of oxidation of the PbO_n according to the gradient of the graph (φ'_p, pH). Calculation according to the data quoted in [23]) shows that in the pH interval from -1 to 3 $n \approx 1.95$ for both modifications of lead dioxide. The absence of accurate experimental values of potentials of α- and β-PbO in the aforementioned area of pH of the solution gives no possibility of evaluating the difference in the degree of oxidation of the α and β modifications.

The dependence of the value of n on the composition of the solution which is in equilibrium with the electrode may turn out to be the reason for the considerable influence of the conditions of synthesis of the lead dioxide on the degree of oxidation. As an example of this influence, we can instance the fact that the gradient of the graphs (φ'_p pH) for α and β-PbO_2 in perchlorate solutions with a constant concentration of ClO_4^- ions, according to the data of [23]) amounts to approximately - 0.08V/pH. This value, in accordance with formula (2.49), leads to the value of n = 1.75.

---

*) The equation 2.47, and also many other relationships of the thermodynamics of oxide electrodes of variable composition can be obtained as a special case of the usual kinetic equations quoted in the work [40]) by Engel for the description of the electro-chemical behaviour of the ion crystals.

It must also be noted that the influence of the composition of the contacting solution on the degree of oxidation of the lead dioxide impedes accurate analytical determination of the value of n. The difficulties in principle are connected here with the necessity of washing off the dioxide from the compounds of bivalent lead and of subsequent reduction in the solution: $Pb^{4+} \rightarrow Pb^{2+}$. The long exposure to the preparation being analysed in solutions of varying composition may lead to a change of oxidation, and in particular to a levelling out of the differences in the value of n for α and β modifications of lead dioxide.

The theory of oxide electrodes was developed by Vetter for the case of fairly dilute solutions, in particular, where it is possible to calculate that the activity of water $\alpha_{H_2O} = 1$. This condition, as has already been shown, is applicable for a lead dioxide electrode only at very low concentrations of H_2SO_4. This electrode also differs in some specific properties caused by the presence in the system of a not very soluble salt - sulphate of lead.

In connection with this a special examination is made below of the thermodynamic characteristics of a lead dioxide electrode with a variable degree of oxidation[41]). In deducing the conditions of thermodynamic equilibrium use is made of a somewhat modified Vetter method.

We examine lead dioxide $PbO_n (1 < n \lesseqgtr 2)$ in equilibrium with a H_2SO_4 solution saturated with $PbSO_4$. Let us designate by $\Delta G(n)$ the free energy of formation of PbO_n at constant pressure as a result of the reaction.

$$Pb + nH_2O \rightleftarrows PbO_n + 2n\,H^+ + 2ne \qquad (2.50)$$

and examine the process of reverse anodic oxidation of PbO_n into $PbO_{n+\Delta n}$ assuming that the magnitude Δn is quite small. This oxidation can be carried out in two ways:

$$\frac{1}{\Delta n} PbO_n + H_2O \rightleftarrows \frac{1}{\Delta n} PbO_{n+\Delta n} + 2H^+ + 2e \qquad (2.51)$$

$$\left(\frac{n}{\Delta n} + 1\right) PbO_n + H_2SO_4 \rightleftarrows \frac{n}{\Delta n} PbO_{n+\Delta n} + PbSO_4 + 2H^+ + 2e \qquad (2.52)$$

The equations of reactions (2.51) and (2.52) can be obtained by algebraic summation of equation (2.50), the equation of the reaction of formation of $PbO_{n+\Delta n}$

$$Pb + (n+\Delta n)H_2O \rightleftarrows PbO_{n+\Delta n} + 2(n+\Delta n)H^+ + 2(n+\Delta n)e \qquad (2.53)$$

and of the reaction of anodic formation of $PbSO_4$.

$$Pb + H_2SO_4 \rightleftarrows PbSO_4 + 2H^+ + 2e \tag{2.54}$$

In reality, equation (2.51) is obtained from the summation of (2.50) and (2.53), if equation (2.50) is individually multiplied by $(-1/\Delta n)$ and (2.53) by $(1/\Delta n)$. Equation (2.52) can be obtained by summation of the following equations: (2.53), all members of which are multiplied by $(n/\Delta n)$, (2.50) individually multiplied by $-[(n/\Delta n)+1]$, and (2.54). If we are to designate the change of free energy corresponding to reaction (2.51) by ΔG_I, and the corresponding reaction (2.52) by ΔG_{II}, then in accordance with the earlier accepted designation

$$\Delta G_I = \frac{\Delta G\,(n+\Delta n) - \Delta G(n)}{\Delta n} \tag{2.55}$$

$$\Delta G_{II} = \frac{n}{\Delta n}\,\Delta G\,(n+\Delta n) - \left(\frac{n}{\Delta n} + 1\right)\Delta G(n) + \Delta G_{Pb/PbSO_4} \tag{2.56}$$

where $\Delta G_{Pb/PbSO_4}$ is the change of free energy with anode formation of lead sulphate according to reaction (2.54). From equations (2.55) and (2.56) it follows that

$$\lim_{\Delta n \to 0} \Delta G_I = \lim_{\Delta n \to 0} \frac{\Delta G(n+\Delta n) - \Delta G(n)}{\Delta n} = \frac{d\Delta G(n)}{dn} \tag{2.57}$$

$$\lim_{\Delta n \to 0} \Delta G_{II} = \lim_{\Delta n \to 0} \left\{ \frac{n\,[\Delta G(n+\Delta n) - \Delta G\,(n)]}{\Delta n} - \Delta G(n) + \right.$$
$$\left. + \Delta G_{Pb/PbSO_4} \right\} = n\frac{d\Delta G(n)}{dn} - \Delta G(n) - \Delta G_{Pb/PbSO_4} \tag{2.58}$$

The values of the equilibrium potential of the lead dioxide electrode (in relation to a hydrogen electrode in the same solution), corresponding to reactions (2.51) and (2.52) in accordance with (2.57) and (2.58) are equal to

$$\varphi'_I = \frac{1}{2F}\,\frac{d\Delta G(n)}{dn} - \frac{\nu}{2}\lg \alpha_{H_2O} \tag{2.59}$$

$$\varphi'_{II} = \frac{n}{2F} - \frac{d\Delta G(n)}{dn} - \frac{\Delta G(n)}{2F} + \varphi^0_{Pb/PbSO_4} - \frac{\nu}{2}\lg \alpha_{H_2SO_4} \tag{2.60}$$

Formula (2.60) can also be written down in the form

$$\varphi'_{II} = \frac{n}{2F}\,\frac{d\Delta G(n)}{dn} - \frac{\Delta G(n)}{2F} + \varphi'_{Pb/PbSO_4} \tag{2.61}$$

where $\varphi'_{Pb/PbSO_4}$ is the potential of a lead sulphate electrode ($\varphi^0_{Pb/PbSO_4}$), is the standard value of this potential.

Equilibrium at the phase boundary PbO_n-$PbSO_4$ (H_2SO_4) is possible only on condition that $\varphi'_I = \varphi'_{II} (= \varphi'_p)$. Equating the right-hand parts of equations (2.59) and (2.60), we can write down the conditions of equilibrium in the form

$$(n - 1)\frac{d\Delta G(n)}{dn} - \Delta G(n) = \nu F \lg \frac{\alpha_{H_2SO_4}}{\alpha_{H_2O}} - 2F\varphi^0_{Pb/PbSO_4} \tag{2.62}$$

Equation (2.62) characterises in a general form the dependence of the composition (degree of oxidation) of the lead dioxide on the concentration of the H_2SO_4 solution which is in equilibrium with it. The formulae (2.59)-(2.62) can be used particularly for calculation of the degree of oxidation n.

Let us look at the dependence of the electrode potential on the activity of the sulphuric acid. Differentiating the equation (2.60) according to $\lg \alpha_{H_2SO_4}$ we obtain

$$\frac{d\varphi'_p}{d \lg \alpha_{H_2SO_4}} = \frac{n}{2F}\,\frac{d^2 \Delta G(n)}{dn^2}\,\frac{dn}{d \lg \alpha_{H_2SO_4}} - \frac{\nu}{2} \tag{2.63}$$

To calculate the value of $d^2\Delta G(n)/dn^2$ we shall differentiate according to $\lg \alpha_{H_2SO_4}$ and (2.62).

$$\frac{d^2 \Delta G(n)}{dn^2}\,\frac{dn}{d \lg \alpha_{H_2SO_4}} = \frac{\nu F}{n-1}\left(1 - \frac{d \lg \alpha_{H_2O}}{d \lg \alpha_{H_2SO_4}}\right) \tag{2.64}$$

Substituting the expression (2.64) in formula (2.63) we shall have

$$\frac{d\varphi'_p}{d \lg \alpha_{H_2SO_4}} = \frac{\nu}{2(n-1)}\left(1 - n\frac{d \lg \alpha_{H_2O}}{d \lg \alpha_{H_2SO_4}}\right) \tag{2.65}$$

In a similar manner from equations (2.59)-(2.62) expressions can be obtained which characterise the influence of the acidity of the solution and the concentration (activity) of the sulphate ions on the potential of a lead dioxide electrode. These dependencies have the form

$$\frac{d\varphi'_p}{dpH} = \frac{\nu}{1-n}\left(1 + \frac{1}{2}\,\frac{d \lg \alpha_{SO_4^{2-}}}{dpH} - \frac{n}{2}\,\frac{d \lg \alpha_{H_2O}}{d\,pH}\right) \tag{2.66}$$

$$\frac{d\varphi'_p}{d \lg \alpha_{SO_4^{2-}}} = \frac{\nu}{2(n-1)}\left(1 - 2\frac{d\,pH}{d \lg \alpha_{SO_4^{2-}}} - 2n\frac{d \lg \alpha_{H_2O}}{d \lg \alpha_{SO_4^{2-}}}\right) \tag{2.67}$$

In the special case

$$\left(\frac{\partial \varphi'_p}{\partial\, pH}\right)_{SO_4^{2-},H_2O} = \frac{\nu}{1 - n} \tag{2.68}$$

$$\left(\frac{\partial \varphi'_p}{\partial\, \lg \alpha_{SO_4^{2-}}}\right)_{pH,H_2O} = \left(\frac{\partial \varphi'_p}{\partial\, \lg \alpha_{H_2SO_4}}\right)_{H_2O} = \frac{\nu}{2(n - 1)} \tag{2.69}$$

Equation (2.68) is similar to equation (2.48) with, however, this difference that as can be seen from (2.68), this dependency is correct only on the condition of a constancy of the activity of the water in the solution *).

Differentiating equations (2.59) and (2.60) by temperature and solving them simultaneously, we have

$$\frac{d\varphi'_p}{dT} = \frac{\nu}{2(n-1)T} \lg \frac{\alpha_{H_2SO_4}}{\alpha^n_{H_2O}} + \frac{\nu}{2(n-1)}\left(\frac{d \lg \alpha_{H_2SO_4}}{dT} - n\frac{d \lg \alpha_{H_2O}}{dT}\right) - \frac{1}{n-1}\frac{d\varphi^0_{Pb/PbSO_4}}{dT} = \frac{1}{n-1}\left[\frac{2.3026R}{2F}\lg \alpha_{H_2SO_4} - \frac{\bar{L}_{H_2SO_4}}{2FT} - n\left(\frac{2.3026R}{2F}\lg\alpha_{H_2O} - \frac{\bar{L}_{H_2O}}{2FT}\right) - \frac{d\varphi^0_{Pb/PbSO_4}}{dT}\right] \tag{2.70}$$

where $\bar{L}_{H_2SO_4}$ and $\bar{L}_{H_2O}$ are the relative partial molar heat contents of sulphuric acid and water respectively. In a similar manner, it is possible to obtain from (2.59) and (2.60) a formula characterising the dependence of the potential of the electrode under consideration on pressure

$$\frac{d\varphi'_p}{dp} = \frac{1}{n-1}\left(\frac{\bar{V}_{H_2SO_4} - n\bar{V}_{H_2O}}{2F} - \frac{d\varphi^0_{Pb/PbSO_4}}{dp}\right) \tag{2.71}$$

where $\bar{V}_{H_2SO_4}$ and $\bar{V}_{H_2O}$ are the relative molar volumes of the H_2SO_4 and H_2O in the solution.

Equations (2.65)-(2.71) makes it possible to calculate the degree of oxidation of the lead dioxide according to the experimental values of

---

*) The condition $\alpha_{SO_4^{2-}}$ = const, used in the formula (2.68) is equivalent to the condition $\alpha_{Pb^{2+}}$ = const in formulae (2.48) since the production of solubility $PbSO_4$ $\alpha_{Pb^{2+}}\alpha_{SO_4^{2-}}$ is a constant value.

the equilibrium potentials of the lead dioxide electrode and to the thermodynamic characteristics of H_2SO_4 solution. The most accurate calculation of the magnitude of n can be carried out with the use of the dependency of the potential on the activity of H_2SO_4. Solving (2.65) in respect of n with account being taken of the relationship resulting from the Gibbs-Duhem Law, we obtain

$$n = \frac{(d\varphi'_p/d\lg\alpha_{H_2SO_4})_{T,p} + \nu/2}{(d\varphi'_p/d\lg\alpha_{H_2SO_4})_{T,p} + \nu m/111.02} \qquad (2.72)$$

where m is the molar concentration of the H_2SO_4.

Table 2.5: Thermodynamic characteristics of α and β modifications of lead dioxide[41])

$m_{H_2SO_4}$ mol/kg	φ'_α V	φ'_β V	n_α	n_β	$\Delta\varphi^0_\alpha$ mV	$\Delta\varphi^0_\beta$ mV	ΔG_α kcal/mol	ΔG_β kcal/mol
0.1000	1.57503	1.56509	1.9407	1.9409	+7.69	+7.66	-52.502	-51.931
0.1996	1.59267	1.58284	1.9580	1.9589	+4.58	+4.48	-52.280	-52.678
0.2917	-	1.59266	-	1.9704	-	+2.89	-	-52.503
0.4717	1.61557	1.60550	1.9867	1.9894	+1.10	+0.88	-51.777	-52.198
1.129	1.64194	1.63195	2.0324	2.0357	-1.75	-1.92	-50.933	-51.338
2.217	1.66962	1.65943	2.0997	2.1059	-2.62	-2.77	-49.525	-49.923

The results of the calculation of the degree of oxidation of the α and β modifications of lead dioxide according to formula (2.72) are given in table 2. 5 in the interval of H_2SO_4 concentration m = 0. 1 - 2. 217. At m > 2.217 the equilibrium on an electrode made of α-PbO_2 is not established owing to the fairly rapid conversion α-PbO_2 → β-PbO_2 [20]).

According to the results obtained, the degree of oxidation of both modifications of the dioxide increases somewhat with an increase in the concentration of H_2SO_4 ($dn/dm > 0$), which is a mathematical consequence of the inequality

$$\frac{d\varphi'_p}{d\lg\alpha_{H_2SO_4}} > 0, \quad \frac{d}{dm}\,\frac{d\varphi'_p}{d\lg\alpha_{H_2SO_4}} < 0$$

and the equation (2.72).

The deviation of the equilibrium values n from 2 does not exceed 0. 1. The data obtained show further that in the interval of concentrations of the solution researched $n_\alpha < n_\beta$, although the difference between n_α and n_β is not great. This relationship of the degrees of oxidation of α- and β-PbO_2 is in conformity with the experimental data considered above.

It is essential to notice that the dependence of the oxidation of the electrode on the composition of the solution should lead to a well defined influenced on the standard potential of the electrode by the concentration of the solution. This standard potential is a function of the nature of the electrode potential-producing process, which generally changes with a change in the degree of oxidation[41]).

The potential-producing process occurring on lead dioxide, the composition of which is expressed by the formula PbO_n can be written down in the form

$$PbO_n + (2n-1)H^+ + HSO_4^- + 2(n-1)e \rightleftarrows PbSO_4 + nH_2O \tag{2.73}$$

It is not difficult to see that the equation of the reaction (2.27) is a special case of (2.73) with n = 2. The potential of the electrode (in relation to a hydrogen electrode in the same solution), corresponding to equilibrium (2.73), is equal to

$$\varphi'_p = \varphi^{0\prime} + \frac{\nu}{2(n-1)} \lg \frac{\alpha_{H_2SO_4}}{\alpha^n_{H_2O}} \tag{2.74}$$

Here $\varphi^{0\prime}$ is the value of the standard potential of a lead dioxide electrode, corresponding to the given composition of the oxide and being a function of the figure n. For determination of the dependence of $\varphi^{0\prime}$ on n we shall differentiate the formula (2.74) according to $\lg \alpha_{H_2SO_4}$ and we shall compare the result obtained with the equation (2.65)

$$\frac{d\varphi'_p}{d \lg \alpha_{H_2SO_4}} = \frac{\nu}{2(n-1)} \left(1 - n \frac{d \lg \alpha_{H_2O}}{d \lg \alpha_{H_2SO_4}} \right) + \left[\frac{d\varphi^{0\prime}}{dn} - \frac{\nu}{2(n-1)^2} \lg \frac{\alpha_{H_2SO_4}}{\alpha_{H_2O}} \right] \frac{dn}{d \lg \alpha_{H_2SO_4}} \tag{2.75}$$

Since, as can be seen from the data in table 2. 5, $dn/d\lg \alpha_{H_2SO_4} \neq 0$, a comparison of (2.75) and (2.65) shows that

$$\frac{d\varphi^{0\prime}}{dn} = \frac{\nu}{2(n-1)^2} \lg \frac{\alpha_{H_2SO_4}}{\alpha_{H_2O}} \tag{2.76}$$

Equation (2.76) characterises the dependency of the standard potential of the lead dioxide electrode on the composition of the oxide and the concentration of the solution. In the interval of concentrations of H_2SO_4 under consideration $\lg(\alpha_{H_2SO_4}/\alpha_{H_2O}) < 0$[17]), and consequently, $d\varphi^{0'}/dn < 0$, i.e. a lower value of the standard potential corresponds to a greater oxygen content. A comparison of the values $\varphi^{0'}$ and n for α- and β-PbO_2 shows that $\varphi^{0'}_{\alpha} > \varphi^{0'}_{\beta}$ since $n_{\alpha} < n_{\beta}$.

Equation (2.76) is used in the[42]) to explain a certain increase in equilibrium potential of a lead dioxide electrode (in 1.25N H_2SO_4) in time. An increase in potential is linked by the authors[42]) with a gradual decrease in the degree of oxidation. From equation (2.76) it also follows that

$$\frac{d\varphi^{0'}_{\alpha}}{dn_{\alpha}} \Big| \frac{d\varphi^{0'}_{\beta}}{dn_{\beta}} = \left(\frac{n_{\beta} - 1}{n_{\alpha} - 1}\right)^2 \qquad (2.77)$$

i.e. the standard potentials of α and β modifications of lead dioxide change with a change of the degree of oxidation in one and the same direction.

The integration of (2.76) needs knowledge of the functional dependency of the value of n on the composition of the solution. A connection between $\varphi^{0'}$, n and the activities of the components can, however, be obtained in an integral form on a comparison of equations (2.29) and (2.74). Equating the right-hand parts of these equations leads to the following result

$$\varphi^{0'} = \varphi^{0} + \frac{\nu}{2}\,\frac{n - 2}{n - 1}\,\lg\frac{\alpha_{H_2SO_4}}{\alpha_{H_2O}} \qquad (2.78)$$

The equation (2.78) can be considered as the result of the integration of (2.76). In this, the value of φ^0, which is known with sufficient accuracy to be independent of the concentration of the solution, plays the part of the integration constant. Differentiation of (2.78) with respect to n leads to the equation (2.76) (if φ^0 is not a function of n).

Thus, the dependency of the standard potential of the lead dioxide electrode on the concentration of the solution can be read with the introduction of the correction $\Delta\varphi^0$ as equal to

$$\Delta\varphi^{0} = \frac{\nu}{2}\,\frac{n - 2}{n - 1}\,\lg\frac{\alpha_{H_2SO_4}}{\alpha_{H_2O}} \qquad (2.79)$$

Since, as has already been shown, in the concentration intervals of the solution being considered $\lg(\alpha_{H_2SO_4}/\alpha_{H_2O}) < 0$, then $\Delta\varphi^0 > 0$ at

$n<2$ and $\Delta\varphi<0$ at $n>2$. It is natural that at $n = 2$, in accordance with (2.78) and (2.79) $\Delta\varphi^0 = 0$ and $\varphi^{0'} = \varphi^0$.

The values of $\Delta\varphi^0$, calculated according to equation (2.79), as can be seen from table 2.5, lie with the limits 1-8mV, which considerably exceeds the measurement error of the equilibrium potentials of a lead dioxide electrode. Simultaneous solving of the equations (2.59) and (2.60) leads to the following formula for calculation of $\Delta G(n)$

$$\Delta G(n) = 2F\,(\varphi^0_{Pb/PbSO_4} - \varphi'_p) - 2.3026RT\ \lg \alpha_{H_2SO_4} + \\ + n\,(2F\varphi'_p + 2.3026RT\ \lg \alpha_{H_2O}) \qquad (2.80)$$

Hence, it is also possible to calculate the free energy of formation of lead dioxide $\Delta G_{\alpha,\beta}$ connected with the value $\Delta G(n_{\alpha,\beta})$ by the relationship

$$\Delta G_{\alpha,\beta} = \Delta G(n_{\alpha,\beta}) + n_{\alpha,\beta}\,\Delta G_{H_2O} \qquad (2.81)$$

where ΔG_{H_2O} is the change of free energy corresponding to the reaction of formation of water

$$2H^+ + \frac{1}{2}O_2 + 2e \rightleftarrows H_2O$$

The results of the calculation (table 2.5) show that the difference in the free energies of formation of α- and β-PbO_2 does not depend on the concentration of the equilibrium solution and constitutes

$$\Delta G_{\alpha-\beta} = \Delta G_\alpha - \Delta G_\beta = 0.41 \pm 0.01\ \text{kcal/mol}$$

An equation for the calculation of the value $\Delta G_{\alpha,\beta}$ can be obtained also from the expression for free energy ($\Delta G'$), corresponding to the equilibrium (2.73). In accordance with (2.74)

$$\Delta G' = 2(n-1)\,F\varphi^{0'} - RT\ \ln \frac{\alpha_{H_2SO_4}}{\alpha^n_{H_2O}} \qquad (2.82)$$

Hence the change of free energy at the phase transition α-$PbO_{n\alpha} \rightleftarrows$ $\rightleftarrows \beta$-$PbO_{n\beta}$, occurring through the intermediate formation of $PbSO_4$, i.e. by way of electro-chemical recrystallisation, will be equal to

$$\Delta G_{\alpha-\beta} = -2F\left[(n_\beta - 1)\varphi^{0'}_\beta - (n_\alpha - 1)\varphi^{0'}_\alpha\right] + (n_\beta - n_\alpha)RT\ \ln \alpha_{H_2O} \qquad (2.83)$$

If $n_\alpha \approx n_\beta$ (=n), then equation (2.83) will have the form

$$\Delta G_{\alpha-\beta} \approx 2F\,(n-1)\,(\varphi^{0\prime}_{\alpha} - \varphi^{0\prime}_{\beta}) \qquad (2.84)$$

If n = 2, then we obtain an equation for the calculation of $\Delta G_{\alpha-\beta}$ on the condition of a constancy of composition of both modifications, which is used in the paper quoted[23]).

A calculation of the variable oxidation of the lead dioxide brings increased accuracy also to the formula for calculation of the enthalpy of phase transformation ($\Delta H_{\alpha-\beta}$). This value is generally expressed by the formula

$$\Delta H_{\alpha-\beta} = 2F\left\{(1-n_\beta)\left[\varphi'_\beta - T\left(\frac{\partial \varphi'_\beta}{\partial T}\right)_p\right] - (1-n_\alpha)\left[\varphi'_\alpha - T\left(\frac{\partial \varphi'_\alpha}{\partial T}\right)_p\right]\right\} \qquad (2.85)$$

The increased thermodynamic stability of the β-modification of lead dioxide, as has already been shown, causes gradual spontaneous transformation $\alpha \rightarrow \beta$-PbO_2. In connection with the above-noted difference in the degree of oxidation of α and β-PbO_2 this process may be accompanied by an increase in the oxygen content in the oxide grid owing to oxidation of the initial phase according to the scheme:

$$\alpha\text{-PnO}_{n_\alpha} + \frac{n_\beta - n_\alpha}{2}\,O_2 \rightarrow \beta\text{-PbO}_{n_\beta} \qquad (2.86)$$

It is of some interest to consider, from the point of view of the theoretical assumptions expounded above, the equilibrium established on an interface of the type Pb/PbO_n

$$PbO_n + 2nH^+ + 2ne \rightleftarrows Pb + n\,H_2O \qquad (2.87)$$

The potential corresponding to equilibrium (2.87) will, obviously, be determined by the formula

$$\varphi_p = \varphi^{0\prime} + \frac{\nu}{2n}\lg\frac{\alpha^{2n}_{H^+}}{\alpha^{n}_{H_2O}} = \varphi^{0\prime} + \frac{\nu}{2}\lg\frac{\alpha^{2}_{H^+}}{\alpha_{H_2O}} \qquad (2.88)$$

From the formula (2.88) it follows that in the given instance (unlike the equilibrium $PbO_n \rightarrow PbSO_4$ considered above) the change of degree of oxidation shows no influence on the character of the dependence of the equilibrium potential on the composition of the solution. The degree of oxidation of PbO_n only influences the value of the standard potential. A similar conclusion may be drawn in a more particular form from a comparison of the equations (2.12) and (2.13) according to which $\varphi^{0'} = +0.248V$ at n = 1 and $\varphi^{0'} = +0.677V$ at n = 2.

In conclusion, it must be noted that quite small deviations from the stoichiometric composition of the lead dioxide, which is in equilibrium with the $PbSO_4$ in the H_2SO_4 solution, do not bring any essential changes in the understanding of the basic scheme of the current producing process in a lead acid battery.

Chapter 3: The influence of the porous structure of the active masses on the electrode process in a lead acid battery

Distribution of polarisation over the thickness of battery electrodes

Porous electrodes

In present day lead acid batteries, as also in the overwhelming majority of other systems of chemical sources of current, electrodes are used which are characterised by a highly porous structure. The active mass of battery electrodes represents a relatively strong electron-carrying frame pierced by a considerable number of pores. The volumetric porosity of the active masses constitutes ~50%.

The use of porous electrodes makes it possible to increase substantially the specific active surface on which the electro-chemical reactions occur. Thanks to this, a considerable increase in discharge capacity is achieved both as a result of an increase in the quantity of active substances participating in the discharge process, which are basically localised on the walls of the pores, and also as a result of the lowering of the density of the discharge current.

The electro-chemical processes occurring on the surface of porous electrodes differ in some particulars. In particular, the specific character of these electrodes is caused by the fact that, generally speaking, their surface is not of equal potential over the thickness of the electrode. The ohmic resistance of the pores (which are filled with electrolyte) and also of the solid-phase base, leads to a more or less uneven distribution of potential and density of current over the surface of the electrode. The character of this distribution depends on the quantity and structure of the pores, the nature of the electrode reactions, the conditions of polarisation, and the physico-chemical properties of the electrode material and the electrolyte. A well-known role can also be played by the presence of a concentration gradient in the electrolyte along the depth of the pores, which is caused by the delayed nature of the diffusion of the solution into the pores of the electrode.

The theory of porous electrodes, the experimental bases of which were laid already in the 1930's, was developed in work carried out in the course of the last 25 years[1]. An important role in the establishment of this field of applied electro-chemistry was played by the fundamental research of V S Daniel-Beck published in 1948[2].

The further development of theoretical premises about porous electro-chemical systems is chiefly connected with the work of A N Frumkin, O S Ksenzhek, V V Stender, V S Daniel-Beck, Newman and Tobias, Winzel, Posey, Euler, Micki etc.

In the literature there are individual attempts at using the theoretical premises about porous electrodes for an examination of the distribution of current in the plates of a lead acid battery. In particular the theory of the porous electrode was used in the work of Euler and others for analysis and modelling of the processes occurring in tubular armoured electrodes of a lead acid battery, which have in recent years achieved considerable popularity abroad. Some results of the current theory of two-phase porous electrodes with reference to the paste-covered electrodes of a lead acid battery are examined in[3].

Experimental investigations devoted to porous electrodes are comparatively few. However, experimental data obtained up to the present time, which we shall examine below, is basically in conformity with theoretical assumptions about current distribution in a porous electrode.

Basic relationships

The processes of flow of current through a porous electrode which are being examined lead to a system of differential equations which take into account the influence of the concentration, diffusion and migration of ions under the action of the forces of the electrical field[4][5]. In general the behaviour of a porous electrode can be described by the following equations:

$$\frac{\partial c_i}{\partial t} = \text{div}(D_i \text{ grad } c_i) + \text{div}(c_i U_i \text{grad } \varphi_2) - \Delta_i - \text{div}(c_i v) \qquad (3.1)$$

$$j_1 = -\varkappa_1 \text{ grad } \varphi_1 \qquad (3.2)$$

$$j_2 = -F \Sigma z_i D_i \text{ grad } c_i - F \Sigma z_i U_i c_i \text{ grad } \varphi_2 \qquad (3.3)$$

$$\text{div}(\sigma_1 j_1 + \sigma_2 j_2) = 0 \qquad (3.4)$$

$$\varphi = \varphi_1 - \varphi_2 \tag{3.5}$$

$$\Sigma c_i z_i = 0 \tag{3.6}$$

where c_i is the concentration of the i component in the solution, D_i the coefficient of diffusion, and U_i the mobility of the i matter, v the rate of flow of the electrolyte through the pores of the electrode, Δ_i the rate of decrease of the i matter as a result of electrode or chemical reaction, φ_1 and φ_2 the values of the potential respectively in the solid phase and in the solution, φ the potential at a given point of the surface of the electrode measured in relation to the solution, σ_1 and σ_2 the parts of the cross-section of the electrode pertaining to the solid and liquid phases, z_i the valency (charge) of the component of the solution, j_1 and j_2 the densities of the current flowing respectively in the solid phase and in the pores of the electrode, $\varkappa_1$ the electrical conductivity of the solid phase. The summation in equations (3.3) and also (3.6), which represents the condition of electrical neutrality, is carried out for all components of the solution.

It must be noted that in equations (3.1) and (3.3) we disregard the properties of movement of the electrolyte in an electric double layer, assuming that its thickness is small in comparison with the radius of the pores. This assumption is fully correct for not too dilute solutions [5]).

The equations quoted give the possibility in principle of determining the current density j at any given point of the porous electrode. The value j is directly linked with the value Δ_i, if the change of concentration on the electrode-electrolyte interface is caused only by the occurrence of the electrode reaction. In this case

$$j = \frac{F}{S} \Sigma z_i \Delta_i \tag{3.7}$$

where S is the specific surface of the electrode per unit of capacity.

Naturally, accurate solving of the system of equations (3.1)-(3.7), cannot be carried out. In principle the use of numerical integration is possible; however, this is generally also linked with quite considerable mathematical difficulties. Therefore use is generally made of a number of simplifications in relation to one concrete objective or another.

Assumptions about the macroscopic uniformity and the unidimensional structure of the electrode [6]) are quite widespread in literature.

The first of these assumptions makes it possible to use for the characteristics of the porous system mean values of such magnitudes as σ_1, σ_2, S, $\varkappa_1$, and also in a number of cases U_i and D_i, although the assumption about the constancy of the mobilities and coefficients of diffusion in the presence of a concentration gradient in the electrolyte in the pores cannot be considered truly strict.

The assumption *) about the unidimensional nature of the electrode, makes it possible to simplify substantially the initial differential equations, reckoning $c_i = c_i(x)$ and $\varphi = \varphi(x)$, is correct in the event of the mean diameter of the pores δ_π being quite small in comparison with the distance over which a marked change of potential or concentration takes place. This condition can be written down[6] in the form

$$\delta_\pi \ll \frac{\varphi}{\partial\varphi/\partial x}, \quad \delta_\pi \ll \frac{c_i}{dc_i/dx} \tag{3.8}$$

Considering battery electrodes, it can be assumed that convective transfer of the electrolyte in the pores plays an insignificant role ($v \approx 0$) owing to the quite small diameter of the pores. If it is necessary to calculate the convection of the electrolyte, this can be done by means of introducing appropriate corrections to the value of the coefficients of diffusion. In a number of cases it can be reckoned that the concentration of the electrolyte is constant over the thickness of the electrode or along the depth of the pores. This assumption is similar to the assumption about the absence of noticeable diffusion difficulties during the occurrence of the electrode process. Data obtained as a result of the study of the discharge characteristics of the negative electrode of a lead acid battery are evidence of the fact that, as a rule, the diffusion of the electrolyte is not a factor limiting the discharge capacity (at least, at not very high currents), As is shown in chapter 4, the rate of the process (2.20) at moderate currents is limited by the electro-chemical stage.

Thus, in consideration of the discharge process occurring on the negative electrode of a lead acid battery, it is possible within known approximation to neglect the influence of diffusion stages on the total rate of reaction. It must be noted that for a similar process on the positive electrode of the battery, the assumption about the absence of a concentration

---

*) It is assumed that the axis x is orientated perpendicularly to the outer surface of the electrode and that the electrode dimensions are sufficiently large for it to be possible to neglect local effects.

gradient in the electrolyte along the depth of the pores is correct, obviously, only at low discharge currents. In particular, this difference is caused by the considerably greater dependence of the equilibrium potential of the positive electrode of the battery on the composition of the electrolyte in comparison with the similar dependency for the negative electrode, which follows from the composition of the formulae (2.21) and (2.28).

It will be later shown that in the absence of a noticeable concentration polarisation the inequalities (3.8) are observed fairly strictly for electrodes of a lead acid battery. This makes it possible to consider the distribution of polarisations in battery electrodes as a function of just the one co-ordinate x. The question of the influence of diffusion of the electrolyte on the work of the battery electrodes will be specially examined below.

With corrections for the assumptions made $[c_i = \text{const}(x)]$ and in the conditions of the stationary state ($\partial c_i / \partial t = 0$) simple conversions of the equations (3.1)-(3.7) make it possible to establish a link between the values of current density j and of potential φ at any point of the surface of a flat porous electrode:

$$j = \frac{A_\sigma}{S} \frac{d^2\varphi}{dx^2} \qquad (3.9)$$

where

$$A_\sigma = \sigma_2 \varkappa_2 \left(1 - \frac{\sigma_2 \varkappa_2}{\sigma_1 \varkappa_1}\right) \qquad (3.10)$$

$\varkappa_2 = F\Sigma z_i U_i c_i$ is the specific electrical conductivity of the electrolyte. Formula (3.9) was first obtained by V S Daniel-Beck on analysis of an electrical model of a porous electrode [2]).

As has already been said, the volumetric porosity of the active masses of a lead acid battery constitutes approximately 50%. Therefore it is possible to calculate with a known degree of approximation that $\sigma_1 \approx \sigma_2$. It is not difficult to show further that with reference to the objective under consideration here $A_\sigma = \sigma_2 \varkappa_2$, since $\varkappa_1 \gg \varkappa_2$.

In fact the specific electrical conductivity of the H_2SO_4 solution serving as the electrolyte of a lead acid battery constitutes $\varkappa_2 = 0.7 \text{ohm}^{-1} \cdot \text{cm}^{-1}$, while the specific electrical conductivity of lead $\varkappa_1 = 0.46 \cdot 10^5 \text{ ohm}^{-1} \cdot \text{cm}^{-1}$. Thus the relationship of the electrical conductivities of the liquid and the solid phases in a charged negative electrode of the battery amounts to $\varkappa_2/\varkappa_1 \approx 10^{-5}$. In the process of discharge the resistance of the active mass increases as a result of the formation of the lead sulphate. However, in normal discharge the electrical conductivity of the negative active mass decreases approximately 1.5 times in all[7]). In this it must be taken into account that in the discharge process a fall in the electrical conductivity of the electrolyte also takes place owing to a decrease in its concentration. So it can be reckoned that the quoted relationship of the values $\varkappa_1$ and $\varkappa_2$ is maintained through all the periods of utilisation of the lead acid battery. This gives a basis for simplification *) of the equation (3.9), which can be rewritten in the form

$$j = \frac{\varkappa\sigma}{S}\,\frac{d^2\varphi}{dx^2} \tag{3.11}$$

This simplification is correct, although with slightly less accuracy, for the positive electrode of the battery too. Having made use of the results of measurement of the specific electrical resistance of PbO_2 (see chapter 4), it is not difficult to show that the relationship of the electrical conductivity of the liquid and solid phases in the charged positive electrode amounts to $\varkappa_2/\varkappa_1 \approx 10^{-3}$. In the process of discharge the resistance of the positive active mass increases approximately 10 times[7]). Thus, in the discharged state of the electrode, the aforementioned relationship of the electrical conductivities should not exceed 10^{-2}.

As was shown in[7]), contact resistance occurs on the grid-active mass interface of the electrode, the specific value of which in the charged state amounts to $4 \cdot 10^{-1/2}\,\text{ohm}\cdot\text{cm}^2$. Although this value is small in comparison with the specific resistance of the battery electrolyte, the presence of transitional layer, which obviously causes the appearance of contact resistance, can show a definite influence on the character of the polarisation distribution over the thickness of the positive electrode of a lead acid battery.

If we write down the electrode potential φ as the sum of the equilibrium value of the potential φ_p and the overvoltage of the electrode reaction η

$$\varphi = \varphi_p + \eta \tag{3.12}$$

and use the equation linking the rate and the overvoltage of the electrochemical stage of the process[8])

*) We omit the indices in the designations $\varkappa$ and σ ($\varkappa_2 \equiv \varkappa$, $\sigma_2 \equiv \sigma$).

$$j = i_0 \left(e^{\frac{\alpha z F \eta}{RT}} - e^{-\frac{\beta z F \eta}{RT}} \right) \tag{3.13}$$

where i_0 is the density of the exchange current, α and β the transfer coefficients, F the Faraday number and z the number of electrons participating in the electrode reaction, then substituting (3.13) with account taken of (3.12) in equation (3.11) we shall have

$$\frac{d^2\eta}{dx^2} = \frac{i_0 S}{\varkappa\sigma} \left(e^{\frac{\alpha z F \eta}{RT}} - e^{-\frac{\beta z F \eta}{RT}} \right) \tag{3.14}$$

In this it is assumed that the value of φ_p does not depend on x, which is correct for a constant concentration of the potential-determining components of the solution over the thickness of the porous electrode under consideration.

For integration of the equation (3.14) it is possible to use the following boundary conditions [2]):

$$\left(\frac{d\eta}{dx}\right)_{x=L} = 0, \quad \left(\frac{d\eta}{dx}\right)_{x=0} = -\frac{j_r}{\varkappa\sigma} \tag{3.15}$$

where j_r is the overall current density on the external surface of the electrode, and L is a value equal, for bilateral polarisation of an electrode with a symmetrically located lead, to half its thickness.

The result of single integration (3.14) under boundary conditions (3.15) has the form:

$$\frac{\left(e^{\frac{\alpha z F \eta_0}{RT}} - e^{\frac{\alpha z F \eta_L}{RT}} \right)}{\alpha} + \frac{\left(e^{-\frac{\beta z F \eta_0}{RT}} - e^{-\frac{\beta z F \eta_L}{RT}} \right)}{\beta} = \frac{j_r^2 z F}{2 i_0 RT \varkappa\sigma S} \tag{3.16}$$

Here η_0 and η_L are the values of overvoltage on the external surface (x = 0) and in the depth (x = L) of a porous electrode respectively. With integration (3.14) it is accepted that $i_0 \neq i_0(x)$, which also assumes the absence of a concentration gradient in the solution along the depth of the pores.

The exponential differences in the left-hand part of equation (3.16) characterise the uniformity of the polarisation of a porous electrode. From this equation it follows that the electrode is polarised the more uniformly (i.e. the values of η_0 and η_L are all the nearer to each other) the less the density of the polarising current and the greater the electrical conductivity of the electrolyte, the porosity and the true surface of the electrode, and also the exchange current of the electrode process.

An increase in temperature, according to equation (3.16) contributes to an improvement of the uniformity of polarisation of the porous electrode, since there the values of T, $\varkappa$ and i_0 increase.

An analysis of equation (3.16) makes it possible to draw a conclusion to the effect that in a lead acid battery at uniform current loads and in the absence of a marked concentration polarisation the positive electrode should work more uniformly than the negative one[3]), since $S_+ > S_-$ and $i_{0+} > i_{0-}$. The different criteria of uniformity of distribution of the process in the pores of the electrode are examined in the works [9])[10]).

The presence of a concentration gradient in the electrolyte along the depth of the pores of the electrode can show a marked influence on the uniformity of polarisation, since, besides the ohmic drop of the potential in the electrolyte of the pores, there will also take place a concentration change of the potential.

In fact, a decrease in the concentration of sulphuric acid in the discharge process should occur most intensively on the external surface of the electrodes (at the mouths of the pores), where the true density of current has the maximum value, and least intensively at the centre of the electrode. Thanks to this, in accordance with formula (2.29), the equilibrium potential of the positive electrode in the plane $x = 0$ will have a lower value than in the plane $x = L$. For the negative electrode at $x = 0$ the value of the equilibrium potential, in accordance with (2.22) will be higher (less negative) than at $x = L$.

From what has been said it follows that the presence of a concentration gradient in H_2SO_4 along the depth of the pores of the battery l has a bad effect on the uniformity of distribution of polarisation in the discharge process. This refers particularly to the positive electrode, on the surface of which there occurs a more marked change of concentration of the electrolyte. In addition a decrease in the values $\varkappa$, σ and S in the discharge process as a result of a decrease of the concentration of the acid and of the active surface of the electrodes should, according to (3.16), lead to a rise in the potential gradient over the thickness of the electrode.

With $\alpha = \beta = 0.5$ equation (3.16) can be rewritten in the form

$$\cosh \frac{\eta_0}{b_1} - \cosh \frac{\eta_L}{b_1} = \frac{j_T^2}{4b_1 i_0 \varkappa \sigma S} \tag{3.17}$$

where $b_1 = 2RT/(zF)$. Naturally all the consequences following from equation (3.17). With integration of the equation (3.14), which in the case $\alpha = \beta = 0.5$ takes on the form

$$\frac{d^2\eta}{dx^2} = \frac{2i_0S}{\varkappa\sigma} \sinh \frac{\eta}{b_1} \tag{3.18}$$

O S Ksenzhek and V V Stender[11]) use the boundary condition at infinity:

$$\eta_{x=\infty} = 0 \tag{3.19}$$

Let us apply the results obtained in this to electrodes of finite dimensions in the case when the value L at least exceeds by 2-3 times the so-called 'effective depth of penetration of the process' Λ[11])

$$\Lambda = \sqrt{\frac{b_1 \varkappa\sigma}{2Si_o}} \tag{3.20}$$

For an electrode of infinite thickness ($L \gg \Lambda$) the value Λ represents the distance over which the initial density of current decreases e $\approx$ 2.7 times[11]). As can be seen from formula (3.20), the value Λ increases with an increase in the electrical conductivity of the electrolyte in the pores and with a decrease in the exchange current and specific internal surface of the electrode.

It must be noted that the identification of the parameter Λ with the thickness of layer of the porous electrode at which the occurrence of the electrode process is limited, which is encountered in some works, does not correspond to the physical concept of this value. Such an identification, as will be shown in chapter 4, in particular, leads to the obtaining of a decreased value of exchange current. For porous electrodes of finite thickness, representing the greatest practical interest, the value Λ can serve principally as a criterion of the applicability of the boundary condition (3.19) in the integration of equation (3.14). The use of Λ as a parameter for determination of the rational thickness of battery plates, as is done in some works[12])[13]), cannot be considered justified.

For evaluation of the value of 'effective depth of penetration' in the case of the negative electrode Λ_- it is possible to use the following data as a starting point: $b_1 = 0.026V$ (at 25°C and $z = 2$), $\varkappa = 0.7$ $ohm^{-1} \cdot cm^{-1}$, $\sigma = 0.5$, $S = 10^4\ cm^2/cm^3$, $i_0 = 5 \cdot 10^{-6} A/cm^2$ [12]). Calculation according to formula (3.20) leads to the following result $\Lambda_- \cong 0.3cm$. Comparison of this value with the thickness of the battery plates shows that $\Lambda \gtrsim L$. From this following the inapplicability of the boundary condition (3.19) in the evaluation of the polarisation distribution over the thickness of the negative electrode of a lead acid battery.

A corresponding calculation for the positive electrode of a lead acid battery characterised by the following parameters: $b_1 = 0.026V$, $\varkappa = 0.7 ohm^{-1} \cdot cm^{-1}$, $\sigma = 0.5$, $S = 7 \cdot 10^4 cm^{-1}$ and $i_0 = 3.2 \cdot 10^{-4} A/cm^2$ (see §4.2), shows that $\Lambda_+ \cong 0.014cm$. Thus in the case of the positive electrode the use of condition (3.19) is fully permissible. This leads to a marked simplification of the equations (3.16)-(3.17), in which it is possible to reckon $\eta_L = 0$.

For the case under consideration here, that of the constancy of composition of the electrolyte along the depth of the pores the value Λ can also be used as a criterion of the possibility of describing a porous electrode with the aid of a unidimensional model. The first of the above-mentioned conditions (3.8) at grad $c_i = 0$ takes on the form[14])

$$\frac{\eta_o/b_1}{sh(\eta_o/2b_1)} \gg \frac{2\delta_\Pi}{\Lambda} \tag{3.21}$$

The mean diameter of the pores of the active mass of the positive electrode $\delta_+ \approx 15\mu m$. A similar value for the negative electrode of the battery δ_- shows the strong dependence on the nature of the organic expansion and the condition of the plates[15]). On average the value of δ_- can be taken as equal to $10\mu m$. Hence, it follows that the value in the right-hand part of the inequality (3.21) constitutes for the positive electrode $\sim 2.2 \cdot 10^{-2}$, and for the negative one $\sim 0.7 \cdot 10^{-2}$. The order of this magnitude does not depend thus on the sign of the battery electrode.

The value standing in the left-hand part of the inequality under consideration decreases with the rise of overvoltage on the external surface of the electrode, as follows from the data quoted below

η_o mV	10	50	100	200	300	400	500
$\frac{\eta_o/b_1}{sh(\eta_o/2b_1)}$	2.02	1.72	1.15	0.33	0.07	0.015	0.006

A comparison of the values shown bears witness to the fact that the inequality (3.21) is correct right up to quite considerable overvoltages (0.2-0.3V), so the use of a unidimensional model for the characteristics of porous electrodes of a lead acid battery is shown to be fully justified.

Features of the behaviour of electrodes at low polarisations

The electrodes of a lead acid battery are characterised by a quite considerable true surface which, as has already been shown, amounts to approximately 10^4 cm^2 in one cubic centimetre of the active mass. Therefore, in spite of the comparatively high current loads, the true current density on the surface of the battery plates is generally small. This gives a basis for using in a number of cases the equations obtained for low polarisations ($\eta \lesssim b_1$). Such equations are considerably simpler than the relationships mentioned above and they make it possible to analyse more clearly the work of the porous electrodes.

Substantial simplification allows, in particular, at $\eta \lesssim b_1$ the use of equation (3.16)[16]. In this case it is possible, expanding in series the exponential values and limiting oneself in to the three first members of the expansion, to obtain after simple conversions the following expression

$$\eta_0^2 - \eta_L^2 \cong \frac{b_1 j_r^2}{2i_0 \varkappa \sigma S} \tag{3.22}$$

If we are further to designate the difference of overvoltages on the external surface of a porous electrode and in its thickness by $\Delta\eta = \eta_0 - \eta_L$, then, neglecting the value $(\Delta\eta)^2$, it is easy to convert the equation (3.22) to the form

$$\Delta\eta \approx \frac{b_1 j_r^2}{4i_0 \varkappa \sigma S \eta_0} \tag{3.23}$$

The value $\Delta\eta$ characterises the maximum change of potential over the thickness of a porous electrode.

Let us note that equation (3.22) can be obtained also from equation (3.17) at $\eta_{0,L} \lesssim b_1$ by means of substitution of $ch(\eta/b_1)$ by $1 + (\eta^2/2b_1^2)$. The relative error in the result of such a substitution increases from 0.01% at $\eta/b_1 = 0.2$ to 2,8% at $\eta = b_1$.

The values of overall density of current and overvoltage on the external surface of the electrode coming into equation (3.23) are mutually linked. As is well known, in many cases there is observed a linear dependence of η_0 on j_r which can be written down[17]) in the form

$$\eta = \frac{RT}{zF}\frac{j_r}{j_0} = \frac{b_1}{2j_0} j_r \tag{3.24}$$

where j_o is the density of exchange current, calculated for the geometric surface of the electrode (S_r).

Obviously

$$j_o = \frac{i_o S V}{S_r} \tag{3.25}$$

where V is the volume of the electrode.

Substituting the expression (3.24) and (3.25) in formula (3.23) and disregarding the area of the side surfaces of the electrode, i.e. reckoning that $V/S_r = L$, we shall have[16])

$$\Delta\eta \cong \frac{j_r L}{2\sigma\varkappa} \tag{3.26}$$

From equation (3.26) it follows that the uniformity of polarisation of the electrode increases ($\Delta\eta$ decreases) with a rise in electrical conductivity of the electrolyte in the pores and a decrease of density of the polarising current and thickness of the electrode.

As an example of the use of the aforementioned formula (3.26) let us calculate the maximum potential drop over the thickness of a plate of a lead acid battery under starting conditions. The overall current density at starter discharge amounts to $j_r \cong 0.1 A/cm^2$. Accepting $\varkappa = 0.7 ohm^{-1} \cdot cm^{-1}$, $\sigma = 0.5$ and $L = 0.15 cm$, we shall have, in accordance with (3.26), $\Delta\eta \approx 0.2 j_r = 0.02V$. Thus, the maximum potential drop over the thickness of the electrode amounts approximately to 20mV. This value is comparatively small. However, it must be reckoned that the overvoltages of the charge-discharge processes on the electrodes of a lead acid battery do not depend much on the current. Lead sulphate, and especially lead dioxide electrodes, are characterised by low polarisability owing to the considerable exchange currents of the corresponding oxidation-reduction equilibria. Therefore, the difference in the true current density on the external surface of a plate and in its thickness can be quite large.

Thus, if we use the dependence of the overvoltage η on the current density j, for the process of anode oxidation $Pb \rightarrow PbSO_4$ obtained by B N Kabanov

$$\eta \cong 0.018 \lg j \tag{3.27}$$

it is not difficult to show that $\Delta\eta = 0.02V$ the value of current density on the external surface of the electrode should exceed more than 10 times the corresponding value at the centre of the plate[16]).

It is natural that, with the presence of a concentration gradient in the electrolyte along the depth of the pores, to the value of $\Delta\eta$ calculated according to formula (3.26) we must add a value equal to the difference of the equilibrium potentials on the surface and in the centre of a porous electrode.

It is quite understandable that the lower the density of the polarising current (or the overvoltage) the greater the justification that the concentration polarisation can be disregarded. In accordance with the data of Grins[6]) the assumption about the uniform distribution of concentration along the depth of the pores is completely correct for the condition

$$\eta_0 \ll \frac{b_1}{2}\left(1 + \frac{z}{|z'|}\right) \tag{3.28}$$

where z is the number of electrons participating in the electrode process and z' the valency of the ions taking part in the current transfer. For processes occurring on the electrodes of a lead acid battery ($z = 2$, $z' = 1$ and $b_1 = 0.026V$) the inequality (3.28) takes on the form $\eta_0 \ll 0.04V$, which already points to the approximate character of the given assumption at comparatively small values of overvoltage.

In the preceding chapter the differential equation (3.14), equivalent in a special case to the equation (3.18), was used for the characteristic of uniformity of polarisation of a porous electrode. This latter formula, taking into account (3.20), can be rewritten in the form

$$\frac{d^2\eta}{dx^2} = \frac{b_1}{\Lambda^2} \sinh \frac{\eta}{b_1} \tag{3.29}$$

or in integral form

$$\int\left(\frac{2b_1^2}{\Lambda^2} \cosh \frac{\eta}{b_1} + C_1\right)^{-1/2} d\eta = x + C_2 \tag{3.30}$$

where C_1 and C_2 are the integration constants.

The integral in the left-hand part of (3.30) cannot be expressed by elementary functions. However, for the field of low overvoltages under consideration here, it is possible to obtain simple integral dependencies describing the profile of the change of potential over the thickness of the electrode.

Thus at $\eta \ll b_1$, i.e. in conditions corresponding approximately to the fulfilment of inequality (3.28), it may be reckoned that $\cosh(\eta/b_1) \simeq 1$. In this case from equation (3.30) it follows that

$$\eta = \eta_0 - \frac{\eta_0 - \eta_L}{L} x \tag{3.31}$$

Equation (3.31) describes the linear voltage drop from the value η_0 at $x = 0$ to η_L at $x = L$, taking place in the field of very low polarisations.

At $\eta \lesssim b_1$, as has already been said, it is possible to calculate with sufficient accuracy that $\cosh(\eta/b_1) = 1 - (\eta^2/2b_1^2)$. In this case integration of (3.30) with the use of the first of the boundary conditions (3.15) gives the following dependency η (x)

$$\eta = \eta_0 \frac{\cosh\,[(1 - x)]\,/\Lambda}{\cosh\,(L/\Lambda)} \tag{3.32}$$

Equation (3.32), as also (3.31), characterises the decrease of η with the rise of x from η_0 on the external surface of the electrode to $\eta_L = \eta_0$ sech(L/Λ) at its centre. However, in the given case, the dependency of η on x bears a more complicated character. From equations (3.26) and (3.32) come formulae for the calculation of the extreme values of overvoltage on the external surface and in the centre of the electrode

$$\left.\begin{aligned} \eta_0 &= \frac{\dfrac{Lj_r}{2\varkappa\sigma}}{\left(1 - \operatorname{sech}\dfrac{L}{\Lambda}\right)} \\ \eta_L &= \frac{\dfrac{Lj_r\,\operatorname{sech}(L/\Lambda)}{2\varkappa\sigma}}{\left(1 - \operatorname{sech}\dfrac{L}{\Lambda}\right)} \end{aligned}\right\} \tag{3.33}$$

The formulae obtained here show that at $L/\Lambda \approx 0.5$ (which is the case for the negative electrode of the battery) the relationship is $\eta_L/\eta_0 \approx 0.78$. At $L \gg \Lambda$ (which is correct with reference to the positive electrode of the battery) $\eta_L \gg 0$. This result points to the fundamental advisability of some reduction in the thickness of the plates of the positive electrode.

Change of current density over the thickness of the electrode in the case of linear dependence of the current on overvoltage is described by equations similar to (3.31) or (3.32). If the factor $j(\eta)$ is determined by formula (3.13), then the curve of change of j with the thickness of the electrode cannot in the usual form be described with the aid of elementary functions. For this case (at $\alpha = \beta$) in the work[12]) the following approximate formula is proposed

$$j = j_o \frac{2\left(1 + \sqrt{1 + y_o^2}\right)}{\left(1 + \sqrt{1 + y_o^2}\right)^2 - y_o^2 \exp(-2x/\Lambda)} \frac{\sinh[(L - x)\Lambda]}{\sinh(L/\Lambda)} \qquad (3.34)$$

where j_o is the value of current density on the external surface of the electrode and $y_o = j_o/4\sqrt{b_1 i_o \varkappa/\delta_\pi}$.

Equations of polarisation graphs

The link between the potential of the external surface of a porous electrode and the overall density of current with activation control of the rate of the electrode process can be obtained by means of a second integration of the equation (3.14) or, in a special case (3.18), with the use of boundary conditions (3.15)[18]). The result of integration of[18]), describing the polarisation graph of a porous electrode, has the form

$$\eta_O = 2b_1 \ \mathrm{Arc\ sinh} \frac{Hj_r}{\mathrm{sn}(u, k)} \qquad (3.35)$$

where sn(u, k) are the Jacobean elliptic sines.

$$u = \frac{L}{\Lambda}\sqrt{\cosh^2 \frac{\eta_O}{2b_1} - (Hj_r)_2}, \quad k = 1/\sqrt{\cosh^2 \frac{\eta_O}{2b_1} - (Hj_r)^2}$$

$$H = 1/\sqrt{8b_1 S\sigma\varkappa i_0}$$

If $L \gg \Lambda$, then sn(u, k) = 1 and formula (3.35) converts into the equation of the polarisation curve of a porous electrode of infinite thickness, which is obtained in the work[11]).

The link between the values η_O and j_r can be expressed in a clear form also in the same case, when the parameter u is sufficiently small. Then, it is possible to reckon *) that $\mathrm{sn}(u, k) \simeq u$ and equation (3.35) takes on the form

*) Using the table values of the elliptic sines, it is not difficult to show that at any value of parameter $(1 > k > 0)$ the difference between u and sn(u, k) does not exceed 1.5% at $u < 0.2$ and does not exceed 5% at $u < 0.4$.

$$\eta_0 \cong 2b_1 \text{Arc sinh} \sqrt{\frac{[(Hj_r)^2 - 1]L + \sqrt{[(Hj_r)^2 - 1]^2 L^2 + (2H\Lambda j_r)^2}}{2L}} \quad (3.36)$$

This equation is correct, especially in the case when the thickness of the electrode is small in comparison with the value Λ. At the given relationship L/Λ the value u increases with a rise in polarisation. Therefore equation (3.36) can be used at comparatively low currents of polarisation and in the case of fairly thin electrodes.

With $(Hj_r)^2 = j_r^2/8b_1 S\sigma\varkappa i_o \ll 1$, in accordance with (3.36)

$$\eta_0 \cong b_1 \text{ Arc sinh } \frac{j_r}{2SLi_o} \quad (3.37)$$

Equation (3.37) is similar to the expression for the polarisation curve of a smooth electrode, the surface area of which is equal to the area of the true surface of a porous electrode. The result obtained shows that the surface of a thin porous electrode in the range of low current densities is polarised practically uniformly.

Let us note that the conclusion drawn about the influence of current density on the uniformity of polarisation is in the usual form correct for a porous electrode of any thickness. This follows from equation (3.16) or (3.17), in accordance with which $\eta_L \to \eta$ at $j_r \to 0$.

At $(Hj_r)^2 \gg 1$ the equation (3.36) can be written down in the form

$$\eta_0 \approx b_1 \ln \frac{2H^2}{L} + 2b_1 \ln j_r \quad (3.38)$$

from which it follows that the slope of the polarisation curve for a porous electrode at high current densitives, plotted against semi-logarithmic co-ordinates, is twice the corresponding value for a smooth electrode[18]).

This result also follows from equation (3.17). In fact, in the field of high current densities $\eta_0 \gg \eta_L$ whence

$$\cosh \frac{\eta_0}{b_1} - \cosh \frac{\eta_L}{b_1} \cong 0.5\, e^{\eta_0/b_1} \quad (3.39)$$

Substituting (3.39) in (3.17) and converting the equation obtained to logarithms, it is not difficult to obtain an equation similar to (3.38).

Over a wide interval of overall current densities the dependency

$(\eta_0, \ln j_r)$ is characterised by a curve with a variable coefficient of slope, the value of which increases with an increase in current[10]. In the case of the influence of diffusion on the working of a porous electrode the equation of the polarisation curve has the form[4]

$$\eta = 2b_1 \ln [j_r/(zFc_0\sqrt{SD'k})] \tag{3.40}$$

where c_0 is the concentration of the reacting matter in the solution, D' the coefficient of diffusion in the pores of the electrode, k the constant of the rate of electrode reaction.

With the use of the above-mentioned formulae it is necessary to bear in mind the possibility of the change of active surface of a porous electrode in the process of polarisation. As is shown in the paper[15], the pores of the negative plates of a lead acid starter battery generally contain 23-36% of hydrogen. The content of the gas oscillates in dependence on the form of expander used and the state of the electrode. Gas filling in the pores of the positive plates amounts to 10-15%.

It is natural that the screening effect on the electrode surface from gas depends on the conditions of polarisation, which determine both the degree of uniformity of gassing over the thickness of the electrode and also the surface tension on the electrode-solution interface. At low current densities, when the process of gassing occurs with relatively uniform speed over the whole surface of the electrode, a considerable amount of gas bubbles can remain in the depth of the pores, insulating the internal part of the electrode from the electrolyte. With an increase in current, as was shown above, there is an increase in the unevenness of distribution of the process. At high current densities a basic quantity of gas is liberated on the external surface of the electrode. Naturally the possibility of the screening of the internal surface is thereby decreased.

It must also be noted that a rise in polarisation, often leading to a considerable shift of electrode potential with reference to the point of zero charge, causes a decrease in surface tension on the metal-solution boundary, thanks to which there is a decrease in the local wetting angle and the breakaway of gas bubbles from the surface of the electrode[8] is made easier.

Thus both the effects described above should lead to an increase in the active surface of a porous electrode with a rise in polarisation. This phenomenon should in its turn lessen the slope of the polarisation curves $(\eta_0, \ln j_r)$ owing to the decrease in true current density in proportion to the increase in polarisation. The surface screening by gas bubbles leads to more uniform polarisation of a porous electrode.

It is natural that the surface tension depends (at a given temperature and composition of the solution) exclusively on the situation of the potential in relation to the point of zero charge. Therefore the decrease in gas filling the plates of the negative electrode of a lead acid battery, noted in[15]), in the process of their deep discharge with a 50-hour regime can be explained by the considerable shift of the electrode potential to the positive side in relation to the potential of zero discharge of lead.

Using the condition of equilibrium of a gas bubble on the surface of the electrode[8]), it is not difficult to show that an increase in temperature of the electrolyte should also cause a decrease of the gas filling of the electrode as a result of reduction in surface tension and local wetting angle.

Let us consider the question of the change of potential and density of current in the thickness of a porous electrode with unlimited increase in polarisation of the external surface[3]). In the work[19]) it is shown that the value of current and potential at any distance from the external surface of the electrode ($x > 0$) has a finite value even with an infinite increase in these on the external surface ($x = 0$). This result is obtained with the use of the equations deduced for a porous electrode of infinitely large thickness ($L \gg \Lambda$). A similar task may be solved for an electrode of finite thickness with the aid of equations[17])[36]). Simultaneous solution of these equations leads to the following result

$$\eta_L = 2b_1 \operatorname{Arc\,sinh} \sqrt{\frac{1 - (L/\Lambda)^2}{\cosh^2(\eta_0/2b_1) + (L/\Lambda)^2}} \tag{3.41}$$

whence

$$\eta_L^\infty = \lim_{\eta_0 \to \infty} \eta_L = 2b_1 \operatorname{Arc\,sinh} \frac{L}{\Lambda} \sqrt{1 - \left(\frac{L}{\Lambda}\right)^2} \tag{3.42}$$

Using equation (3.13) at $\alpha = \beta = 0.5$ and (3.42), it is possible to obtain an expression for the limiting value of current density in the depth of a porous electrode

$$j_L^\infty = \lim_{\eta_0 \to \infty} j_L = \frac{4 i_0 \Lambda^2}{L^2} \sqrt{1 - \left(\frac{L}{\Lambda}\right)^2} \tag{3.43}$$

From equations (3.42) and (3.43) it can be seen that the limiting values of overvoltage and current density in the depth of a porous electrode at $\eta_0 \to \infty$ are quite small. Thus, if we use the above-mentioned values of the parameters characterising the negative electrode of a lead acid battery ($i_0 = 5 \cdot 10^{-6}$ A/cm^6, $b_1 = 0.026$V, L = 0.15cm, $\Delta = 0.3$cm), then, in accordance with (3.42), $\eta_L^\infty = 0.07$V and, in accordance with (3.43) $j_L^\infty = 10^{-4}$ A/cm^2.

The comparatively small values of η_L^∞ and j_L^∞ are explained by the sharp increase in the unevenness of polarisation at high currents. Naturally, with polarisation of the electrode in the sphere of considerable currents the concentration polarisation must not be neglected, which should lead, however, to a still greater increase of the gradients of potential and current over the thickness of the electrode, thus causing a decrease in the limiting values η_L and j_L.

At the same time from formulae (3.42) and (3.43) it follows that at $L \to 0$ the values of j_L^∞ and η_L^∞ tend towards infinity, i.e. in proportion to the decrease in thickness of the porous electrode its characteristics even at high polarisation come closer to the characteristics of the smooth electrode. From the formulae quoted it can also be seen that a rise in the value of Λ leads to an increase of η_L^∞ and j_L^∞. At the limit with $\Delta \to \infty$ the values η_L^∞ and j_L^∞ also tend towards infinity.

In accordance with equation (3.20), the value of Λ increases with a rise in the electrical conductivity of the electrolyte, and also in the relationship σ/S, which, as will be shown below [see (3.67)], is proportional to the diameter of the pores. These results bear witness to the fact of the benefit of decreasing the thickness of the battery plates and increasing the diameter of the pores of the active mass for an improvement in the uniformity of polarisation over the thickness of the electrode.

The influence of surface-active substances on the uniformity of polarisation of the negative electrode of a lead acid battery

In the manufacture of the negative electrode of a lead acid battery as is well known, various organic additives are used. The mechanism of the action of these substances will be examined in detail in chapter 4. Here, however, it is necessary to go into the question of how the adsorption of these compounds, which possess considerable surface activity, influences the distribution of polarisation over the thickness of the electrode[20][21].

Equation (3.16), characterising the dependence of the uniformity of polarisation of a porous electrode on the overall current density, the parameters of the electrode reaction and the porosity, is quoted without taking into account the influence of the structure of the double layer on the overvoltage of the electrode reaction. In this equation no account is taken either of the possibility of the screening of the electrode surface by the adsorbed particles. Therefore, this equation is unsuitable for showing the influence of surface-active substances on the distribution of the potential and current over the surface of a porous electrode.

If we reckon that the rate of the charge-discharge process (2.23) occurring on the negative electrode of the battery is limited by the electro-chemical stage, then the relationship between the rate of the electrode process j and the overvoltage η with the presence of adsorbed particles on the surface of the electrode can be written in the form

$$j = j_o (1 - \theta) e^{-\frac{\beta z F \psi_1'}{RT}} \left(e^{\frac{\beta z F \nu}{RT}} - e^{-\frac{\alpha z F \eta}{RT}} \right) \tag{3.44}$$

where θ is the degree of filling up of the surface with adsorbed substances, and ψ_1' is the value of the potential measured in direct proximity (at a distance of the order of ion radius) to the surface of the electrode in relation to the thickness of the solution with the presence on the electrode of adsorbed particles. The previously used equation (3.13) represents a special case (3.44) with $\theta = 0$ and $\psi_1' = 0$.

Substituting the equation (3.44) in formula (3.11) taking into account (3.12) and carrying out integration in boundary conditions (3.15), it is possible to obtain the following expression for overall current density

$$j_r = \sqrt{2 i_0 \varkappa \sigma S \int_{\eta'_L}^{\eta'_0} (1 - \theta) e^{-\frac{\beta z F \psi_1'}{RT}} \left(e^{\frac{\beta z F \eta}{RT}} - e^{-\frac{\alpha z F \eta}{RT}} \right) d\eta} \tag{3.45}$$

In the absence of surface-active substances equation (3.45) may be written down in the form

$$j_r = \sqrt{2 i_0 \varkappa \sigma S^o \int_{\eta^o_L}^{\eta^o_0} e^{-\frac{\beta z F \eta_1^o}{RT}} \left(e^{\frac{\beta z F \eta}{RT}} - e^{-\frac{\alpha z F \eta}{RT}} \right) d\eta} \tag{3.46}$$

The limits of integration in the formula (3.45) η'_0 and η'_L represent the overvoltage values on the external surface and in the thickness of a porous electrode in the presence of matter being adsorbed. There are similar values in formula (3.46): η°_0 and η°_L are the values of η on the external surface and at the centre of an electrode which does not contain special surface-active additives, S° is the value of the specific internal surface of this electrode and ψ°_1 the value of the ψ_1 potential in the absence of surface-active additives. The value of $\psi^\circ_1 < 0$ in fairly concentrated H_2SO_4 solutions is caused by the adsorption on the electrode of sulphate ions.

Equating the right-hand parts of equations (3.45) and (3.46), i.e. comparing the distribution of polarisation over the thickness of the two electrodes being polarised at one and the same overall current density in the presence of surface-active additives and in pure electrolyte, we obtain

$$S \int_{\eta'_L}^{\eta'_0} (1-\theta)\, e^{-\frac{\beta z F \psi'_1}{RT}} \left(e^{\frac{\beta z F \eta}{RT}} - e^{-\frac{\alpha z F \eta}{RT}} \right) d\eta = S^\circ \int_{\eta^0_L}^{\eta^0_0} e^{-\frac{\beta z F \psi^0_1}{RT}} \left(e^{\frac{\beta z F \eta}{RT}} - e^{-\frac{\alpha z F \eta}{RT}} \right) d\eta \qquad (3.47)$$

The difference in the potentials on the external surface and in the thickness of the electrode, i.e. (with constant electrolyte concentration along the depth of the pores) the values $\eta'_0 - \eta'_L$ and $\eta^\circ_0 - \eta^\circ_L$ can serve as a natural characteristic of the uniformity of polarisation of the electrodes being compared. If the introduction of surface-active matter causes a more uniform current distribution then obviously

$$\eta'_0 - \eta'_L < \eta^\circ_0 - \eta^\circ_L \qquad (3.48)$$

In accordance with equation (3.47), the inequality (3.48) is fulfilled on the condition

$$S(1-\Theta)\, e^{-\frac{\beta z F \psi'_2}{RT}} > S^\circ\, e^{-\frac{\beta z F \psi^0_1}{RT}} \qquad (3.49)$$

or (at $z > 0$)

$$\Delta\psi_1 < \frac{RT}{\beta z F} \left[\ln \frac{S}{S^\circ} + \ln (1-\Theta) \right] \qquad (3.50)$$

where $\Delta\psi_1 = \psi_1' - \psi_1^\circ$ the shift of ψ_1 potential under the influence of adsorption of surface-active matter. If in the special case the introduction of an additive does not cause any marked change of active surface of the electrode ($S \approx S^\circ$ and $\Theta \ll 1$), i.e. the action of the additive is connected exclusively with its influence on the structure of the electrical double layer, then the inequality (3.50) is simplified and takes on the form

$$\Delta\psi_1 < 0 \tag{3.51}$$

In accordance with (3.51), the introduction of surface-active additives improves the uniformity of current distribution over the thickness of a porous electrode on the surface of which a discharge of cations or an ionisation of the metal occurs. In the case when adsorption of the corresponding additive causes a shift of the ψ_1 potential to the negative size, since $\psi_1^\circ < 0$, the value of ψ_1' should exceed ψ_1°, according to absolute values. The negative shift of the ψ_1 potential, as is well known, is observed with adsorption of anion-active compounds[8]).

Naturally, the use of inequality (3.51) assumes unchangeability of the active surface of the electrode. In general, for analysis of the influence of one or the other surface-active substance on the behaviour of a porous lead electrode, it is necessary to use inequality (3.50).

If $S = S^\circ(1 - \Theta)$, i.e. the effect of adsorption of the surface-active substances on the value of the active surface of the electrode leads to a screening of part of the surface, then, according to (3.50)

$$\Delta\psi_1 < \frac{RT}{\beta z F} \ln(1 - \Theta) < 0 \tag{3.52}$$

Obviously, the inequality (3.52) is analogous in a sense to the inequality (3.51). However, in the given case, the influence of the surface active additives on the uniformity of distribution of polarisation over the thickness of the electrode should increase.

Let us note that the results obtained are shown to be correct also in the case when the resistance of the material is commensurate with the resistance of the electrolyte. The distribution of potential over the thickness of such an electrode is described by equation (3.9), the boundary conditions of which for integration of[9]) have the form

$$\left(\frac{d\eta}{dx}\right)_{x=0} = -\frac{j_r}{\varkappa_1\sigma_1} \quad \text{and} \quad \left(\frac{d\eta}{dx}\right)_{x=L} = \frac{j_r}{\varkappa_2\sigma_2} \tag{3.53}$$

The change of sign of the derivative $\partial\eta/\partial x$ in the interval of $0 \leqslant x \leqslant L$ is evidence of the fact that between the external surface of the electrode and its centre there is a value of x at which $\partial\eta/\partial x = 0$ and the overvoltage η_m is minimal.

For the characteristic of uniformity of behaviour of a porous electrode with a comparatively low electrical conductivity of the solid phase, the values of the differences of overvoltage $\eta_0 - \eta_m$ and $\eta_L - \eta_m$ may serve as the most corresponding limits of integration and of the pre-integral factors in formulae (3.45) and (3.46); however, it does not change the final result. Instead of the inequality (3.48) in the case given we shall have

$$\left.\begin{array}{l} \eta'_0 - \eta'_m < \eta^o_0 - \eta^o_m \\ \eta'_L - \eta'_m < \eta^o_L - \eta^o_m \end{array}\right\} \qquad (3.54)$$

The values of η' as before refer to an electrode on the surface of which there is adsorbed matter, and η^o to an electrode being polarised in a 'pure' solution. The inequalities (3.54), and also the inequality (3.48), which is correct for electrodes with low resistance of the solid phase, leads to (3.50). Therefore, the results described above bear witness to the fact that, if the introduction of an organic additive does not change the active surface of the negative electrode of a lead acid battery or decreases it, the uniformity of polarisation of the electrode over its thickness should improve under the effect of anion-active additives.

As will be shown in chapter 5, many of the expanders used in the production of storage batteries evidently belong to the group of anionic materials. The previously described[22]) improvement in the uniformity of current distribution when the active mass of the negative electrode contains organic expanders can therefore be explained in terms of the presented ideas. The non-dependence of the specific weight discharge capacity on the thickness of the negative plates (in a specific thickness range of 1.1-4.4mm), established in the literature[23]), is probably also explained by the effect of anionic components of the expander on the uniformity of distribution of polarisation in the discharge process.

The introduction of organic expanders, as is well known, causes an increase in the true surface of the electrode. Therefore, in accordance with (3.50), at $S > S^o$ the field of favourable values of the ψ_1 potential is broadened in the direction of more positive values. If adsorption leads to a reduction of the active surface of the electrode as a result of a rise in the value of Θ (which obviously takes place with the introduction into the active mass of some inhibitors in the absence of corresponding depassivators), then, in accordance with inequality (3.50), the field of favourable values of the ψ_1 potential shifts to the negative side.

The values of ψ_1 and Θ are clearly, generally speaking, functions of the potential of the electrode[8]). The conclusions drawn do not depend, however, on the form of the functional dependencies $\psi_1(\eta)$ and $\Theta(\eta)$, since they do not require the carrying out of integration of the equation (3.47). If, in the special case, we reckon the values of ψ_1 and Θ as constant in the interval of change $\eta : \eta_0 \geqslant \eta \geqslant \eta_L$, then integrating (3.47) with the use of the boundary conditions (3.15), we shall have (at $\alpha = \beta = 0.5$)

$$\frac{\cosh(\eta'_0/b_1) - \cosh(\eta'_L/b_1)}{\cosh(\eta^0_0/b_1) - \cosh(\eta^0_L/b_1)} = \frac{S^0}{S(1-\theta)}\, e^{\frac{zF\Delta\psi_1}{2RT}} \tag{3.55}$$

From the equation (3.55) it follows that the expression standing in the left-hand part is the smaller, the higher the negative value of $\Delta\psi_1$ and the lower the ratio S^0/S. In other words, a shift to the negative side of the ψ_1 potential and an increase of the specific internal surface of the electrode under the influence of an organic additive causes a decrease in the difference in the values of the potential on the surface and in the thickness of the electrode. This result is in complete conformity with the conclusions drawn above. In this, as can be seen from equation (3.55), the change of ψ_1 potential should have an effect on the character of the distribution of polarisation over the thickness of the electrode much more markedly than a change of specific internal surface.

Analysis of the influence of surface-active substances on the polarisation of a porous electrode shows therefore that one of the important functions of organic additives used in the production of lead acid batteries is the improvement of the uniformity of the behaviour of the active mass over the thickness of the negative electrode.

The theory of the discharge process

Discharge graphs of battery electrodes

Mathematical analysis of the discharge process occurring on a porous electrode is generally linked with considerable difficulties. In the discharge process there is observed, especially, a substantial change of phase composition of the electrode base, caused by partial conversion of the electrical conducting material into a compound which does not possess noticeable conductivity. On discharge of the electrodes of a lead acid battery, a layer of lead sulphate is formed on the walls of the pores. This leads to a decrease in time in the diameter of the pores and a change in their structure ture. This last phenomenon is connected with the difference in the volumes of the initial active materials (Pb and PbO_2) and lead sulphate. The consumption of sulphuric acid in the discharge process and the difficulty in diffusion of it from the solution as a result of a narrowing of the pores, should inevitably lead to a progressive decrease in the concentration of the electrolyte in the pores of the battery plates. In addition, the formation of lead sulphate leads to screening of part of the active surface of the electrodes of the battery and, in time, to a corresponding increase in true current density. Thus, the battery electrodes in the process of discharge represent essentially non-stationary systems, all the basic properties of which change in time. This circumstance does not permit us at the present time to give a strict quantitative treatment of the phenomenon under consideration.

In the literature there are different attempts to examine the current distribution in a porous electrode with variable diameter of the pores[24]). However, the results obtained are marked by considerable complexity and cannot be directly used for the case in point. Mathematical description of the discharge process is possible with the introduction of a number of simplifying propositions.

The discharge theory of porous electrodes developed by Winzel[18]) is worthy of the greatest interest. The author examines the current distribution in cylindrical pores of length L and radius r, the internal surface of which is uniformly filled with an active mass with capacity q_o Kl/cm^2. Discharge in the pore is carried out with a constant current strength I. It is also suggested that between overvoltage η and the current density j there is a linear dependence with constant polarisation resistance R_π.

The active mass at the mouth of the pores (x = 0) is rapidly discharged, which leads to a rise in resistance and a displacement of the pores to the depth of the pores. At the moment of time τ the area of the wall of the pore from the mouth to a certain value of $x_o(\tau)$ is fully discharged (passivated) and takes no part in the process.

It is possible thus to write down the following initial equations:

$$\left.\begin{array}{l} j = R_\pi^{-1}\,\eta \quad \text{at} \quad x_o \leqslant x \leqslant L \\ j = 0 \quad \text{at} \quad 0 \leqslant x < x_o \end{array}\right| \qquad (3.56)$$

Using formula (3.11) and boundary conditions (3.15) (at $i_r = I/\pi r^2$), it is not difficult taking account of (3.20) to convert the system of equations (3.56) into the form

$$\left.\begin{aligned} \eta &= \frac{I\Lambda}{\pi r^2 \varkappa} \frac{\cosh\left[(L - x)/\Lambda\right]}{\sinh\left[(L - x_0)/\Lambda\right]} \\ j &= \frac{I\Lambda}{\pi r^2 \varkappa R_\pi} \frac{\cosh\left[(1 - x)\,\Lambda\right]}{\sinh\left[(L - x_0)\Lambda\right]} \end{aligned}\right\} \text{ at } x_0 < x < L \qquad (3.57)$$

and

$$\left.\begin{aligned} \eta &= \frac{I}{\pi r^2 \varkappa}\left\{x_0 - x + \Lambda \coth\left[(1 - x_0)\Lambda\right]\right\} \\ j &= 0 \end{aligned}\right\} \text{ at } 0 < x < x_0 \qquad (3.58)$$

The polarisation measured at the mouth of the pore is given, in accordance with (3.58), by the equation

$$\eta_0 = \frac{I}{\pi r^2 \varkappa}\left(x_0 + \Lambda \coth \frac{L - x_0}{\Lambda}\right) \qquad (3.59)$$

The value of x_0 increases in the discharge process. The dependence of x_0 on τ, obtained with the aid of the second of the equations (3.57), has the form[18])

$$\tanh \frac{L - x_0}{\Lambda} + \frac{x_0}{\Lambda} = \tanh \frac{L}{\Lambda} + \frac{I\Lambda}{\varkappa} \frac{\tau - \tau_0}{\pi r^2 q_0 R_\pi} \qquad (3.60)$$

where the constant

$$\tau_0 = \frac{\pi r^2 q_0 \varkappa R_\pi \tanh (L/\Lambda)}{I\Lambda} \qquad (3.61)$$

characterises the interval of time from the switching on of the discharge current to that moment when the active mass in the plane $x = 0$ is shown to be fully passivated. As follows from (3.61), τ_0 decreases with a rise in discharge current and 'effective depth of penetration' and increases with a rise in the radius of the pores, the electrical conductivity of the electrolyte, the specific discharge capacity and the polarisation resistance.

In Winzel's work[18]) an equation defining the time of complete discharge was also obtained

$$\tau_m = \frac{\pi r^2 q_o R_\pi L \varkappa}{\Lambda^2 I} = \frac{2\pi r L q_o}{I} \tag{3.62}$$

From (3.61) and (3.62) it follows that the relationship

$$\tau_o/\tau_m = \frac{\tanh(L/\Lambda)}{L/\Lambda} \tag{3.63}$$

does not depend on the discharge current.

Equation (3.63) makes it possible, in particular, to determine Λ according to the known values τ_o and τ_m. Substituting the value τ_o (3.61) and (3.60), it is possible to express the dependency $x_o(\tau)$ by the following transcendental equation

$$x_o + \Lambda \tanh \frac{L - x_o}{\Lambda} = \frac{I\tau}{2\pi r q_o} \tag{3.64}$$

The calculation of the graphs $(x_o/L, \tau/\tau_m)$ and $(\eta_o/\eta_i, \tau/\tau_m)$ *) carried out in ref. [18]), the results of which are represented in figs. 3.1 and 3.2, showed that the ratio L/Λ exerts a substantial influence on the course of the discharge process. If the length of the pores L is small in comparison with Λ, then the walls of the pores are discharged practically uniformly and for almost the whole time τ_m the overvoltage η_0 is constant. Only at the end of the discharge is a rapid rise in polarisation noticeable, when the zone of passivation spreads to the whole pore.

On the other hand, if $L \gg \Lambda$ (which is realised, as has been shown above, in the case of the positive electrode of the battery), then the constancy of polarisation is observed for a comparatively short time. Yet the overvoltage rises approximately in proportion to the time. A sharp rise in polarisation takes place at the end of the discharge. The sharp rise in polarisation, causing a deflection of the discharge graph at the end of the discharge, follows directly from equation (3.59), according to which $\eta_0 \to \infty$ at $x_o \to L$.

Considering in the first approximation the porous electrode as a system of cylindrical pores disposed in parallel, the mean number of which at 1cm² electrode section is equal to N, it is possible to write

$$\sigma = \pi r^2 N \tag{3.65}$$

$$S = 2\pi r N \tag{3.66}$$

---

*) $\eta_i = LI/(\pi r^2 \varkappa)$ the ohmic voltage drop

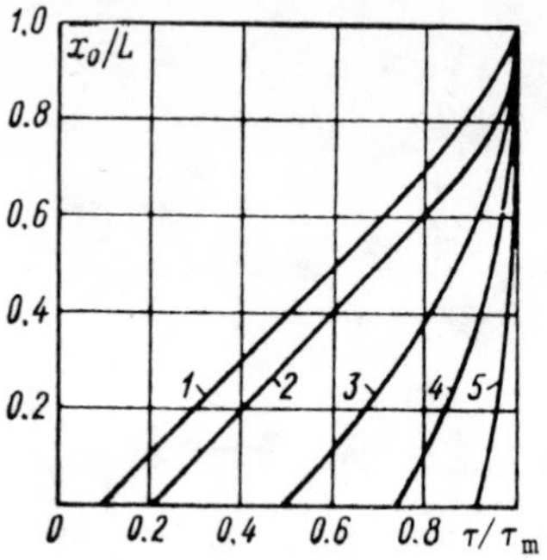

Fig. 3.1 Time-dependence of the relative extent of the passivated zone at the discharge of a cylindrical pore. 1 - $L/\Lambda = 10$; 2 - $L/\Lambda = 5$; 3 - $L/\Lambda = 3$; 4 - $L/\Lambda = 1$; 5 - $L/\Lambda = 0.1$.

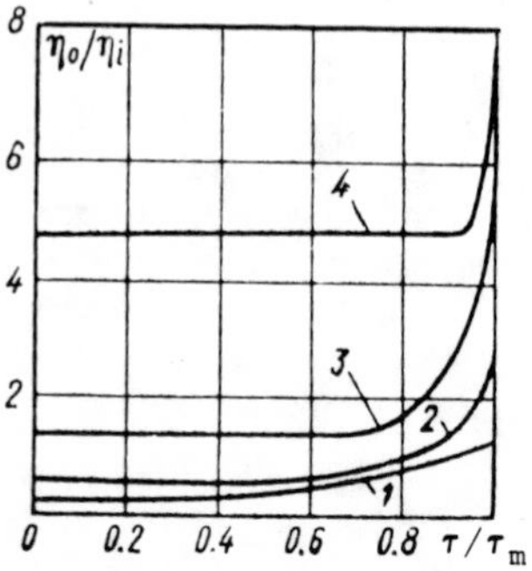

Fig. 3.2 Calculated discharge graphs of a cylindrical pore. 1 - $L/\Lambda = 10$; 2 - $L/\Lambda = 2$; 3 - $L/\Lambda = 1$; 4 - $L/\Lambda = 0.5$.

Individual division of equations (3.65) and (3.66) leads to the following expression for the radius of the pores

$$r = 2\sigma/S \qquad (3.67)$$

The value of I can be expressed with the aid of formulae (3.65)-(3.67) through the overall current density:

$$I = \frac{j_r}{N} = \frac{4\pi\sigma j r}{S^2} \qquad (3.68)$$

Taking account of the formulae (3.67) and (3.68), it is possible to write down the equations (3.59) and (3.64) in the form[3])

$$\eta_0 + \frac{j_r}{\sigma\varkappa}\left(x_0 + \Lambda \coth \frac{L - x_0}{\Lambda}\right) \tag{3.69}$$

$$x_0 + \Lambda \tanh \frac{L - x_0}{\Lambda} = \frac{j\,\tau}{Sq_0} \tag{3.70}$$

In the initial period of discharge $x \ll L$. Simultaneous solving of equations (3.69) and (3.70) leads in this case to the following dependence of the overvoltage on the external surface of the electrode (η_0^{init}) on the time of discharge

$$\eta_0^{init} = \frac{j_r}{\sigma\varkappa}\left(\frac{j_r\tau}{Sq_0} + 2\Lambda \operatorname{cosech} \frac{2L}{\Lambda}\right) \tag{3.71}$$

whence it can be seen that the initial part of the discharge graph is linear with a slope proportional to the square of the overall current density

$$\partial\eta_0^{init}/\partial\tau = j_r^2/\sigma\varkappa Sq_0$$

If the difference $L-x_0$ is small in comparison with the value of Λ, then the hyperbolic functions in equations (3.69) and (3.70) can be expanded in series and replaced by the two first members of the expansion *). In this case the solving of equations (3.69) and (3.70) makes it possible to eliminate the value x_0 and lead to the following equation of the discharge graph of a porous electrode[3])

$$\eta_0 \approx \frac{j_r L}{\varkappa\sigma}\left[1 - 0.96(\Lambda/L)^{2/3}\left(1 - \frac{j_r\tau}{Sq_0 L}\right)^{1/3} + 0.69(\Lambda/L)^{4/3}\left(1 - \frac{j_r\tau}{Sq_0 L}\right)^{-1/3}\right] \tag{3.72}$$

By expanding in series the binomials in the right-hand part of equation (3.72), it is possible to represent the dependence of η_0 on τ in the form of an exponential series

$$\eta_0 = A_0 + A_1\tau + A_2\tau^2 + A_3\tau^3 + \ldots + A_k\tau^k + \ldots \tag{3.73}$$

---

*) $\tanh \approx z - (z^3/3)$; $\coth z \approx (1/z) + z/3)$

where

$$A_o = \frac{j_r L}{\varkappa\sigma}\left[1 - 0.96\left(\frac{\Lambda}{L}\right)^{2/3} + 0.69\left(\frac{\Lambda}{L}\right)^{4/3}\right],$$

$$A_1 = \frac{j_r^2}{\varkappa\sigma S q_o}\left[0.32\left(\frac{\Lambda}{L}\right)^{2/3} + 0.23\left(\frac{\Lambda}{L}\right)^{4/3}\right],$$

$$A_2 = \frac{j_r^3}{\varkappa\sigma S^2 q_o^2 L}\left[0.11\left(\frac{\Lambda}{L}\right)^{2/3} + 0.15\left(\frac{\Lambda}{L}\right)^{4/3}\right],$$

$$A_3 = \frac{j_r^4}{\varkappa\sigma S^3 q_0^3 L^2}\left[0.06\left(\frac{\Lambda}{L}\right)^{2/3} + 0.12\left(\frac{\Lambda}{L}\right)^{4/3}\right],$$

....

$$A_k = \frac{j_r^{k+1}}{\varkappa\sigma S^k q_o^k L^{k-1}}\left[a_k\left(\frac{\Lambda}{L}\right)^{2/3} + b_k\left(\frac{\Lambda}{L}\right)^{4/3}\right]. \qquad (3.74)$$

The values of coefficients a_k and b_k in formula (3.74), which are correct at $k \neq 0$, decreases with a rise in k.

Considering the discharge of a porous lead electrode, it must be noted that the presence of surface-active additives/expanders (depassivators) leads also to a rise in the values of S and q_o. An increase in q_o is clearly a consequence of an increase in the porosity and the thickness of the passivating sulphate film appearing at the discharge. Thanks to this, coefficients A_k ($k = 1.2, ..$) decrease, which should lead to a smoother slope of the discharge graph and to an increase in discharge capacity, which is determined by the time required for attaining the determined given value of η_0.

The coefficients A_k in the formula (3.73) decrease quickly with a rise in k. Calculation of the first three coefficients for discharge of the negative electrode of a lead acid battery at starter regime *) leads to the following values: $A_o = 0.052$V, $A_1 = 2.4 \cdot 10^{-3}$ V/min, $A_2 = 6.2 \cdot 10^{-5}$ V/min^2. Hence it follows that in the course of the basic discharge time (excluding the initial and final periods) the factor $\eta_0(\tau)$ is close to linear, which is confirmed by analysis of experimental discharge graphs.

---

*) In calculation the value of q_o = 1.3A·min/cm^2, obtained at the discharge of a smooth Pb electrode in the presence of humic acid, is used.

Naturally, the formula (3.73), quoted with the use of a number of approximations, cannot serve for an accurate quantitative description of the discharge graph of the electrodes of a lead acid battery. In the discharge process, as has already been shown, changes are possible in the structure of the pores of the electrode. In addition, at discharge, particularly in its final period, there can take place the well known shift of equilibrium potential of the electrode as a result of the decrease in concentration of H_2SO_4 in the pores*). Finally, the features of the change of potential of a lead electrode in the initial discharge graph, cannot be described either with the aid of equation (3.73) without additional complication to it. Equation (3.73) can, nevertheless, be used as a semi-empirical formula, suitable for the discharge characteristics of a lead acid battery.

An equation of the discharge graph was obtained above as a consequence of Winzel's theory[18]). This method is not, however, the only possible one. In ref.[25]) an empirical formula was put forward by L S Greenberg characterising the change of voltage with time on the discharge of different sources of current (including lead acid batteries). Taking into account the fact that in the basic period of discharge the voltage U drops in the time τ according to the linear law and only in the final period does it decrease more sharply, the author[25]) obtained an equation of the discharge graph, representing the discharge voltage as the sum of the linear and exponential members:

$$U = \frac{u_1 \tau_2 - u_2 \tau_1}{\tau_2 - \tau_1} + \frac{u_2 - u_1}{\tau_2 - \tau_1} \tau + Ae^{\beta\tau} \tag{3.75}$$

where u_1 and u_2 are the values of voltage at the moments of time τ_1 and τ_2 respectively on the linear section of the graph (U, τ) and A and B are the empirical constants. The equation (3.75) can be used for predicting the capacity of the batteries from the initial points of the discharge graph.

In the work of B V Byelyayev[26]) a formula was proposed characterising the discharge of a battery at constant load resistance τ

$$\frac{U}{U_0} = 1 - k_c \left(\frac{r_{c.s}\,\tau}{rT_0} \right)^{p\alpha} - (1 - k_c) \left(\frac{r_{c.s}\,\tau}{rT_0} \right)^{p\beta} \tag{3.76}$$

---

*) For description of discharge graphs in co-ordinates (φ, τ) with the aid of formula (3.73) the value of the potential can be included as an additional item in parameter A_0.

where U_0 is the initial value of the tension, $r_{c.s.}$ the initial internal resistance with short circuit current, T_0 the constant characterising time

$$k_c = c_1 e^{-c_2 \frac{r}{r_{c.s}}} \tag{3.77}$$

$$p_\alpha = p_\alpha^0 \left[1 \pm a_1 \left(1 - e^{-a_2 \frac{r}{r_{c.s}}}\right)\right] \tag{3.78}$$

$$p_\beta = p_\beta^0 \left[1 \pm b_1 \left(1 - e^{-b_2 \frac{r}{r_{c.s}}}\right)\right] \tag{3.79}$$

Equation (3.76) is correct also at discharge with constant current, if we replace the value r by the product of the initial load resistance and the coefficient of the form of the discharge graph $\eta_{\alpha\beta}$ [26])

$$\eta_{\alpha\beta} = 1 - \frac{k_c}{1 + p_\alpha} - \frac{1 - k_c}{1 - p_\beta} \tag{3.80}$$

The semi-empirical equation of the discharge graphs was also obtained by Shepherd[17]). This equation has the form

$$U = U_S - k\left(\frac{Q}{Q - j\tau}\right)j - Nj + A \exp\left(-BQ^{-1} j\tau\right) \tag{3.81}$$

where j is the density of the discharge current.

The empirical constants: U_S, k, Q, N, A and B can be found at four points on two discharge graphs. Here two points are selected on a graph taken at comparatively low current density, and two others on a graph taken at high current density. For a lead acid battery at 25°C in ref.[17]) the following values of constants were obtained: U_S = 2.003V, k = 0.0189ohm, Q = 58.31A·hr, N = -0.015ohm.

In many cases, disregarding the initial part of the graphs, it is possible to use the equation

$$U = U_S - B_1 j \tag{3.82}$$

where

$$B_1 = k[Q/(Q - j\tau)] + N$$

The results calculated according to equation (3.81) show a marked divergence from the experimental data if the concentration of the electrolyte in the discharge process changes substantially. In this case assuming that the voltage drop is proportional to the change in concentration of the electrolyte it is possible to write

$$U = U_S - k\left(\frac{Q}{Q - j\tau}\right) j - Nj + A \exp\left(- BQ^{-1} j\tau\right) - Cj\tau \qquad (3.83)$$

where C is also an empirical constant.

If $Q/(Q - j\tau) = 1$, then according to (3.82)

$$U = U_S \; (k + N)\, j \qquad (3.84)$$

Formulae (3.82) and (3.84) are well confirmed by experiment (fig. 3.3).

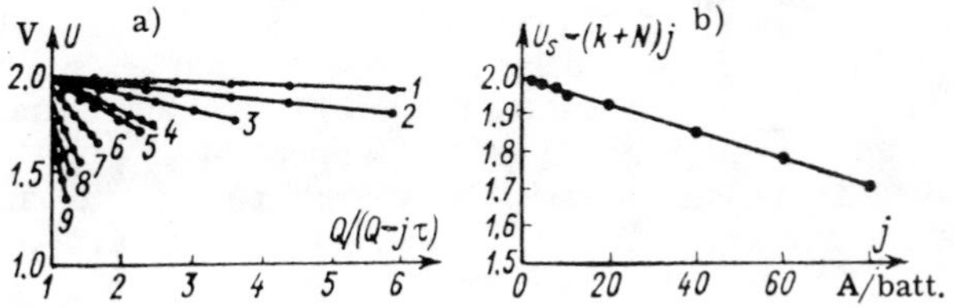

Fig.3.3 Graphs of change of discharge voltage of a lead acid battery with relation to: a - on the amount of electricity transmitted; b - on the current at $Q/Q-j\tau)=1$. 1 - discharge current 0.8A; 2 - 2A; 3 - 4A; 4 - 8A; 5 - 10A; 6 - 20A; 7 - 40A; 8 - 60A; 9 - 80A.

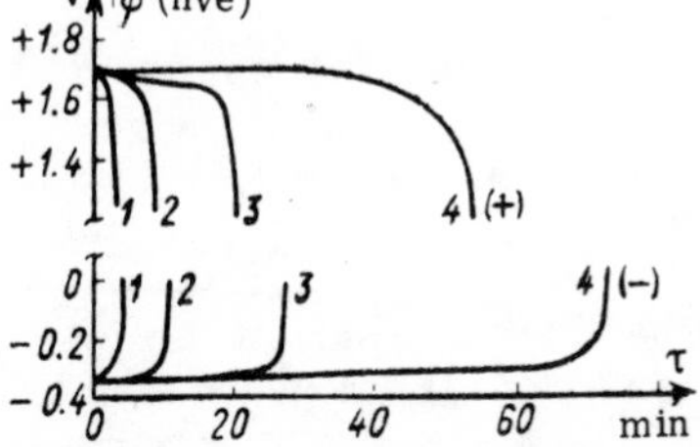

Fig. 3.4 Discharge graphs of the plates of a lead acid battery taken at temperature $21 \pm 1^{\circ}C$ in $6M \cdot H_2SO_4$. Dimensions of the plate: 14 x 12 x 0.2cm. Discharge current: 1 - 100A; 2 - 40A; 3 - 20A; 4 - 10A.

Experimental discharge graphs of pasted plate battery electrodes (fig. 3.4) were obtained in quite precise conditions by Gillibrand and Lomax[27]). According to the data of these authors the discharge graphs have a uniform shape for positive and negative electrodes. A stable value of the potential established approximately 5 s. after the beginning of the discharge. As can be seen from fig. 3.4, the graphs (φ, τ) are characterised by the presence of a considerable linear section.

The equations (3.69) and (3.70) obtained above, resulting from the theory of discharge of a cylindrical pore[18]), give the possibility in principle of establishing a link between the discharge potential and the current density. In special cases this relationship is expressed by the formulae (3.71) or (3.72). Naturally a change of active surface and structure of the electrode in the discharge process also causes inconstancy in the true current density, which substantially complicates the question under consideration.

The calculation of the dependence of the initial value of the discharge voltage on the current presents considerable interest in connection with this. In the initial period of discharge the surface of the battery electrodes does not suffer any substantial changes. In addition, in this period the concentration of the electrolyte in the pores also does not change noticeably, which makes it possible to disregard entirely the concentration polarisation.

Thus the shift of the potentials of the electrodes from the respective equilibrium values will be caused only by the activation overvoltage of the discharge process. The discharge voltage of the battery can in this case be written in the form

$$U = E - \Delta U_{act} - IR \qquad (3.85)$$

where I is discharge current, R is internal resistance of the battery, and ΔU_{act} is the algebraic sum of the overvoltages of the discharge reactions, which, in principle, can be expressed by equations (3.35)-(3.38).

As was shown by experimental study of the laws of discharge of lead acid starter batteries[28]), the dependence of the overvoltage on current density is described with sufficient accuracy by Tafel's equation[8]), the coefficients of which, however, are shown to be empirical constants. Therefore the formula (3.85) can be rewritten in the form[29])

$$U = E - \gamma \lg \frac{I}{I_c} - IR \qquad (3.86)$$

where the constants γ and I_c can be determined experimentally.

The internal resistance of the battery is composed of the ohmic resistances of all its constituent parts (electrolyte, separators, grids, active masses and current-carrying parts). Its magnitude is quite small. Thus, according to the data of I A Selitsky[28]), for starter batteries $R = (1\text{-}2) \cdot 10^{-3}$ ohm. The value of R decreases with a rise in temperature.

At $U = 0$ the value of I in formula (3.85) or (3.86) represents the short circuit current ($I_{s.c}$). According to (3.86)

$$R = \frac{E - \gamma \lg (I_{s.c}/I_c)}{I_{s.c}} \qquad (3.87)$$

Formula (3.87) can be used for determination of the internal resistance of a source of current in the absence of noticeable concentration polarisation[29]).

Dependence of capacity in discharge conditions

Winzel's theory[18]) set out above makes it possible to obtain equations describing the dependence of discharge capacity of a porous electrode on its physico-chemical characteristics and on current density.

If we designate τ_k the time of discharge of the electrode to a given value of the potential at which the overvoltage value of the discharge process on the external surface constitutes η_0^k, then in accordance with (3.72)

$$\eta_0^{(k)} \simeq \frac{j_r L}{\varkappa\sigma} \left[1 - 0.96 \left(\frac{\Lambda}{L}\right)^{2/3} (1 - \theta_q)^{1/3} + \frac{0.69}{(1 - \theta_q)^{1/3}} \left(\frac{\Lambda}{L}\right)^{4/3} \right] \qquad (3.88)$$

where $\Theta_q = Q/Q_0$ - the coefficient of utilisation of the active mass, $Q = i/\tau_k$ - the discharge capacity of the electrode pertaining to a unit of its geometric surface, and $Q_0 = SLq_0$ - the maximum theoretical discharge capacity in a volume corresponding to the geometric surface. Solving the equation (3.88) with respect to Θ_q, we obtain

$$\Theta = 1 - \frac{\left[\sqrt{\left(1 - \frac{\eta_0^{(k)}\varkappa\sigma}{j_r L}\right)^2 + 2.65\,(\Lambda/L)^2} + 1 - \frac{\eta_0^{(k)}\varkappa\sigma}{j_r L}\right]^3}{7.1\,(\Lambda/L)^2} \qquad (3.89)$$

From equation (3.89) it follows that the coefficient of utilisation of the active mass increases with decrease in overall current density and thickness of the electrode, and also with an increase in the electrical conductivity of the electrolyte and the porosity of the electrode. All these consequences of the equation of the discharge graph of a porous electrode find experimental confirmation in the study of the discharge characteristics of the electrodes of a lead acid battery.

Equation (3.89) allows a marked simplification on the condition

$$\left(\frac{\Lambda}{L}\right)^2 \gg 0.38\left(\frac{\eta_0^{(k)}\varkappa\sigma}{j_r L} - 1\right)^2 \qquad (3.90)$$

In this case it is possible to represent the relationship of the capacity to overall current density in a series of the form [3])

$$Q = \alpha_0 + \frac{\alpha_1}{j_r} + \frac{\alpha_2}{j_r^2} + \frac{\alpha_3}{j_r^3} + \dots \qquad (3.91)$$

The coefficients α_0, α_1, α_2, α_3 etc. are determined by the values of the parameters $\varkappa$, σ, L, Λ, q_0 and $\eta_0^{(k)}$. It is not difficult to show that the inequality (3.90), and consequently also formula (3.91), is correct at sufficiently high densities of discharge current.

If we disregard the members containing current density in the second and higher degrees, then the formula (3.91) show that Q has a linear relationship to j_r^{-1}. As is shown by the elaboration of experimental data obtained in the work of Gillibrand and Lomax [27]), such a relationship in fact occurs at $j > 0.1 A/cm^2$ (fig. 3.5). In the field of relatively low discharge currents the graphs (Q, I^{-1}), as can be seen from fig. 3.5, diverge from a rectilinear course.

There is a charge number of experimental formulae in the literature giving the relationship of current to the discharge rate of the battery. The most widely used has been the well known Peikert's equation, put forward already in 1897 [30]). According to this equation the discharge time is in inverse proportion to the discharge current at any degree of $\eta > 1$. In other words, the relationship between the capacity Q and the current I has the form

$$Q = K/I^{n-1} \tag{3.92}$$

where K is an empirical constant depending on temperature, concentration of the electrolyte and also the constructional features of the battery.

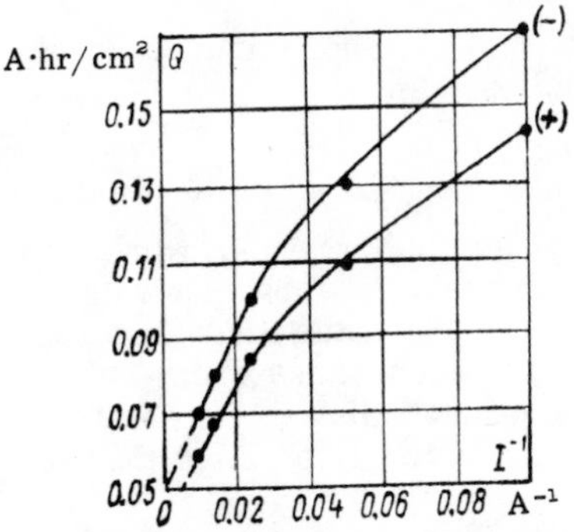

Fig. 3.5 Dependence of the specific discharge capacity Q of battery plates on the value I^{-1}, reverse discharge current (dimensions of the electrodes and conditions of discharge - see fig. 3.4:

As has been shown by precision measurements of recent years[27)31)], this equation is fully suitable also for the characteristics of discharge of the separate electrodes of a lead acid battery over a fairly wide interval of discharge current densities (0.02-0.2A/cm²) and temperatures (-20 - +20°C).

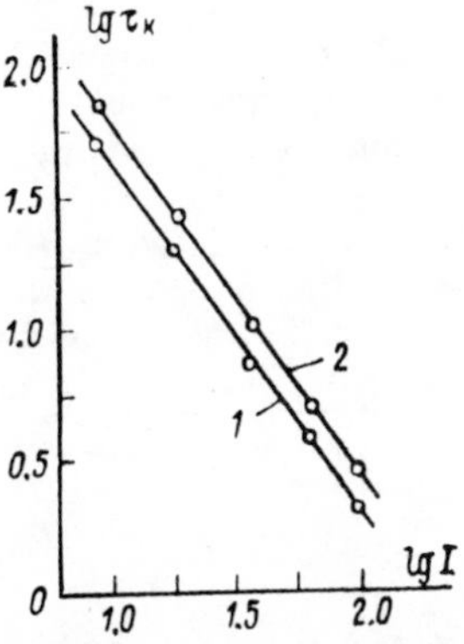

Fig. 3.6 The logarithmic relationship of the discharge time lg τ_k on the logarithm of the current lg I (dimensions of the electrodes and conditions of discharge - see fig. 3.4). 1 - positive electrode; 2 - negative electrode.

The correctness of equation (3.92) is confirmed by the presence of a rectilinear dependence of the discharge time (min) on the current (A) in the logarithmic co-ordinates (fig. 3.6). From fig. 3.6 it follows that the slope of the graphs (lg τ_k, lg I) does not depend on the sign of the discharge of the battery electrode and is n = 1.4[31]).

In ref.[31]) the equation (3.92) is supplemented by the introduction of a temperature correction

$$Q = K_0(1 + \alpha t)/I^{n-1} \tag{3.93}$$

According to the data of the author of this work, in the interval of current densities and temperatures shown above for the negative electrode α = 0.015min/deg. Thus, the discharge capacity of both electrodes of the battery, in accordance with (3.93), increases with an increase in temperature according to the linear law, while the rate of this rise is higher for negative plates than for positive ones.

In spite of individual attempts at providing a theoretical base, Peukert's equation must be reckoned a purely empirical formula suitable for a specified interval of currents. In the field of low currents of discharge this equation becomes unacceptable. In accordance with (3.92), at $I \to 0$, $Q \to \infty$, which has no physical sense.

For relatively small discharge currents satisfactory results are given by Liebenow's equation[30])

$$Q = \frac{A}{B + I} \tag{3.94}$$

characterising the hyperbolic relationship Q(I). The values of A and B in formula (3.94) are empirical constants, the relationship of which (A/B) represents the maximum value of capacity at $I \to 0$.

Dolezalek[30]) proposed an inference from (3.94) based on the use of an equation of stationary diffusion. Assuming that the discharge current is determined by the diffusion of the sulphuric acid into the pores of the active mass, according to Dolezalek it is possible to write that

$$I = \frac{k_1 Ds \text{ grad } c}{L} \tag{3.95}$$

where D is the coefficient of diffusion of H_2SO_4, s the cross-section of the pores, grad c the gradient of concentration of H_2SO_4 which is reckoned independent of I.

It is further assumed that the effective value of the length of the pores L is proportional to the amount of electricity transmitted in the discharge process, i.e.

$$L = k_2 Q \tag{3.96}$$

In addition it is reckoned that, in time, a decrease of the cross-section of the pores also occurs proportionally to Q

$$s = s_0 - k_3 Q \tag{3.97}$$

where s_0 is the value of s at the beginning of the discharge.

Substituting (3.96) and (3.97), it is not difficult to obtain equation (3.94). Here $A = \frac{k_1}{k_2} D s_0 \text{ grad } c$ and $B = \frac{k_1 k_3}{k_2} D \text{ grad } c$, and the limit to the maximum value of the capacity is directly proportional to the cross-section of the pores: $\lim\limits_{I \to 0} Q = s_0/k_3$.

Equation (3.94) was deduced subsequently by I A Selitsky[32]), who also set out from the premise of the limiting role of the diffusion of the electrolyte in the kinetics of the discharge process. The expressions obtained in ref.[32]) for the constants A and B in (3.94) only keep one arbitrary coefficient characterising the effective porosity of the electrodes.

It must, however, be noted that the assumption about the diffusion mechanism of the discharge, as has already been said above, cannot be reckoned correct, particularly at low discharge currents. Therefore Liebenow's equation (3.94), as also Peukert's equation (3.92), shows itself to be empirical. As was shown by B V Byelyayev[26]), both these equations can be recognised with certain assumptions as special cases of a more general relationship which has the form

$$Q = Q_0 \frac{U_0}{E} \eta_{\alpha\beta} \left(1 - \frac{U_k}{U_0}\right)^d \tag{3.98}$$

where U_0 and U_k are the initial and the final value of the discharge voltage, and d a coefficient depending on the load.

Let us consider how the concentration of the electrolyte influences the capacity of a lead acid battery. From the point of view of the representations of the theory of porous electrodes set out above, the most important property of the electrolyte is shown to be its conductivity. According to equation (3.89), the coefficient of utilisation of the active mass increases with an increase in the specific electrical conductivity of the electrolyte. In addition, as follows from formula (3.85), a rise in electrical conductivity leads to an increase in the discharge voltage as a result of a decrease in the internal resistance of the battery.

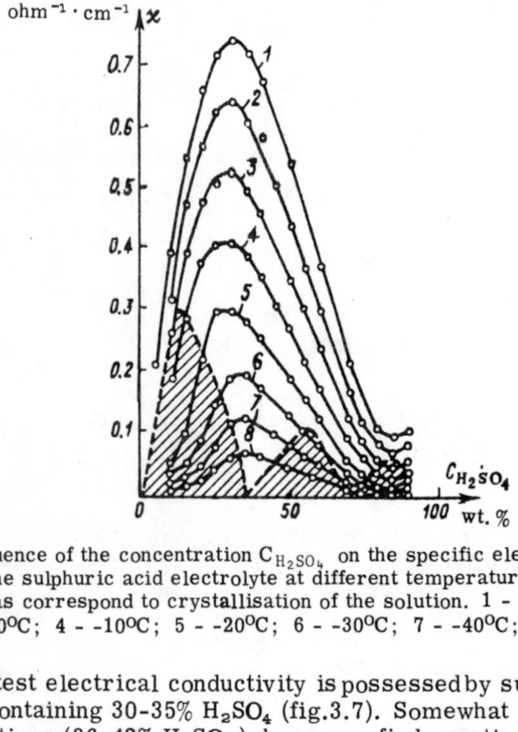

Fig. 3.7 Influence of the concentration $C_{H_2SO_4}$ on the specific electrical conductivity of the sulphuric acid electrolyte at different temperatures. The shaded areas correspond to crystallisation of the solution. 1 - +18°C; 2 - +10°C; 3 - 0°C; 4 - -10°C; 5 - -20°C; 6 - -30°C; 7 - -40°C; 8 - -50°C.

The greatest electrical conductivity is possessed by sulphuric acid solutions containing 30-35% H_2SO_4 (fig.3.7). Somewhat more concentrated solutions (36-42% H_2SO_4), however, find practical application in batteries. This is caused, above all, by the fact that in conformity with the basic equation of the theory of double sulphation (2.34), sulphuric acid is in fact in a lead acid battery an active substance participating in the current producing process. Therefore, the H_2SO_4 content in the electrolyte should ensure the possibility of carrying out long discharges at the quite limited volume pertaining to the electrolyte in current batteries. Here it must be reckoned that too big a fall in the concentration of H_2SO_4 in the discharge process is undesirable, owing to the increase in resistance of the electrolyte and consequently also in the internal resistance of the battery.

As a rule, the final concentration of the electrolyte should amount to not less than 10% H_2SO_4 ($d \geqslant 1.07 g/cm^3$).

It is also necessary to bear in mind the circumstance that a rise in the concentration of H_2SO_4 leads to a decrease in freezing temperature of the solution. This plays an important role in the selection of the concentration of the electrolyte of batteries employed in the winter time in the open air.

On the other hand, as will be shown below (chapters 4 and 5), a rise in concentration of the H_2SO_4 causes passivisation and self-discharge of battery electrodes, which limits the possibility of using strong solutions of the acid.

The influence of diffusion of sulphuric acid on the discharge of battery electrodes

The direct participation of the sulphuric acid in the current-producing process determines the marked influence of the diffusion of the electrolyte into the pores of the active mass on the course of the discharge of the battery electrodes. As has already been shown, this influence is particularly substantial for the positive electrode, at the discharge of which a decrease in the concentration of H_2SO_4 in the pores occurs not only due to the formation of lead sulphate, but also as a result of the dilution of the solution with water forming in conformity with the equation of the reaction (2.27).

The influence of the diffusion of the acid on the capacity of the battery increases in proportion to the rise in the discharge current and the corresponding decrease in time of discharge. We can use, as direct evidence of the marked role of diffusion in the kinetics of the discharge process the fact that the capacity of a lead acid battery discharged in an interrupted regime, in which the load is alternated with periods of switching off of the current, exceeds the capacity of a battery continuously discharged by the same current. Here the difference in capacity obtained at interrupted and continuous discharge increases with an increase in current. At long-term rates of discharge this difference practically disappears.

The noted increase in capacity can be explained in the given case by the fact that in the period of absence of current in the pores of the active masses the concentration of the electrolyte is increased thanks to the diffusion of the H_2SO_4 from the inter-electrode areas.

The influence of the diffusion of sulphuric acid on the discharge of a lead acid battery was thoroughly examined by Lening[33]). The author, starting out from quite general premises, obtained a differential equation determining the change in time and space of the concentration of H_2SO_4 (c mol/l)

$$\frac{\partial c}{\partial \tau} = \left(\Delta_c \varkappa \frac{\partial \varphi}{\partial x} + D\right) \frac{\partial^2 c}{\partial x^2} + \left[\frac{\partial D}{\partial c} + \Delta_c \frac{\partial}{\partial c}\left(\varkappa \frac{\partial \varphi}{\partial c}\right)\right]\left(\frac{\partial c}{\partial x}\right)^2 \qquad (3.99)$$

where Δ_c is the rate of decrease of the concentration of sulphuric acid as a result of the discharge. For the negative electrode this value constitutes $4.19 \cdot 10^{-6}$ mol/Kl, and for the positive (taking into account the dilution of the solution by water formed) $\Delta_c = [6.16 + 0.1865c : (1 - 0.037c)] \cdot 10 \cdot ^{6}$ mol/Kl. For the dependence of the coefficient of diffusion of H_2SO_4 on the concentration there was quoted in ref. [33]) the formula

$$D = (1.47 + 0.155c) \cdot 10^{-5} \ \mathrm{cm^2/s} \qquad (3.100)$$

In deducing the equation (3.99) use is made of a unidimensional model of a porous electrode and it is calculated that the specific electrical conductivity $\varkappa$ does not depend on x. Convection of the electrolyte is not taken into consideration. In addition, the author only takes account of the dependence of the potential on the concentration, completely disregarding the activation polarisation.

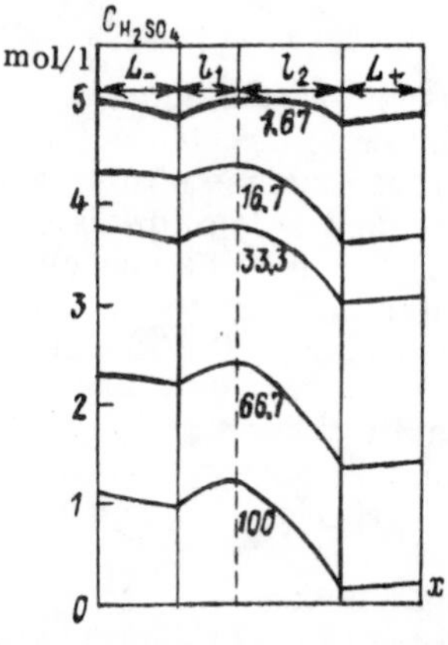

Fig. 3.8 Profile of the concentration $C_{H_2SO_4}$ in the pores of the negative and positive plates of a lead acid battery and in the inter-electrode area in the different periods of discharge. Thickness of the plates ($2L_-$ and $2L_+$) and distance between the plates ($l_1 + l_2$) - 2mm, porosity of the plates - 50%.The figures on the diagram are the percentage of capacity taken up.

The results of numerical integration of (3.99) are represented in fig. 3.8. From the figure it can be seen that in the discharge process the biggest fall in the concentration of H_2SO_4 takes place at the mouths of the pores, i.e. on the external surface of the electrodes. The decrease in concentration in the pores of the positive electrode markedly exceeds the decrease in concentration in the negative plate. Here the difference in the concentration of the electrolyte in the pores of the positive and the negative plates increases in the discharge process. The concentration gradient of the acid in the pores in the initial period of discharge is quite small and increases with time.

As can be seen from fig. 3.8, the maximum value of the concentration is to be found within the limits of the inter-electrode area. The situation of the maximum is determined by the parameters of the electrodes and the figures for transfer of the ions of the electrolyte in conformity with the relationship[33])

$$\frac{\gamma_+ L_+ + l_2}{\gamma_- L_- + l_1} = \frac{2 - n_{H^+}}{n_{H^+}} \qquad (3.101)$$

where $n_{H^+} = 0.81$ - the figure for the transfer of the hydrogen ions in the sulphuric acid solution, γ_+ and γ_- are the porosity of the active masses of the positive and negative electrodes, l_1 and l_2 are the distance from the surface of the negative and the positive plates to the maximum concentration, and L_+ and L_- are half of the thickness of the positive and negative electrodes. At $\gamma_+ = \gamma_- = 0.5$; $L_+ = L_- = 1$mm and an inter-electrode distance equal to 2mm, in accordance with (3.101), $l_1 \approx 0.7$mm and $l_2 \approx 1.3$mm.

H Lening[33]) notes that the calculations carried out by him are based on a certain idealisation of the discharge process. In particular, in the deduction of the basic differential equation (3.99) the volume changes at discharge were not taken into account. As an elementary calculation shows, with the flow of 2F of electricity the total increase in volume on the negative electrode constitutes $0.7cm^3$, and on the positive one $15.9cm^3$. This increase in volume should cause an outflow of electrolyte from the pores of the active masses in the discharge process, hindering the diffusion equalisation of the concentration.

Substantial complications of the phenomena under consideration are linked, as has already been noted, with the formation of lead sulphate. The sulphate deposit appears initially at the mouths of the pores at the beginning of the discharge. The negative influence of this phenomenon can be decreased by means of a decrease in the thickness of the battery plates and in the distances between them with a corresponding increase in the number of plates.

Such constructional changes cause a decrease in the concentration gradients at an equal current load and a corresponding decrease in the radial component of the discharge current, which causes passivation of the pores. A decrease in the inter-electrode distances leads to a decrease in the differences in concentration of the electrolyte which is in the inter-electrode area, thanks to which the carrying out of deep discharges becomes possible. Thus, the examination of the diffusion mechanism of the discharge leads to conclusions similar to those obtained by us earlier in the evaluation of the activation mechanism of the process.

In conclusion, let us note that the data accumulated up to the present time are, obviously, insufficient for an unambiguous evaluation of the relative influence of the electro-chemical and the diffusion stages on the kinetics of the discharge process occurring in a lead acid battery. Obviously, the conditions of carrying out the discharge can substantially influence the kinetic weight of these stages of the discharge. Attempts in the literature to explain the discharge mechanism solely by the laws of diffusion cannot be recognised as justified.

Distribution of polarisation along the length of the battery electrodes

The distribution of polarisation in chemical sources of current and, in particular, in the lead acid battery, includes within itself two mutually connected spheres: the distribution of potential and current over the thickness of the electrodes and over the external surface of the electrodes.

Hitherto we have considered the first problem. Here a description will be given of the results of the calculation of the distribution of current along the height of the battery. We shall assume here that the unevenness of polarisation over the thickness is small and it can be disregarded. The results of the study of the distribution of polarisation along the height of the electrodes is of interest, especially with respect to batteries of large dimensions, and also batteries with tubular (armoured) construction of the positive electrode.

Analysis of the distribution of current along the height of the battery plates was carried out in refs.[34-36]). We shall consider this question using the results obtained by V N Kosholkin and O S Ksenzhek[36]) who examined a unidimensional model of the battery, which is correct with the following assumptions: the electrodes have a rectilinear form and are polarised from both sides (the current outflow is situated in the centre of the electrode), the inter-electrode distances d_e are uniform along the whole height of the battery and are well below the width and height of the electrodes, current output is realised at the top over the whole width of the electrodes (fig. 3.9). Obviously, the majority of types of lead acid batteries satisfy these conditions.

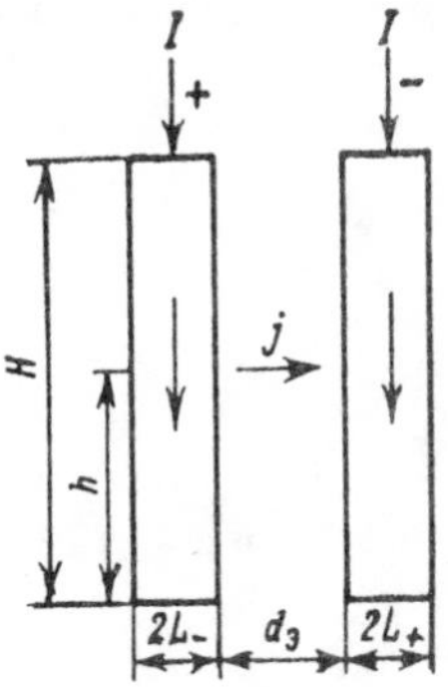

Fig. 3.9 Scheme of disposition and work of battery electrodes.

For the initial distribution of current J calculated per unit of width of the electrode (A/cm), in ref.[36]) the following differential equation was obtained

$$\frac{d^2 j}{dh^2} - \frac{1}{H_C^2} J = 0 \qquad (3.102)$$

where J is the value of the current in the electrodes at point h (see fig. 3.9) and H_C the characteristic height of the electrode

$$H_C = \sqrt{\frac{\frac{d_e}{\varkappa} + R_n^+ + R_n^-}{\frac{1}{L_+\varkappa_+} + \frac{1}{L_-\varkappa_-}}} \qquad (3.103)$$

$\varkappa_+$ and $\varkappa_-$ are the specific electrical conductivities of the active masses of the positive and negative electrodes, and R_n^+ and R_n^- are the polarisation resistances of the electrodes, with the condition of linear dependence between overvoltage and current density equal to

$$R_\pi = \frac{RT}{zFi_o} = \frac{0.013}{i_o} \tag{3.104}$$

The current density j on the surface of the electrodes at point λ constitutes

$$j = \frac{dj}{dh} \tag{3.105}$$

Integrating (3.102) with the use of boundary conditions

$$J = 0 \text{ at } h = 0 \text{ and } J = I \text{ at } h = H \tag{3.106}$$

and taking account of (3.105), we have

$$j = \frac{I}{H_C} \frac{\cosh(h/H_C)}{\sinh(H/H_C)} \tag{3.107}$$

The maximum value of current density in the upper part of the electrodes, in accordance with (3.107) and (3.106), is given by the equation

$$j_{max} = \frac{I}{H_C} \coth \frac{H}{H_C} \tag{3.108}$$

and the minimum value in the lower part

$$j_{min} = \frac{I}{H_C} \operatorname{cosech} \frac{H}{H_C} \tag{3.109}$$

The relationship

$$j_{max}/j_{min} = \cosh(H/H_C) \tag{3.110}$$

does not depend on the current and can serve as a criterion characterising the uniformity of current distribution along the height of the electrodes. The electrode is ideally polarised uniformly at $j_{max} = j_{min}$, which, in accordance with (3.110) take place if $H/H_C \to 0$ ($H_C \to \infty$). With $H = H_C$ $j_{max}/j_{min.} = 1.54$, i.e. the current density in the upper part of the plates exceeds the corresponding value in the lower part approximately 1.5 times.

Thus the parameter H_C plays an important role in the characteristics of uniformity of behaviour of the electrodes. This parameter is determined by the formula (3.103), which in the case of the lead acid battery admits of marked simplification.

As is shown by calculation according to (3.104), $R_{\pi}^{-} \cong 0.26 \cdot 10^4$ ohm·cm² and $R_{\pi}^{+} = 0.43 \cdot 10^2$ ohm·cm². On the other hand, at $d_e = 0.2$cm $d_e/\varkappa \approx 0.3$ohm·cm², i.e. $R_{\pi}^{-} \gg R_{\pi}^{+}$ and $R_{\pi}^{-} \gg d_e/\varkappa$. Further $\varkappa_- = 0.24 \cdot 10^4$ ohm⁻¹·cm⁻¹, $\varkappa_+ = 0.83 \cdot 10^2$ ohm⁻¹·cm⁻¹ [7]), and $L_+ \approx L_-$, whence it follows that $1/L_+\varkappa_+ \gg 1/L_-\varkappa_-$. Taking into account the relationships of the values coming into (3.103) quoted, it is possible to rewrite this formula with sufficient accuracy in the form

$$H_C \cong \sqrt{R_{\pi}^{-} L_+ \varkappa_+} \tag{3.111}$$

At $L_+ = 0.15$cm calculation according to (3.111) shows that $H_C \cong 180$cm. For starter batteries where the height of the plates generally varies within the limits H = 12-14cm, the relationship $H/H_C \approx 0.07$, whence, in accordance with (3.110), $j_{max}/j_{min} \approx 1.0025$, i.e. the plates work practically uniformly along their height. However, for batteries with a considerable height of the plates ($H \sim H_C$) the value j_{max} can markedly exceed j_{min}.

An increase in the characteristic height of the electrode H_C, as can be seen from formula (3.111), can be attained principally by means of changing the parameters of the positive electrode of the battery: increases in the thickness of the plates and the electrical conductivity of the active mass. An increase in the thickness of the plates should, however, lead to a deterioration in the uniformity of polarisation along the depth of the pores. Therefore, this method of increasing H_C must be reckoned unacceptable. As far as an increase in the electrical conductivity of the positive electrode is concerned, this way obviously has known possibilities, since the resistance of the active mass is connected with its structure and phase composition. These last characteristics, in principle, can be changed in the necessary direction as a result of a corresponding change of conditions of manufacture of the electrode.

The value R_{π} depends on the presence on the surface of the negative electrode of the battery of adsorbed particles, which influence ψ_1 - potential and the dimension of the active surface. According to equation (3.44)

$$R_{\pi}^{-} = \frac{RTe^{\frac{\beta zF\psi_1'}{RT}}}{zFi_0^{-}(1-\Theta)} \tag{3.112}$$

whence it follows that R_{π} increases with an increase in the positive potential (or with a decrease in its negative value), and also with a rise in the degree of filling up the surface θ. The anion-active expanders which cause more uniform polarisation over the thickness of the negative electrode, as has been shown above, at the same time have a bad effect on the current distribution along the height of the electrode. On the other hand, the use of H_C, the adsorption of which increases the potential gradient over the thickness of the electrode, should produce a more uniform behaviour of the electrode along its height. Hence it is inappropriate to increase the value of H_C on account of the influence of the surface-active additives on the negative electrode of the battery.

It must be emphasised that equation (3.102) and all the consequences flowing from it, strictly speaking, refer exclusively to the initial distribution of current when the physico-chemical properties of the active masses are isotropic. In the discharge process different sections of the plates discharge at a different rate. The maximum rate of discharge of the upper part of the plates leads to a gradual decrease of the effective value of H, since the capacity of the upper parts is exhausted and they are excluded from the discharge process. This phenomenon leads, in accordance with (3.110), to continuous smoothing out of the unevenness of the discharge of the plates along their height.

In calculation of the parameter H_C we have not taken into account the influence of the grid of the positive electrode. In conformity with the basic pre-requisites of the theory set forth[36]) it was accepted that the active mass uniformly fills the plate and is characterised by a constant value of specific electrical conductivity $\varkappa_+$. In reality the electrical conductivity of the positive electrode should exceed the value accepted for the calculations as a result of the participation of the grid in the passage of current. The difference between the electrical conductivity of the positive active mass and the effective value of the electrical conductivity of the electrode is particularly great at the beginning of the period of service. In the process of utilisation or testing of the battery the grids of the positive plates are subjected to corrosion, as a result of which the influence of the grids on the electrical conductivity of the plates decreases.

From what has been said, it follows that the value of H_C should decrease with an increase in the number of charge-discharge cycles, which, in turn, leads to a progressive deterioration of current distribution along the height of the battery electrodes. An increase in the corrosion resistance and electrical conductivity of the positive grids causes a more uniform distribution of polarisation in the process of long-term utilisation of batteries.

The character of the distribution of current along the height of tubular elements of battery plates of armoured type has a definite specific form. Such plates (fig. 3.10) are widely used abroad as positive electrodes, resulting in a considerable increase in the period of service of the battery. Present-day armoured electrodes consist of tubular elements with a diameter of the tubes equal to approximately 8mm. Lead rods of diameter ~3mm serve as current outflows. The length of the tubes in the series of constructions exceeds 50cm.

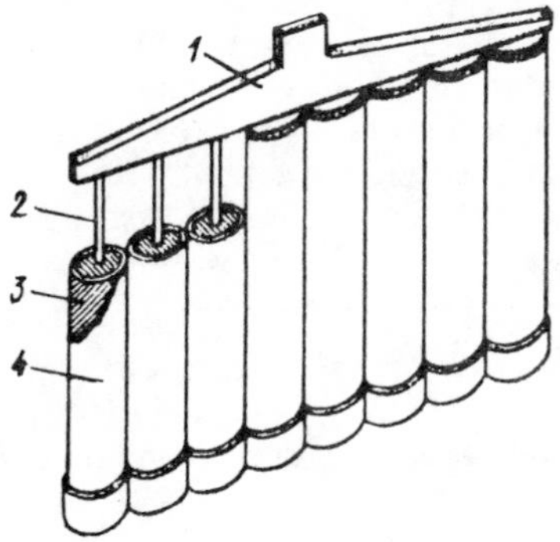

Fig. 3.10 General view of an armoured plate. 1 - contact strip; 2 - rods; 3 - active mass; 4 - cloth strips.

The current distribution over the radius of the tube is subject to the laws of the theory of porous electrodes which were previously examined by us. According to the data of Euler and Horn[37]) the dimensions of armoured electrodes used in practice ensure relatively uniform working of the active mass over the cross-section.

Current distribution along the height of a tubular element of a plate is given by the formula[37])

$$\Delta I = \frac{I \alpha \Delta Z \cosh \alpha Z}{\sinh \alpha H} \tag{3.113}$$

where I is the strength of current, ΔI the change of current on the sector ΔZ, H the height of the tube

$$\alpha = \frac{r_1}{r_2 \Delta Z} \sqrt{\frac{R_a}{R_b}} \tag{3.114}$$

r_1 is the radius of the lead rod, r_2 the internal radius of the tube, R_a the resistance of the element of the active mass, consisting of ohmic and polarisation resistance, R_b the resistance of the electrolyte within the limits of the same element.

In ref.[37]) graphs are calculated for current distribution along the height of an armoured plate in a 5-hour discharge. The distribution is characterised by the relationship of the maximum (at $Z = H$) and minimum ($Z = 0$) values of ΔI. For reasons set out above, this relationship, equal to $\sinh \alpha H$, decreases in the discharge process, i.e. the current distribution becomes more uniform. Thus in the course of the time corresponding to 50% discharge, the ratio $\Delta I_{max}/\Delta I_{min}$ (at $H = 44$cm) decreases for the individual plate from 1.07 to 1.05 and for the battery from 1.27 to 1.20. Naturally an increase in the length of the tube H leads to a deterioration of current distribution. According to the data of Euler and Horn[37]) the permissible limit value of H amounts to 100cm. An increase in the length of tubular elements also leads to an increase in the voltage drop, the maximum value of which constitutes

$$\Delta U_{max} = \frac{\rho I}{\alpha \pi r_1^2 \sinh \alpha H} \quad (\cosh \alpha H - 1)' \tag{3.115}$$

where ρ is the specific resistance of lead ($2.6 \cdot 10^{-5}$ ohm·cm). According to the data quoted in the work under consideration, ΔU_{max} at a 5-hour regime of discharge increases from 7 to 43mV with an increase in H from 40 to 100cm. A similar increase in ΔU_{max} with a 10-minute discharge amounts to one from 32 to 468mV. Thus increasing voltage drop also turns out to be a reason limiting the possibility of lengthening armoured electrodes.

Results of experimental study of the distribution of polarisation in the electrodes of a lead acid battery

Experimental study of the character of the distribution of potential and current over the internal surface of porous electrodes is linked with quite considerable difficulties. Direct measurements of potentials in the pores of the active masses cannot at present be carried out owing to the very low diameter of the pores. If indeed we theoretically allow the possibility of such measurements, then the distortion of the electrical field in the pores as a result of the introduction into them of any sort of probe would be so considerable that this would inevitably lead to substantial errors.

The works devoted to an experimental study of porous electrochemical systems can be provisionally divided into two groups. Research of the first group is carried out with the use of different physical and also analogical models. In the second group are investigations in which the current distribution over the surface of the electrode is studied with the aid of analytical methods. The most often used method is the X-ray diffraction analysis or radio-chemical analysis of battery plates at different stages of the discharge. Here the change of phase composition of the active mass is clearly a source of information about the spatial distribution of the speed of the process.

The method of macro-modelling of the pore was used in the works of Yu D Dunayev, G C Kiryakov and Z N Chernyshev[13]. The authors carried out measurements of the potentials of the internal surface of tubes of diameter 0.4-0.65cm and length 25cm, made of lead and a number of lead alloys, in the process of anodic polarisation with 2N · H_2SO_4. The overall current density changed within the limits 0.1-2A/ cm^2. Here the presence of a considerable potential gradient φ along the length of the tube x was established, thanks to which, with the formation of lead dioxide and the liberation of oxygen on the section situated near the mouth of the tube, the value of the potential in the depth corresponds to the oxidation of the lead to sulphate. The graphs obtained in the investigations under consideration (φ, x) are in qualitative conformity with the theory of distribution of potential in cylindrical pores, which is based on the hypothesis of activation control of the rate of the electrode processes.

In the work of L S Sergeyeva and I A Selitsky[12] current distribution over the thickness of the negative electrode of a lead acid battery was studied with the aid of a specially assembled block, consisting of five plates of a thickness 0.8mm, divided by separators of thickness 0.1mm. The block was polarised from both sides in 37% H_2SO_4. In the process of polarisation (discharge) the portions of current μ flowing through layers that were in identical conditions were determined.

$$\mu_1 = \frac{I_1 + I_5}{I}, \quad \mu_2 = \frac{I_2 + I_4}{I}, \quad \mu_3 = \frac{I_3}{I} \qquad (3.116)$$

Here I is the polarisation current, and I_1, I_2 etc. are the currents in corresponding layers of the electrode under investigation. The results obtained (fig.3.11) show that in conformity with the theory of the porous electrode the current is distributed unevenly, while with an increase in I the unevenness increases. The values of μ, calculated according to equation (3.34), satisfactorily coincide with the corresponding experimental values. This result serves principally as a direct confirmation of the applicability of the basic assumptions of the theory of the porous electrode to the discharge process occurring on the negative plates of the battery. In addition, the quantitative coincidence of theory and experiment are evidence in the given case of the fact that diffusion phenomena do not show any marked influence on the discharge capacity of a negative electrode, insofar as equation (3.34) does not take into account the presence of a concentration gradient of the electrolyte along the depth of the pores.

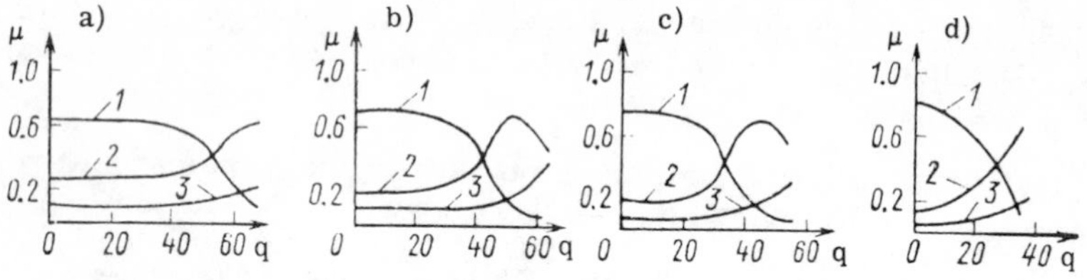

Fig. 3.11 Current distribution (3.116) depending on the amount of electricity transmitted q (mA·hr/cm^2) at the discharge by a current with density: a - 4mA/cm^2; b - 8mA/cm^2; c - 16mA/cm^2; d - 32mA/cm^2. 1 - μ_1; 2 - μ_2; 3 - μ_3.

Euler[38]) used an analogue model for analysis of current distribution over the thickness of the positive electrode of a lead acid battery, including resistors characterising electron, ion, polarisation and diffusion resistances. The results obtained by Euler for the discharge of an electrode at a 3-hour regime show the presence of a considerable gradient of current density, gradually decreasing in the discharge process. However, it must be noted that the parameters used as starting points by Euler are to a known extent arbitrary and do not correspond fully to the real values of the magnitudes shown.

Passing on to an examination of the series of works devoted to analytical determination of the current distribution in battery electrodes, we shall point first of all to the already previously mentioned work[22]). These authors, with the aid of X-ray diffraction analysis of the active mass of a discharged negative electrode, established that the $PbSO_4$ content decreases in proportion to penetration into the depth of the electrode (fig. 3.12). The presence of a concentration gradient of $PbSO_4$ is caused by uneven distribution of the discharge current.

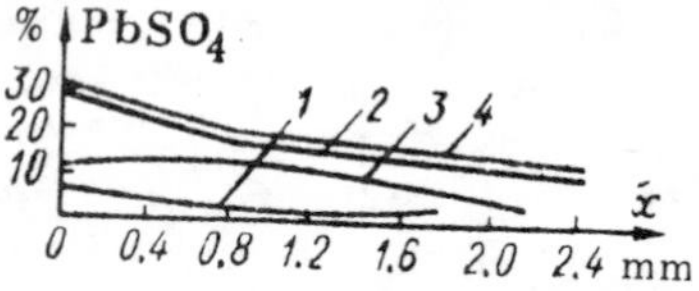

Fig. 3.12 Change of $PbSO_4$ content in the negative active mass over the thickness of the plate. 1, 2 - paste without additions; 3, 4 - paste with the addition of sodium lignosulphonate; 1, 3 - starting discharge; 2, 4 - long-term discharge.

In the works of Bode and Euler[39]) and others, current distribution over the external surface and over the thickness of battery plates was investigated by the auto-radiographic method with the use of radio-active isotopes of sulphur S^{35} and selenium Se^{75}. The isotope S^{35} is characterised by comparatively soft β-radiation, at the same time as Se^{75} possesses the hard γ-radiation. Owing to this the radiograms obtained with the use of radio-active sulphur characterise, basically, the surface distribution of lead sulphate, but the radiograms obtained with the aid of Se^{75} give evidence of the distribution of lead selenate over the whole thickness of the battery plate.

As object of research in the investigation under consideration, plates were used with dimensions 143 x 124 x 2.1mm and 43 x 51 x 1.25mm, which were cycled in electrolyte with d = 1.28g/cm^3. The cycling was carried out, basically, with a 5-hour discharge regime.

First of all the presence of a definite unevenness in the distribution of the sulphate over the surface of the positive plates was established. This phenomenon the authors connect with the influence of the separator, the density of which, and the degree of adherence to the plates, can oscillate within known limits, and also with differences in the density of the initial paste. In the process of cycling, these local differences were gradually smoothed out, which bears witness to the homogenisation of the active mass. It is noted that plates pasted by machine with subsequent pressing are characterised in the initial period of cycling by a more uniform distribution of sulphate than plates coated by hand. The plates of the negative electrode from the very beginning of the test show no lack of uniformity over the external surface.

For determination of the character of the current distribution over the thickness of the plates the most acceptable method is shown to be the use of an electrolyte containing the isotope Se^{75} in the form of Na_2SeO_4. The ion SeO_4^{2-} together with the sulphate ion comes into the crystal lattice of $PbSO_4$, thanks to which the γ-radiation of the isotope mentioned characterises the distribution of $PbSO_4$ forming in the discharge process.

In ref.[39]) it is shown that an increase in current density from 5 to 250mA/cm^2 leads to a marked deterioration in current distribution over the thickness. In the sphere of current densities 5-10mA/cm^2 the formation of lead sulphate (and consequently also $PbSeO_4$) occurs practically uniformly over the whole thickness of the electrode.

In refs.[40-42]) the distribution of $PbSO_4$ over the thickness of the positive electrode of a lead acid battery was studied with the aid of X-ray analysis with the use of the line of K_α of sulphur. Plates with a different degree of discharge were placed beforehand in a thermoplastic solution containing copper powder. After polymerisation a section of the plates was polished and studied with an X-ray micro-analyser.

The data obtained (fig. 3.13) show that on discharge of the plates with relatively low currents, the sulphate is distributed practically uniformly over the whole thickness of the electrode. With an increase in current density an unevenness appears in the rate of the discharge process, with this unevenness becoming more marked in the discharge process. The fall in the concentration of sulphate on the external surfaces of the plates which is observed in fig. 3.13 is obviously the result of the special features of the system of preparation of the samples before X-ray analysis. It can be assumed that the external area turn out to be covered with polymer film not containing $PbSO_4$. As was shown in[42], in the process of washing the plates equalisation of the $PbSO_4$ concentration over the thickness is possible, owing to discharge of the short-circuit concentration element formed by the external and internal layers of the active mass.

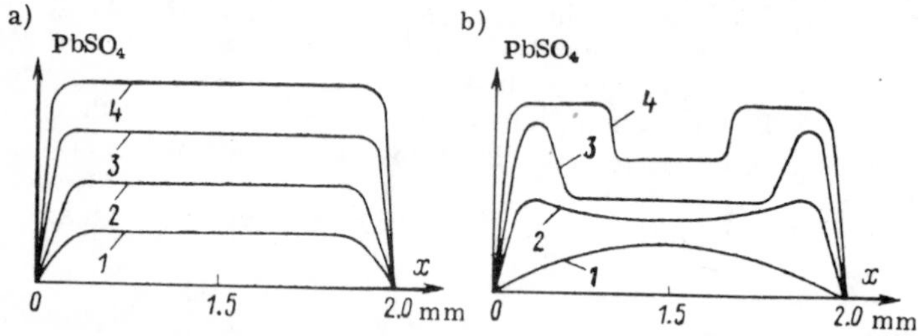

Fig. 3.13 Distribution of $PbSO_4$ over the thickness x of the positive electrode at current density 6mA/cm² (a) and 30mA/cm² (b): 1 - 25% discharge; 2 - 50%; 3 - 75%; 4 - 100%.

A substantial influence on the distribution of the concentration of sulphate over the thickness of the positive plate of a battery is shown by induced circulation of the electrolyte[41]. The character of this influence cannot be explained within the framework of the theory of porous electrodes which has been propounded. However, the very fact of the change of profile of the concentration of $PbSO_4$ over the thickness of the plate is evidence of the obviously important role of diffusion phenomena in the kinetics of the discharge process occurring on the positive electrode.

Summarising the above, it must be emphasised that current theory of two-phase porous electrodes cannot give a quantitative explanation of the whole collection of quite complicated processes occurring in a lead acid battery. Nevertheless, the existing theoretical representations are qualitatively confirmed by experimental data and make it possible in a number of cases to explain the physical essence of the laws proper to this source of current. So taking account of the properties of distribution of polarisation over the surface of porous electrodes must be reckoned necessary in the study of the kinetics of electrode reactions on battery electrodes, and also in the calculation and design of lead acid batteries.

Chapter 4: The positive electrode of a lead acid battery

The structure and physical properties of lead dioxide

The active mass of the positive electrode of a lead acid battery consists basically of lead dioxide in the charged state. In Chapter 2 the thermodynamic properties of this compound were examined. It was shown, in particular, that this oxide exists in the shape of two crystalline forms: α and β-PbO_2. The phenomenon of polymorphism of lead dioxide was discovered in 1950 by A I Zaslavsky, Yu D Kondrashov and S S Tolkachev[1]), who first synthesised the α modification of PbO_2 and studied its basic crystallo-chemical properties.

X-ray investigation of the structure of the crystalline modifications of PbO_2 showed[1-3]), that α-PbO_2 possesses an elementary lattice of the orthorhombic type with axes: a = 4.938Å, b = 5.939Å and c = 5.486Å (fig. 4.1a). A lead ion in each octahedron is surrounded by six oxygen ions, which are at a distance of 2.16Å. Here the radius of the lead ions is 0.84Å, and the radius of the oxygen ions 1.32Å. The α-PbO_2 crystals belong to the rhombo-dipyramidal class; β-PbO_2 is characterised by a tetragonal lattice with dimensions: a = 4.945Å and c = 3.378Å (fig. 4.1b). In its structure the tetragonal modification of PbO_2 is similar to rutile (TiO_2), whilst the structure of α-PbO_2 is close to the structure of columbite.

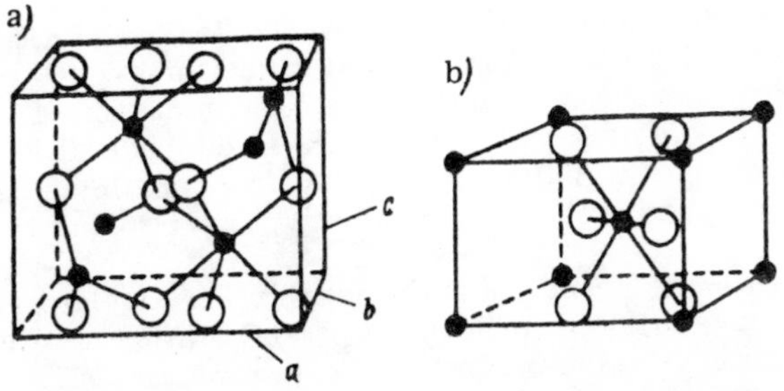

Fig. 4.1 Structure of an elementary cell of α-PbO_2 (a) and of β-PbO_2 (b).

According to the data of S S Tolkachev [2], structural analogies exist in the series Pb-$Pb_{yell.}$-α-PbO_2 and Pb-Pb_2O-PbO_{red}-Pb_2O_3-Pb_3O_4-β-PbO_2 [2]. Compounds of the first series are characterised by hexagonal packing, and in the second series by a denser cubic packing.

The volume reduction to 1 molecule of PbO_2 amounts to 40.3Å^3 for α-PbO_2 and 41.7Å^3 for β-PbO_2 [2]. As can be seen from these data, α-PbO_2 is characterised by increased density of packing. In the formation of lead dioxide as a result of anodic oxidation of metal the volume of β-PbO_2 film exceeds the corresponding value of the volume of α-PbO_2 (with one and the same quantity of oxidised lead). This circumstance from the point of view of general assumptions about the mechanism of film corrosion of metals should cause some increase in the protective properties of lead oxide film in the case when it is β-PbO_2 [4].

The density of the crystalline modifications of PbO_2 according to the data of a number of researchers is given in table 4.1.

Table 4.1: Density of α and β-PbO_2 (g/cm^3)

No.	α-PbO_2	β-PbO_2	Literature
1	9.53	9.375	[2]
2	9.873	9.696	[5]
3	9.7594	9.6483	[6]
4	9.866	9.523	*)

*) The results are given, setting out from the above-mentioned values of molecular volumes at α and β-PbO_2.

The results quoted in table 4.1 show that the density of α-PbO_2 exceeds by approximately 2-3% the corresponding value for β-PbO_2. Let us note that the density values quoted in the first column of table 4.1 were obtained by the pycnometric methods, which, in the case of fine-dispersion and porous bodies, can give lower values. The remaining data were obtained by the X-ray method.

As was shown in the papers of B N Kabanov, I G Kiseleva and I I Astakhov, the crystalline modifications of PbO_2 differ markedly in dimensions of the crystals and in mechanical properties [7][8]. Thus, in deposition on the anode of α-PbO_2 this oxide forms relatively large (~1mkm) crystals, densely adhering to each other. The tetragonal modification of lead dioxide (β-PbO_2) is deposited on the anode in the form of fine needle-like crystals (~0.5 x 0.03μm), not very well connected with each other. It is noted that α-PbO_2 crystals are markedly superior in hardness to β-PbO_2 [8]).

According to Feitknecht, who studied PbO_2 crystals forming in the process of anodic polarisation of a lead electrode, the dimensions of crystals of α- and β-PbO_2 are in this case approximately uniform and amount to ~0.01μm [9]). The whole series of data obtained up to the present time are evidence of the fact that the dimensions of PbO_2 crystals are determined to a greater extent by the conditions of formation than by the type of crystal lattice[4]). Naturally the changes in the macrostructure of the crystals leads to changes in the mechanical properties of the PbO_2 [10]).

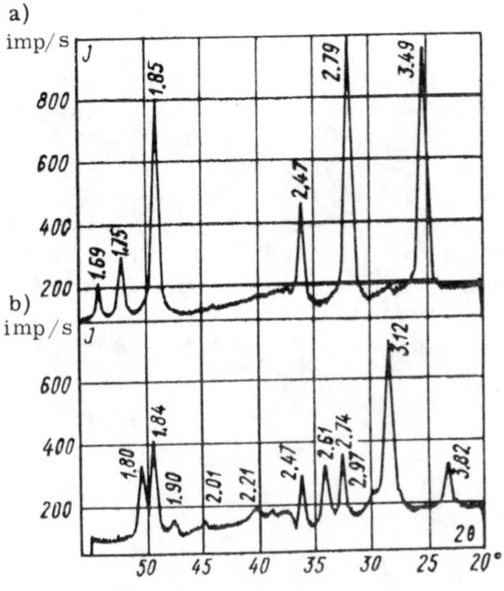

Fig. 4.2 X-ray spectra of crystalline modifications of PbO_2: a - β-PbO_2; b - α-PbO_2. In the diagrams are shown the inter-plane distances(in A) corresponding to the base lines.

The determination of the mechanical characteristics of the compound under consideration is considerably impeded owing to the presence of defects (microcracks, scratches etc.), which appear in the preparation of samples for mechanical tests. Therefore the data quoted by various authors in this sphere are noticeably different from each other. In the work of Shibasaki[11]) a study was made of lead dioxide which was obtained in the optimum conditions of electrolysis. According to the data of this author PbO_2 is characterised by a high rigidity [Young's modulus $E = (2.5 \pm 1.5) \cdot 10^{11}$ dynes/cm^2] and a very low strength.

The difference in the structure of the crystal lattice of α and β-PbO_2 causes substantial differences in the X-ray spectra of the oxides (fig. 4.2). This gives the possibility of using X-ray structure analysis for determination of the phase composition of mixtures of crystalline modifications of PbO_2 and, in particular, of the composition of the active masses of the positive electrode of the battery. The system of phase analysis of lead dioxide was first put forward by Dodson[12]), who used for analytical purposes the intensities of lines with inter-plane distances d = 3.49Å and d = 2.79Å for β-PbO_2 and a line with d = 2.61Å for α-PbO_2. The graduated graph obtained in the work[12]) is correct over the range of concentrations of α-PbO_2 in the mixture (C_α) from 20 to 70%.

Later the system of phase analysis of PbO_2 was improved[13])[14]), which made it possible to widen considerably the limits of change of α-PbO_2 content ($10\% \leqslant C_\alpha \leqslant 95\%$). This result was achieved thanks to the use of the most intense line of α-PbO_2 (d = 3.12Å). For quantitative determination of β-PbO_2 a line was selected with d = 3.49Å. The close arrangement of these lines (see fig. 4.2) makes it possible to carry out X-ray photography in quite a limited range of angles $2\Theta = 20$-30°. The X-ray line of α-PbO_2 with d = 3.12Å practically coincides with the corresponding line for PbO. Therefore the system worked out requires previous removal from the preparation being investigated of oxides of bivalent lead. This is achieved by washing the mixture in an acetate solution.

The graduated graph obtained in the work[13]) is shown in fig. 4.3. On the semi-logarithmic scale the graph is described by the linear equation

$$C_\alpha = 65 - 50 \lg (I_\beta / I_\alpha) \qquad (4.1)$$

where I_α and I_β are the intensities of lines of 3.49A for β-PbO_2 and 3.12A for α-PbO_2. The error of the system worked out does not exceed 3%.

It must be noted that, as shown in the thorough investigation of Kordes[15]), the relative intensities of the lines for α-PbO_2 and β-PbO_2 can change depending on the method of obtaining the preparations. These changes are caused by the difference in the degree of perfection

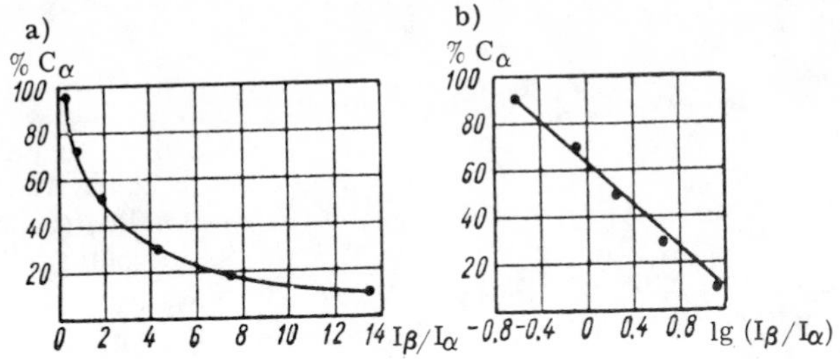

Fig. 4.3 Graduated graphs for phase analysis of mixtures of α and β-PbO_2: a - in normal co-ordinates, b - in semi-logarithmic co-ordinates.

of the crystals, by deformation of the structure of the crystals etc. However, since the method used in[13]) for obtaining the initial preparations was close to the methods used in the production of the positive electrode of a lead acid battery, the suitability of the system worked out for quantitative phase analysis of the positive active masses does not give rise to any doubt. As far as concerns other forms of lead dioxide, the method worked out here may serve, obviously, only for an approximate evaluation of phase composition. The electrical properties of this compound are of substantial interest for the characteristics of the macro and micro-structure of lead dioxide.

As was shown in Chapter 2, the stoichiometric composition of lead dioxide is in general described by the formula PbO_n, where the degree of oxidation n is a function of the phase composition of the oxide, the method of obtaining it, the composition of the contacting solution, the temperature and a number of other factors. Using the symbol system adopted in the theory of real crystals, it is possible to write down the composition of lead dioxide also in the following form:

with $n < 2$ $(Pb^{4+}/\square^{+})(O^{2-}_{2-\delta}, e_{2\delta}/\square^{-})$, where $\delta = 2 - n$
with $n > 2$ $(Pb^{4+}_{1-\frac{\delta}{2}}, p_{2\delta}/\square^{+})(O^{2-}_{2}/\square^{-})$, where $\delta = n - 2$

From the formulae quoted it follows that with $n < 2$ lead dioxide should possess electron conductivity, and with $n > 2$ hole-type.

As is shown in[16]), where a study was made of the equilibrium β-$PbO_2 \rightleftarrows Pb^{2+} + (HClO_4)$, the value of δ diminishes proportionally to the increase in partial pressure of the oxygen in the degree of $^1/_8$. This dependence is correct, in the opinion of the authors of[16]), in the case when the concentration of free electrons in the lead dioxide is determined, basically, by the divergence of its composition from the stoichiometric ($n < 2$).

A number of papers[17-20]) have been devoted to investigation of the electrical conductivity of lead dioxide. According to the results obtained, all the samples studied possessed electronic conductivity. Evidence of this is to be found in the negative values of Hall's coefficient and of the temperature coefficient of electrical conductivity over a wide interval of change of temperature. According to data in[19]), where a study was made of thin films of lead dioxide produced by cathode sputtering, this oxide represents an n-type semi-conductor with a forbidden band width of ~1.5eV, a carrier density of $5 \cdot 10^{9}$ to 10^{25} cm^{-3} and a mobility of ~1cm^2/V.s. Conductivity of similar nature in PbO_2 was established in[21]) by a method based on the measurement of the photo emf which appears when the oxide is illuminated in its characteristic absorption region.

As far as the values of the electrical resistance of PbO_2 mentioned in literature are concerned, here a considerable diversity is observed. The values of specific resistance mentioned in the articles referred to, differ by more than two orders. This is principally explained by the differences in the method of preparation of the experimental samples, i.e. by the difference in macro-structure of the particles and in the stoichiometric and phase composition of the lead dioxide. It must also be noted that the data from literature examined above refer basically to the tetragonal modification of PbO_2 or to samples of unknown phase composition. This circumstance, and also the abovementioned differences in method of preparation of the samples, do not permit the use of the results described for determination of the influence of the crystalline structure of PbO_2 on the electrical conductivity.

Comparative study of the electrical resistance of α and β-PbO_2 was undertaken in ref. [22]). Samples of crystalline modifications of PbO_2 obtained by the method of forming pasted electrodes were used as objects of investigation[12-14]). The samples of the dioxide were kept for a long time in an acetate solution (15%CH_3COONH_4 + 3% CH_3COOH), thanks to which admixtures of compounds of bivalent lead were removed. It can also be assumed that the long stay of the samples in a uniform solution should have resulted in the obtaining of comparative data corresponding to the equilibrium degree of oxidation of both modifications of lead dioxide.

Measurements of electrical resistance were carried out with powders of α and β-PbO_2, the dimensions of the particles of which were within the limits of 40-80μm, and also with the so-called conducting plastics, containing an organic bond together with PbO_2. AKR-7 resin was used as a bond. Samples of the mixture of PbO_2 and resin were prepared by means of pressing and subsequent polymerisation. For determination of the electrical resistance, measurements were taken of the ohmic voltage drop on the sample being investigated with the passing of continuous current. The electrical conductivity of the powders was determined with the aid of a device that made it possible to carry out measurements with a varying degree of compression of the powder. The porosity of the sample of α-PbO_2 here changed from 58 to 38%, and that of β-PbO_2 from 62 to 44%. The resistance of each sample was measured at 4-5 values of current at +20 to -22°C. The extreme current values differed by approximately 10 times. In all cases the resistance of the dioxide did not depend on the direction and magnitude of the current. The results obtained are given in fig. 4.4, where the logarithm of the specific resistance lg ρ is shown depending on the share of the volume taken up by the lead dioxide (V_{PbO_2}/V, where V_{PbO_2} is the volume taken up by PbO_2, and V the overall volume of the sample). The values of V_{PbO_2} were calculated, setting out from a weighed amount and the density of the corresponding modification of PbO_2. The following averaged density values were used: α-PbO_2 9.8g/cm³, β-PbO_2 9.67g/cm³. The first five points on the graph for α-PbO_2 and six points on the graph for β-PbO_2 (fig. 4.4) refer to samples from conducting plastics, the remaining points to pressed powders.

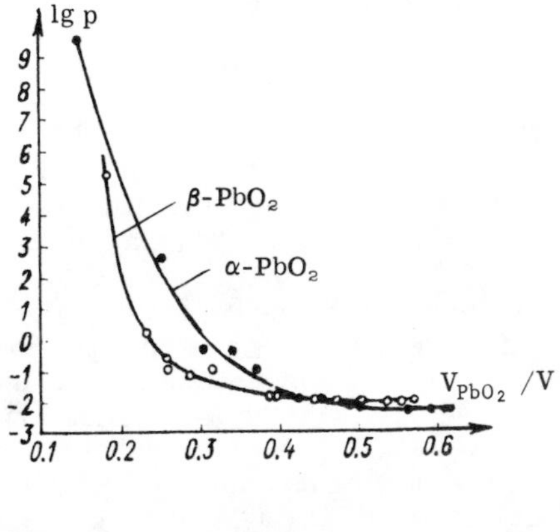

Fig.4.4 Dependence of the specific resistance of α- and β-PbO_2 on volumetric concentration.

As can be seen from fig. 4.4, an increase in the PbO_2 content in the samples in the sphere of relatively low-volume concentrations leads to a quite sharp decrease in the electrical specific resistance ρ. In the field of higher concentrations the influence of V_{PbO_2}/V on the value of ρ becomes less important. The influence of the form of modification of PbO_2 on ρ depends on the volumetric concentrations of lead dioxide. In the field of low values of V_{PbO_2}/V the resistance of α-PbO_2 considerably exceeds the corresponding value for β-PbO_2. With $V_{PbO_2}/V = 0.42$, the graphs ($\lg \rho$, V_{PbO_2}/V) for α- and β-PbO_2 intersect, and with $V_{PbO_2}/V > 0.42$ the specific resistance of α-PbO_2 (ρ_α) becomes less than that of β-PbO_2 (ρ_β).

The values of the specific resistance of dense, poreless samples of α- and β-PbO_2 can be evaluated by means of extrapolation of graphs ($\lg \rho$, V_{PbO_2}/V), which in the field of high volumetric concentrations of PbO_2 are close to straight lines. Extrapolation of $\lg \rho$ to the value $V_{PbO_2}/V = 1$ gives the following values: $\rho_\alpha \approx 10^{-3}$ ohm·cm, $\rho_\beta \approx 4 \cdot 10^{-3}$ ohm·cm. The result obtained can naturally be explained by the fact that the concentration of oxygen vacancies in the α-PbO_2 lattice exceeds the corresponding value for β-PbO_2 (see Chapter 2). The value of specific resistance of PbO_2 obtained by electrolysis of a solution of lead sulphamate is [$\rho = 1.2 \cdot 10^{-3}$ ohm·cm [17])]. The deposit of dioxide obtained in electrolysis of a perchlorate solution, according to the data of Thomas, is characterised by a higher electrical conductivity [$\rho = 0.3 \cdot 10^{-3}$ ohm·cm [17])]. It can be assumed that this deposit possesses an increased concentration of oxygen vacancies in the oxygen sub-lattice, which are equivalent to the free electrons. The results of the calculation of the degree of oxidation of PbO_n in a solution of $HClO_4$ (see Chapter 2) testify in favour of this proposition.

Data obtained in the measurement of the resistance of pressed powders can be used for evaluation of the electrical conductivity of the active mass of the positive electrode of a lead acid battery. As has already been shown in Chapter 3, the volumetric porosity of the positive active mass constitutes ~50%. The specific resistance of powders with the same porosity, according to data represented in fig. 4.4 constitutes $\rho_\alpha = 0.52 \cdot 10^{-2}$ ohm·cm, $\rho_\beta = 1.05 \cdot 10^{-2}$ ohm·cm. The latter value closely coincides with the experimentally determined specific resistance of the active mass of a charged positive electrode [$1.2 \cdot 10^{-2}$ ohm·cm [23])]. This coincidence shows that the active mass studied in [23]) represented basically the β-modification of lead dioxide.

The dependence of the values ρ_α and ρ_β on the volumetric concentration of PbO_2 can be explained by taking account of the influence of contact conductivity. The resistance r of two adjacent particles of PbO_2 is composed of the resistance of the PbO_2 and the contact resistance.

$$r = r_{PbO_2} + r_k \tag{4.2}$$

Since contact resistance r_k is inversely proportional to the square root of the area of contact surface S_k [24]), equation (4.2) can be rewritten in the

$$r = \frac{K_1 \rho}{l} + \frac{K_2 \rho}{\sqrt{S_k}} \tag{4.3}$$

where l is the characteristic dimension of the PbO_2 particles, and K_1 and K_2 are constant coefficients depending on the configuration of the particles.

The summary resistance of the sample r_Σ can be approximately considered as the resistance N_{ch} of parallel chains, each of which consists on average of N particles. In this case, according to (4.3)

$$r_\Sigma = \frac{N}{N_{ch}} r = \frac{N}{N_{ch}} \left(\frac{K_1}{l} + \frac{K_2}{\sqrt{S_k}} \right) \rho \tag{4.4}$$

An increase in PbO_2 content in the sample should principally lead to an increase in the value of N_{ch}, which causes a fall in resistance. In addition the value of S_k should increase here, which leads to a decrease in contact resistance. The higher the concentration of PbO_2 the greater is the resistance of the sample determined by the resistance of the lead dioxide and the less does it depend on the contact surface. At a given concentration of PbO_2 the value of S_k, obviously is determined by the structure of the contacting particles.

Electron microscope study of preparations of lead dioxide showed that particles of α-PbO_2 are characterised by a smooth surface and a round form, while particles of β-PbO_2 at approximately the same dimensions represent crystallites with strongly ramified, dendrite-like surface. Naturally, therefore, at one and the same volumetric concentration the area of contact surface in samples containing β-PbO_2 should considerably exceed the corresponding value for α-PbO_2. This circumstance, obviously, causes higher resistance of samples of α-PbO_2 in the field of relatively low volumetric concentrations, when contact electrical conductivity to a considerable extent determines the conductivity of the sample.

Electro-mechanical properties of lead dioxide

Anode behaviour of a lead dioxide electrode

In the process of polarisation of a lead dioxide anode the liberation of oxygen is observed on the surface.. A study of the mechanism of this process showed that the rate of liberation is limited by the ionisation stage of the water molecules with the formation of adsorbed radicals [25-28]).

$$H_2O \rightarrow OH_{ads} + H^+ + e \qquad (4.5)$$

The dependence of current density of anodic polarisation of a lead dioxide electrode on the potential φ according to the data of I G Kiseleva and B N Kabanov, is expressed by the equation

$$j = ka_{H_2O} \exp\left[\frac{B(\varphi - \psi_1)F}{RT}\right] \qquad (4.6)$$

where β is the coefficient of transfer of the process (4.5), ψ_1 the potential drop in the diffusion part of the electrical double layer (the value of the potential in direct proximity to the surface of the electrode, measured in relation to the corresponding value in the thickness of the solution), k the speed constant. The value of the angular coefficient of the graph (φ, lg j) confirms the course of the process (4.5) according to the single-electron mechanism (at $\beta = 0.5$). Of course, according to data obtained in [29]), the discharge of oxygen on the α-modification of PbO_2 occurs with simultaneous participation of two electrons, i.e. according to the scheme

$$H_2O \rightarrow O_{ads} + 2H^+ + 2e \qquad (4.7)$$

causing a twofold decrease in the pre-logarithmic coefficient. These data, however, were not confirmed in later research [30]).

The rate of diffusion of the oxygen into the PbO_2 lattice depends on the anodic current density j, which points to the marked role of the stage of recombination of the radicals OH with the formation of O_2 molecules or oxygen atoms in the kinetics of the process under consideration [28]).

The mechanism of liberation of oxygen on lead dioxide is determined to a considerable degree by the laws of adsorption on the electrode of sulphate ions [7])[8]). According to equation (4.6), the adsorption of the ions of HSO_4^- should lead to an increase in the rate of discharge of the oxygen as a result of an increase in the negative value of the ψ_1 potential.

The potential of the point of zero charge of PbO_2 in the H_2SO_4 solution is about 1.8V (in respect of a normal hydrogen electrode) [26]). At $\varphi > 1.8$V in conformity with equation (4.6), a sharp increase in the rate of liberation of oxygen is observed. In the graph (φ, lg j) at this potential there occurs a marked inflection; the graphs (φ, lg j), taken with a rise and fall of current, show in 0.1N H_2SO_4 hysteresis in the region of the point of zero charge of PbO_2 (fig. 4.5).

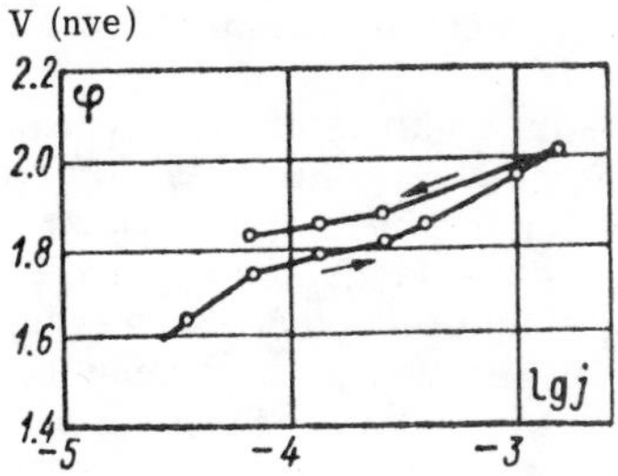

Fig. 4.5 Dependence of the potential of liberation of oxygen on PbO_2 on the current in 0.1N·H_2SO_4.

An increase in the concentration of sulphuric acid causes a shift of the zero charge potential of PbO_2 to the negative side. Thus, if in 0.1N·H_2SO_4 the point of zero charge lies at ~1.9V, then in 8N·H_2SO_4 it is at 1.7V (on the hydrogen scale)[31]). This phenomenon the authors also link with the adsorption of sulphate ions[31]), which increases with an increase in the concentration of H_2SO_4 and, together with the shift of the point of zero charge, causes a decrease in the hardness of the PbO_2 crystals. Radio-chemical study of the adsorption processes on a lead dioxide electrode[27]) showed that adsorption of HSO_4^- ions begins even at a faintly negative surface charge and sharply increases with the change of sign of the charge. Starting at potential $\varphi \approxeq 1.95V$, adsorption practically ceases to change with a further increase in φ.

In dilute solutions of H_2SO_4 adsorption is caused by electrostatic forces. With an increase in concentration of the acid there is an increase in the proportion of specific adsorption, which does not depend much on the potential of the electrode. Strengthening of the bond of the adsorbed ions with the surface of the oxide, which takes place in strong solutions of H_2SO_4, leads to inhibition of the discharge of oxygen and an increase in the oxygen overvoltage.

Adsorption of sulphuric acid shows a marked dependence on the form of the crystalline modification of the PbO_2. The quantity of sulphate ions specifically adsorbed on the surface of β-PbO_2 considerably exceeds the corresponding value for α-PbO_2 [7]). Irreversible adsorption takes place in the process of formation of β-PbO_2 with anodic oxidation of $PbSO_4$ and leads to considerable dispersion of the crystals of the tetragonal modification of PbO_2. Let us note that increased adsorption of anions on the surface of β-PbO_2 (in comparison with α-PbO_2) is possibly linked with the greater density of the positive charges on the faces of an elementary cell of this modification of PbO_2 [32]).

Comparison of the absolute values of the oxygen overvoltage on lead dioxide quoted in literature shows that they differ markedly. The values of oxygen overvoltage on PbO_2, according to the data of the majority of authors, are quite large and approximate to the corresponding values for a platinum electrode. However, the angle of slope and, in particular, the disposition of the graphs (φ, lg j) in different works vary within fairly wide limits. This can be explained principally by the difference in the value of the true surface of the electrodes prepared by different methods. We must also take into account the peculiarity of the electrode under consideration mentioned in literature, consisting in the fact that its surface changes in the process of electrolysis, and the character of this change depends on the regime of polarisation and the stoichiometric composition of the oxide. Finally, an important role is played here, obviously, by the abovementioned difference in the concentration of oxygen vacancies, which can also suffer changes in the process of anode polarisation of the electrode.

According to the opinion of Ruetschi and Delahaye [33]) discharge of OH^- ions on the metal M, which is the first stage of the process of liberation of oxygen, occurs with intermediate formation of the compound M-OH according to the scheme

$$M + H_2O - OH^- - e \rightarrow M - OH + H_2O \qquad (4.7')$$

Using this representation, it is possible to consider the adsorption of the radicals OH on PbO_2 as the intrusion of them into the surface layer of lead dioxide, in the lattice of which there are oxygen vacancies. The process (4.5) may be written down in the form

$$\frac{1}{\Delta n} PbO_n + H_2O \rightarrow \frac{1}{\Delta n} PbO_n(OH)_{\Delta n} + H^+ + e \qquad (4.8)$$

The equation of the reaction (4.8), as also (4.5), leads to the dependence (4.6).

In the event of the process of liberation of oxygen occurring according to the two-electron mechanism (4.7), instead of equation (4.8) we shall have

$$\frac{1}{\Delta n} PbO_n + H_2O \rightarrow \frac{1}{\Delta n} PbO_{n+\Delta n} + 2H^+ + 2e \qquad (4.9)$$

and

$$j = k a_{H_2O} \exp\left[\frac{2\beta F(\varphi - \psi_1)}{RT}\right] \qquad (4.10)$$

The following stage of the process under consideration represents the disintegration of the intermediate complex

$$PbO_n(OH)_{\Delta n} \rightarrow PbO_n + \frac{\Delta n}{2} H_2O + \frac{\Delta n}{2} O \qquad (4.11)$$

$$PbO_{n+\Delta n} \rightarrow PbO_n + \Delta n O \qquad (4.12)$$

Thus the initial oxide, from the point of view of the ideas set forth, is the catalyst of the process.

If we designate the free energy of formation of the intermediate adsorption complex by ΔG_{act}, then we can write down the velocity constant in the form

$$k = k_o e^{-\Delta G_{act}/RT} \qquad (4.13)$$

where the constant k_o can in principle be calculated with the aid of the theory of absolute speeds of reactions. According to the equation of the reaction (4.9) *)

$$\Delta G_{act} = \frac{1}{\Delta n} (\Delta G_{PbO_{n+\Delta n}} - \Delta G_{PbO_n}) - \Delta G_{H_2O} \qquad (4.14)$$

or if the value of Δn is sufficiently small

$$\Delta G_{act} = \frac{dG}{dn} - \Delta G_{H_2O} \qquad (4.15)$$

whence, according to (4.13)

$$k = k_o' e^{-\frac{1}{RT}\frac{dG}{dn}} \qquad (4.16)$$

---

*) Subsequent calculation can be carried out also with the use of equation (4.8).

where

$$k_0' = k_0 e^{-\Delta G_{H_2O}/RT}$$

Insofar as formation of the intermediate complex is thermodynamically possible, $\Delta G_{act} < 0$. This, according to (4.15), means that the derivative dG/dn is a negative value exceeding in absolute value $|\Delta G_{H_2O}|$.

It can be assumed that the lower the degree of oxidation of the initial compound n, the more considerable changes the free energy will suffer in the transition from the initial to the activated state, i.e. the greater will be the value of $|dG/dn|$. An increase in the absolute value of the derivative dG/dn should, in conformity with equation (4.16), lead to an increase in the rate constant k, and consequently also of the anodic current density j. This effect is equivalent to a decrease in the oxygen overvoltage. Thus the lower the degree of oxidation of the lead dioxide, the smaller will be the value of the overvoltage of liberation of oxygen η. The symbiotic dependence between the values n and η makes it possible to explain the dependence of the potential for the liberation of oxygen on PbO_2 on the form of crystalline modification described in the literature. However, numerous data point to the fact that oxygen overvoltage on the β-modification of PbO_2 markedly exceeds overvoltage on α-PbO_2. At the same time, as was shown in Chapter 2 of this book, β-PbO_2 is distinguished by a higher degree of oxidation.

Returning to the article of Ruetschi and Delahaye quoted above, we shall show that, according to the data of these authors, the overvoltage of liberation of oxygen on metal M depends on the energy of the bond M-O or M-OH in the corresponding oxide. Indeed, the latter decreases with an increase in concentration of oxygen in the lattice of the oxide. This decrease in bond energy is shown to be the reason for the increase in oxygen overvoltage. Hence it also follows that samples of lead dioxide with a higher degree of oxidation should possess higher values of the potential for liberation of oxygen than samples containing a lower quantity of oxygen.

As an example illustrating the possible influence of the degree of oxidation on the oxygen overvoltage, let us look at the anode characteristics of the β-modification of lead dioxide in $10N \cdot H_2SO_4$ solution[34]). In fig. 4.6 there is represented the stationary graph of dependence of the anode potential of β-PbO_2 on the logarithm of current density.

The graph (η, lg j) is characterised by two straight-line sections with a coefficient of slope of 0.116V at low current densities and 0.127V in the sphere of high current densities. Deflection in the semi-logarithmic graph is observed in the interval of potentials φ_{π} = 2.05-2.15V (in relation to the normal hydrogen electrode). The values of potentials, measured at subsequent fall and rise of current, coincided with an attained accuracy of ±2-3mV.

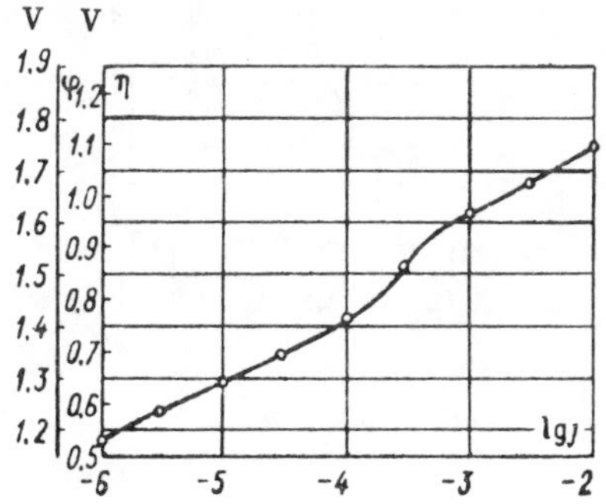

Fig.4.6 Dependence of oxygen overvoltage on β-PbO_2 on the logarithm of current density in 10N·H_2SO_4 (φ is in relation to Hg/Hg_2SO_4).

The inflection in the graph (η, lg j) cannot be explained by the adsorption-desorption processes with the participation of the sulphuric acid. This is evidenced principally by the considerable difference of the φ_{π} from the potential of the point of zero charge of the PbO_2, which in strong solutions of H_2SO_4 is equal to ~1.7V, and also by the absence of hysteresis in the sphere of φ_{π} in the graph under consideration, taken at increase and decrease of the current. It must, besides, be noted that, as can be seen from fig. 4.6, the extrapolated value of the oxygen overvoltage $\eta_{j=1}$ with j = 1A/cm^2 for the upper straight-line section of the graph (φ, lg j) lies at a more positive potential than that for the lower section. In the case when the inflection in the graph (φ, lg j) is caused by change of the ψ_1 potential as a result of the adsorption of sulphate ions on the surface of the PbO_2 (which takes place in dilute solutions of H_2SO_4), the value of $\eta_{j=1}$, in conformity with equation (4.6), decreases in the sphere of potentials lying more positive than the potential of zero charge of PbO_2.

Electrostatic adsorption of the H^+ ions in the sphere of potentials situated at a more negative position than the potential of zero charge of PbO_2 should, according to equation (4.6), lead to an increase in oxygen overvoltage. Thus the resulting effect will be similar to what is described above.

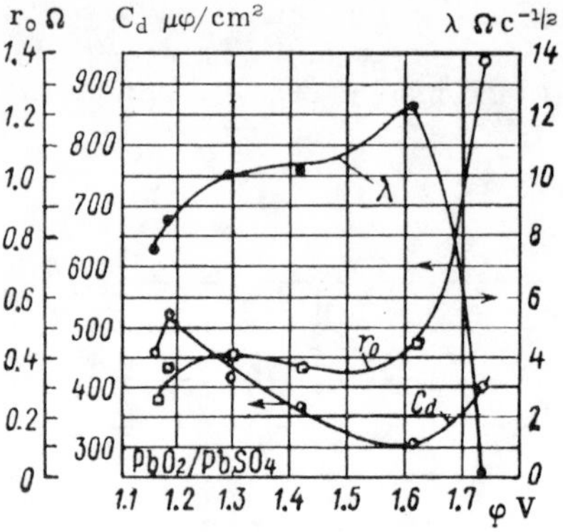

Fig.4.7 Dependence of the parameters of the double layer of β-PbO_2 on the potential of the electrode (in relation to Hg/Hg_2SO_4).

It can be assumed that in $10N \cdot H_2SO_4$ solution considerable irreversible adsorption of sulphuric acid on the surface of the β-PbO_2 takes place [7][28]), as this does not depend much on the sign of the charge of the electrode surface. The quantity of sulphate ions adsorbed owing to electrostatic forces, obviously, is small and shows no marked influence on the value of the oxygen overvoltage. These ideas are confirmed by the comparatively small dependence of the capacity of the double layer of β-PbO_2 on potential (fig. 4.7). At the same time, as can be seen from fig. 4.7, the values of the other parameters of the double electrical layer connected with the course of the electro-chemical reaction (those of polarisation resistance r_0 and of Warburg's coefficient of diffusion resistance λ) change sharply at $\varphi > \varphi_{\pi}$.

The character of the inflection in the graph (φ, lg j), and also the changes in the parameters of the double layer, which have already been mentioned, give a basis for assuming that these phenomena are linked with a reversible change in the degree of oxidation of the surface layers of the electrode. An increase in the anode potential may cause an increase in the oxygen content in the crystal lattice of lead dioxide, which leads to an increase in the overvoltage of liberation of oxygen. With a decrease in potential ($\varphi < \varphi_{\pi}$), obviously, there follows a decrease in the degree of oxidation, causing an increase in the rate of liberation of oxygen.

In studying the anodic behaviour of lead dioxide electro-deposited from nitric acid electrolyte and representing a mixture of approximately equal parts of α and β-PbO_2 [35]), no inflection was found in the graph (η, lg j) (fig. 4.8). In the field of current densities j from $3 \cdot 10^{-5}$ to $3 \cdot 10^{-3}$ A/cm^2 (calculated for the visible surface) the graph of oxygen overvoltage is characterised by the equation

$$\eta = 1.15 + 0.12 \lg j \qquad (4.17)$$

The absence of an inflection obviously is evidence of the stable stoichiometric composition of the given oxide which does not change in the process of polarisation.

The capacity of the double layer of the electrode under consideration ($\alpha + \beta$-PbO_2) constitutes $C_d = 130 \mu F/cm^2$ of visible surface. Hence it follows that the true surface of the electrode exceeds the visible surface by approximately seven times. Therefore, if we calculate the density of the current per unit of true surface, then the value of the first member on the right-hand side of equation (4.17) will constitute ~1.25V.

Modification of the graph η, lg j) for platinum (fig. 4.8) has the form

$$\eta = 1.24 + 0.12 \lg j \qquad (4.18)$$

If we calculate that the coefficient of roughness of Pt is equal to 2, then the value of the first member in the right-hand part of equation (4.18) constitutes approximately 1.27V. Thus the anodic characteristics of $\alpha + \beta$-PbO_2 and Pt are quite close over a wide interval of densities.

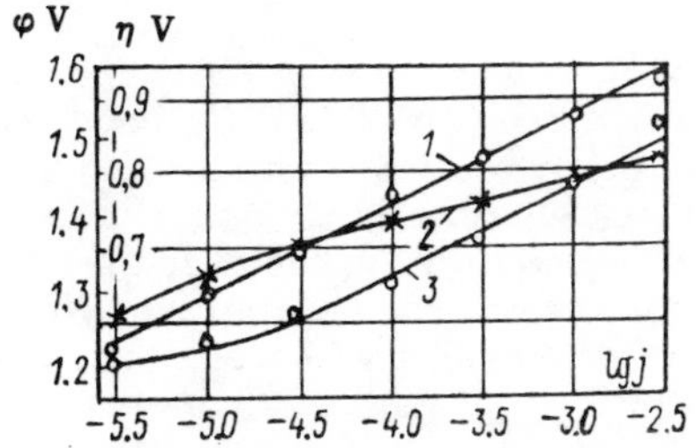

Fig.4.8 Oxygen overvoltage on Pt (1), β-PbO_2 (2), obtained by anodic oxidation of $PbO_{1.68}$ and $\alpha + \beta$-PbO_2 (3).

Fig.4.8 also shows a plot of the semi-logarithmic graph of oxygen overvoltage on lead dioxide obtained by electro-deposition from an alkaline solution of ferro-salt[35]). As will be shown below, this oxide is marked by considerable stoichiometric deficiency of oxygen. According to the data of X-ray structural analysis, the oxide, submitted to a long anodic polarisation until the attainment of stable values of the potential, represents a fine-dispersion tetragonal modification of lead dioxide. The stationary graph (η, lg j) is characterised in this case by the equation

$$\eta = 0.97 + 0.06 \lg j \tag{4.19}$$

Judging by the value of the pre-logarithmic coefficient in (4.19), discharge of oxygen occurs according to the two-electron mechanism, i.e. according to (4.7) or (4.9).

As has been shown above, the kinetics of the liberation of oxygen on oxide electrodes are to a large extent determined by the concentration of the oxygen vacancies in the crystal lattice of the oxide. The likelihood of the occurrence of discharge of oxygen on a lead dioxide electrode according to the scheme of (4.8) or (4.9) also, obviously, depends on the degree of oxidation of the lead dioxide. It can be assumed, therefore, that a low value of the pre-logarithmic coefficient for the process of liberation of oxygen on the β-modification of the dioxide obtained as a result of anodic polarisation of a low-oxide sample is connected with the relatively high stoichiometric deficiency of oxygen in this electrode.

In the sphere of low current densities, as can be seen from fig. 4.8, the semi-logarithmic graphs of oxygen overvoltage on lead dioxide deviate from a rectilinear course. This phenomenon occurs near the equilibrium potential of $PbO_2 \rightleftarrows PbSO_4$, pointing to the essential role of the oxidisation-reduction processes with the participation of lead ions at low polarisations of the electrode. The graph (η, lg j), taken on β-PbO_2 (fig. 4.6), maintains a rectilinear course right down to quite low current densities (10^{-6} A/cm^2). Obviously, this difference is connected with higher overvoltage of the liberation of oxygen and lower rate of spontaneous reduction of β-PbO_2 (in comparison with an electrode made of a mixture of $\alpha + \beta$-PbO_2). Naturally, the graph (η, lg j), taken on a Pt electrode, is characterised, as can be seen from fig. 4.8, by a rectilinear course over the whole range of current densities studied (j $3 \cdot 10^{-6}$ to $3 \cdot 10^{-3}$ A/cm^2).

Exchange current of the equilibrium $PbO_2 \rightleftarrows PbSO_4$

An important characteristic of the positive electrode of a lead acid battery is the exchange current of the equilibrium established on the surface of lead dioxide in a sulphuric acid solution. As is well known[36] the Faraday impedance method may be used for the determination of exchange current.

In refs. [37][38] it was shown that the structure of the electrical double layer of a lead dioxide electrode over a wide range of frequencies ($\nu = 20\text{-}30\,000$Hz) and at potentials $\varphi < 2$v (in relation to a normal hydrogen electrode) can be described by a scheme with parallel combination of the capacity of the dual layer (C_d) and the linear and semi-infinite RC line with uniformly distributed parameters.

Measurements of impedance of a lead dioxide electrode ($\alpha + \beta$-PbO_2), carried out by using the method of N P Gnusin[39][40], showed that the frequency dependence of impedance Z is characterised by a straight line in the co-ordinates Z, $\nu^{-1/2}$ maintained over a wide interval of anodic polarisation currents. With an increase in current density there was observed an increase in the slope of the straight lines (Z, $\nu^{-1/2}$), i.e. the values of $\partial Z/\partial(\nu^{-1/2})$, and some decrease in the dimensions of the section of the axis of the (Z) ordinates that is cut off by the straight lines (Z, $\nu^{-1/2}$) extrapolated to the value of $\nu \to \infty$ ($\nu^{-1/2} \rightleftarrows 0$). At $j < (10^{-4} - 10^{-5})$ A/cm², when the potential of the electrode approaches the value corresponding to the equilibrium $PbO_2 \rightleftarrows PbSO_4$ the disposition of graph (Z, $\nu^{-1/2}$) does not depend, in practice, on the anodic polarisation current right down to $j = 0$ ($\varphi \approx \varphi_{PbO_2/PbSO_4}$).

The frequency dependence of the impedance quoted in fig. 4.9 was obtained in the sphere of low polarisations. The straight line (Z, $\nu^{-1/2}$) is described by the equation

$$Z = 0.1 + \frac{1.8}{\sqrt{\nu}} \qquad (4.20)$$

A comparison was made of the dependence of Z on ν, expressed in logarithmic co-ordinates (fig. 4.9), with a standard graph[40]. For determination of the parameters of the electrical double layer: capacity C_d, polarisation resistance r_o and Warburg's coefficient of diffusion resistance λ. This method is based on the assumption that the double layer can be interpreted as a scheme with parallel combination of capacity C_d, and Faraday impedance representing subsequently combined polarisation and diffusion resistances.

The area of the geometric surface of the electrode constituted 3cm². With $\varphi \approx \varphi_{PbO_2/PbSO_4}$ the following values were obtained: $C_d = 400\mu F$ of $130\mu F/cm^2$ of visible surface, $r_o = 0.12$ohm, $\lambda = 1.77$ohm $\cdot$ $c^{-1/2}$ With an increase in polarisation the value of λ rises slightly, and that of r_o falls. The value of C_d also decreases slightly with an increase in anode polarisation, although the changes in C_d are small. The absence of a strong dependence of the capacitance of the double layer on the potential can be explained by the considerable irreversible adsorption of sulphuric acid taking place in a strong solution of H_2SO_4, and a certain decrease in C_d in the sphere of high anode polarisations, probably as a result of screening of part of the surface of the electrode by oxygen bubbles.

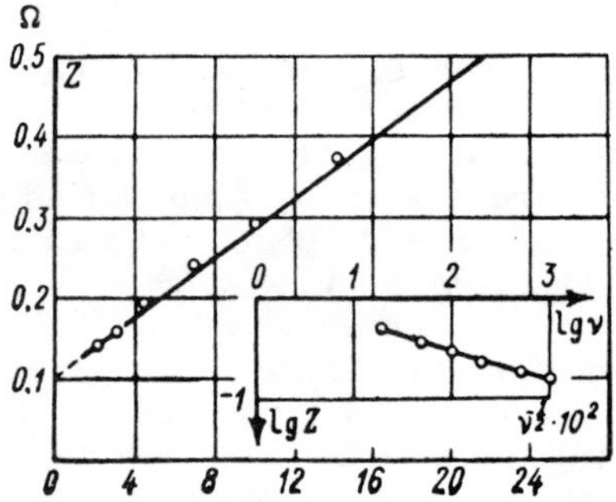

Fig.4.9 Frequency dependence of impedance of the double layer of $\alpha + \beta$-PbO_2 at equilibrium potential of $PbO_2 \rightleftarrows PbSO_4$ (10N·H_2SO_4).

The value of the capacitance can be determined also by means of the construction of a triangle of voltage drops [39]. The value of the capacitance C determined in this way shows a dependence on frequency, as it decreases with an increase in frequency. This is caused by the influence of the capacitance sum and of the diffusion resistance, which depends on frequency. The extrapolated value of C with $\nu \to \infty$ coincides well with the above-mentioned value of C_d determined by the method given in ref. [40]).

It can be shown that the linear dependence of the impedance of the double layer on the frequency to the power of $(-\frac{1}{2})$ is evidence of the fact that the measured values of Z in the frequency range under investigation are close to the Faraday impedance of the electrode Z_ϕ. The frequency dependence Z_ϕ can be written down in the form [41])

$$Z_\phi = \sqrt{\left(r_0 + \frac{\lambda}{\sqrt{2\nu}}\right)^2 + \frac{\lambda^2}{2\nu}} \qquad (4.21)$$

From formula (4.21) it follows that the coefficient of slope of the graph $(Z_\phi, \nu^{-1/2})$

$$\frac{\partial Z_\phi}{\partial(\nu^{-1/2})} = \frac{\lambda(r_0 + \lambda\sqrt{2/\nu})}{\sqrt{2[r_0(r_0 + \lambda\sqrt{2/\nu}) + \lambda^2/\nu]}} \qquad (4.22)$$

depends on the frequency, i.e. is shown to be a variable value. The limits of change of this value constitute

$$\lim_{\nu\to\infty}\left[\frac{\partial Z_\phi}{\partial(\nu^{-1/2})}\right] = \frac{\lambda}{\sqrt{2}} \cong 0.71\lambda; \quad \lim_{\nu\to 0}\left[\frac{\partial Z}{\partial(\nu^{-1/2})}\right] = \lambda \qquad (4.23)$$

Thus, if we rewrite formula (4.22) in the form

$$\frac{\partial Z_\phi}{\partial(\nu^{-1/2})} = K_\nu\lambda \qquad (4.24)$$

then, in accordance with (4.23), the coefficient K_ν takes on values corresponding to the inequality

$$1 > K_\nu > 0.71 \qquad (4.25)$$

and decreases with an increase in frequency.

As can be seen from inequality (4.25), the change of coefficient K_ν with frequency is comparatively small, and in a limited field of frequencies the value of K_ν can with good approximation be reckoned constant. In fact, using the approximate relationship for calculation of the root of the sum of the squares

$$\sqrt{x^2 + y^2} \approx 0.96x + 0.4y \qquad (4.26)$$

where x and y are any positive figures $(x > y)$ the error of which does not exceed 4%, it is possible to rewrite equation (4.21) in the form[41])

$$Z_\phi \approx 0.96\left(r_0 + \frac{\lambda}{\sqrt{2\nu}}\right) + \frac{0.4\lambda}{\sqrt{2\nu}} = 0.96\left(r_0 + \frac{\lambda}{\sqrt{\nu}}\right) \qquad (4.27)$$

From formulae (4.27) and (4.24) it follows that $K_\nu = 0.96$, which is in conformity with inequality (4.25)

$$r_0 = 1.04 \lim_{\nu\to\infty} Z_\phi \text{ and } \lambda = 1.04 \frac{\partial Z_\phi}{\partial(\nu^{-1/2})} \qquad (4.28)$$

Comparison of equations (4.27) and (4.20) taking into account the values of r_o and λ quoted above shows that in the given case $Z \approx Z_\phi$. This equation is possible on the condition

$$R_p \ll Z_\phi \ll R_c \tag{4.29}$$

where R_p is the resistance of the layer of electrolyte at the surface of the electrode, and R_c is the resistance connected with the capacity of the double layer

$$R_c = 1/(2\pi\nu C_d) \tag{4.30}$$

The value R_p in the case of a smooth electrode in a sufficiently electrically conductive electrolyte is quite small. On the other hand, as is shown by calculation according to formulae (4.27) and (4.30), for the electrode under consideration $R_c \gg Z_\phi$. Thus inequality (4.29) is observed in the field of comparatively low frequencies.

If on the electrode oxidation-reduction equilibrium occurs, then [36])

$$r_o = \frac{RT}{zFSi_o} \tag{4.31}$$

$$\lambda = \frac{RT}{\sqrt{2\pi}\, z^2 F^2 S} \left(\frac{1}{c_O \sqrt{D_O}} + \frac{1}{c_R \sqrt{D_R}} \right) \tag{4.32}$$

where i_o is the density of the exchange current, S is the area of the true surface of the electrode, z the number of electrons participating in the electrode reaction, c_O and c_R respectively are the concentration of oxidiser and reducer, D_O and D_R the coefficients of diffusion of the oxidiser and reducer.

With $T = 298^\circ$ and $z = 2$, according to (4.31)

$$i_o = \frac{0.013}{Sr_o} \tag{4.33}$$

Calculation according to formula (4.33) for the electrode under consideration here ($\alpha + \beta$-PbO_2) leads to the value $i_o = 4.9 \cdot 10^{-3} A/cm^2$. Here the value of S is determined by the value of C_d. It must, however, be noted that with the presence of adsorption of sulphate ions the calculation of the value of S according to the capacity of the double layer cannot be considered fully satisfactory.

Calculation of the equations (4.31) and (4.32) makes it possible to eliminate the value S and write down the formula for calculation of exchange current of the oxidation-reduction equilibrium under consideration in the form[41])

$$i_0 = \frac{4.84 \cdot 10^5 \lambda}{r_0 \left(c_{Pb^{2+}}^{-1} D_{Pb^{2+}}^{-1/2} + c_{Pb^{4+}}^{-1} D_{Pb^{4+}}^{-1/2} \right)} \qquad (4.34)$$

From the data on the solubility of $PbSO_4$ in $10N{\cdot}H_2SO_4$ at 25°C[42]) it follows that $C_{Pb^{2+}} = 1.2 \cdot 10^{-8}$ g.eq/cm^3. The coefficient of diffusion of Pb^{2+} ions in the solution is $D_{Pb^{2+}} = 0.98 \cdot 10^{-5}$ cm^2/s[43]).

If we assume that the oxidised form (Pb^{4+}) is found in the solid phase, then, setting out from the values of the density and molecular weight of PbO_2, it is possible to calculate that $c_{Pb^{4+}} = 0.156$ g.eq/cm^3. The coefficient of diffusion of the Pb^{4+} ions in the solid lead dioxide is $D_{Pb^{4+}} = 8.8 \cdot 10^{-16}$ cm^2/s[44]). Substituting these values in formula (4.34), we obtain $i_0 = 3.25 \cdot 10^{-4}$ A/cm^2. If we accept that the oxidised form is found in the solution and its concentration $c_{Pb^{4+}} = 6.2 \cdot 10^{-7}$ g.eq/cm^3 [45]), and also assume that $D_{Pb^{2+}} \approx D_{Pb^{4+}}$, then according to (4.34), $i_0 = 3.22 \cdot 10^{-4}$ A/cm^2. Thus the value of i_0, calculated according to formula (3.34), in practice does not depend on the assumption that has been made in relation to the state of the ions of quadrivalent lead, since in both cases there is observed the condition

$$c_{Pb^{2+}}^{-1} D_{Pb^{2+}}^{-1/2} \gg c_{Pb^{4+}}^{-1} D_{Pb^{4+}}^{-1/2} \qquad (4.35)$$

At the same time calculation according to formula (4.33) leads to a value of i_0 approximately differing by one order from the value of i_0 calculated according to the formula in ref.[34]). Obviously the reason for this divergence is due to the inaccurate determination of the value of the true surface of the electrode S. Adsorption of sulphuric acid should lead to a decrease in the specific capacity of the double layer, which causes a rise in the value of S calculated setting out from the value of C_d and a corresponding decrease in i_0 calculated according to (4.33). It is possible that the values of c and D used for calculation according to formula (4.34) are not fully accurate, since the electrochemical reaction ($Pb^{2+} \rightleftarrows Pb^{4+} + 2e$) takes place in a thin inter-phase layer, where the values of these terms may differ from the corresponding values in the thickness of the solution and of the electrode.

In ref.[46]) a value of the exchange current is quoted for the equilibrium $PbO_2 \rightleftarrows PbSO_4$ in $2N{\cdot}H_2SO_4$, $i_0 = 1.5 \cdot 10^{-5}$ A/cm^2. This value was calculated per unit of visible surface of lead dioxide formed on anodic polarisation of Pb in sulphuric acid. Taking into account the essential difference of the geometric and the true surface of the lead dioxide anodic film, and also the increase in the solubility of the $PbSO_4$ (and, consequently, of the value of $c\,Pb^{2+}$) in proportion to the dilution of the H_2SO_4 solution, it must be noted that the values of i_0 and i_0' differ quite considerably.

The value of i_0' was calculated in ref.[46]) setting out from the graph of distribution of potential along the length of a lead tube being anodically polarised. Here the authors identify the length of the section L, on which the process of formation of PbO_2 occurs, with the depth of penetration of the process, determined by the equation (3.20). In reality, as follows from determination of the value of Λ, $L > \Lambda$, whence, according to (3.20), $i_0' < i_0$.

Impedance measurements with a lead dioxide electrode representing β-PbO_2 give at the equilibrium potential for $PbO_2 \rightleftarrows PbSO_4$ the following values of parameters of the double layer which are independent of frequency: $C_d = 460\mu m/cm^2$, $r_0 = 0.25$ ohm, $\lambda = 7.5 ohm \cdot s^{-1/2}$. Calculation according to formula (4.33) leads to a density of exchange current $i_0 = 6.8 \cdot 10^{-4}\ A/cm^2$. Let us note that this value in order of magnitude coincides with the exchange current of β-PbO_2 Pb^{2+} in a $HClO_4$ solution[47]). Calculation of the exchange current of the equilibrium under consideration (β-PbO_2 $PbSO_4$) according to formula (4.34) leads in this case to a very close value $i_0 = 6.4 \cdot 10^{-4}$ A/cm^2.

It is of interest to compare the results of impedance measurements for electrodes of a mixture of $\alpha + \beta$-PbO_2 and of β-PbO_2 at the equilibrium potential of $PbO_2 \rightleftarrows PbSO_4$. Substantial changes which are suffered by the values of polarisation resistance r_0 and the coefficient of diffusion resistance λ at the transfer from one electrode to the other in one and the same electrolyte ($10N \cdot H_2SO_4$) are evidence of the considerable probability of the participation in the oxidation-reduction process of lead ions present in the oxide phase. The change of phase composition of the electrode, obviously, affects the value of the coefficient of diffusion of the Pb^{4+} ions and their concentration in the surface layer of oxide. In fact, according to equation (4.32)

$$\frac{\lambda S}{c^{-1}_{Pb^{2+}} D^{-1/2}_{Pb^{2+}} + c^{-1}_{Pb^{4+}} D^{-1/2}_{Pb^{4+}}} = \frac{RT}{4\sqrt{2\pi}\,F^2} = \text{const}(T) \qquad (4.36)$$

The data quoted above show *) that $\lambda_{(\beta)} > \lambda_{(\alpha+\beta)}$ and $S_{(\beta)} > S_{(\alpha+\beta)}$. Since the values of $c_{Pb^{2+}}$ and $D_{Pb^{2+}}$, obviously, do not depend on the phase composition of the electrode, from equation (4.36) it follows that

$$\left(c_{Pb^{4+}} D^{1/2}_{Pb^{4+}}\right)^{(\beta)} < \left(c_{Pb^{4+}} D^{1/2}_{Pb^{4+}}\right)^{(\alpha+\beta)} \qquad (4.37)$$

The inequality (4.37) makes sense only in the case where the values of $c_{Pb^{2+}}$ and $D_{Pb^{2+}}$ refer to the solid phase.

Further, the above densities of exchange current of the equilibrium $PbO_2 \rightleftarrows PbSO_4$, calculated according to formula (4.33), correspond to the inequality

$$i_o^{(\beta)} < i_o^{(\alpha+\beta)} \qquad (4.38)$$

The dependence of the exchange current on the concentration of the oxidised and reduced forms can be written down with reference to the equilibrium under consideration in the form

$$i_o = I_o c^{\alpha}_{Pb^{2+}} c^{\beta}_{Pb^{4+}} \qquad (4.39)$$

where α and β are the coefficients of transfer of the cathode and anode reaction, and I_o is a constant which does not depend on the concentration. Since, as has already been shown, $c_{Pb^{2+}}$ cannot depend on the phase composition of the lead dioxide electrode, from equation (4.39) and inequality (4.38) it follows that

$$c^{(\beta)}_{Pb^{4+}} < c^{(\alpha+\beta)}_{Pb^{4+}} \qquad (4.40)$$

This means that the concentration of lead ions in β-PbO_2 is less than in the composition of the mixture α + β-PbO_2, or, in other words, the concentration of oxygen ions in the crystal lattice of β-PbO_2 is greater than in the lattice of α-PbO_2. This result is in full conformity with numerous data quoted above.

The inequalities (4.37) and (4.40) are similar, in the sense that they do not permit us to explain the influence of the phase composition of

---

*) The upper indices in brackets point to the applicability of the corresponding parameter to an electrode of α + β-PbO_2 or of β-PbO_2. The second inequality follows from the relationship of the capacities of the double layer of the electrodes.

the dioxide on the coefficient of diffusion of the Pb^{4+} ions. Hence, judging by the relationship of the exchange currents of $\alpha + \beta\text{-}PbO_2 \rightleftarrows PbSO_4$, calculated according to formula (4.33) and formula (4.34), and analogous results for the equilibrium $\beta\text{-}PbO_2 \rightleftarrows PbSO_4$, it can be assumed that

$$D^{(\beta)}_{Pb^{4+}} < D^{(\alpha+\beta)}_{Pb^{4+}} \tag{4.41}$$

The inequality (4.41) shows that the mobility of the lead ions in the tetragonal modification of PbO_2 is less than in the rhombic one. It is possible that the increased concentration of oxygen vacancies in the crystal lattice of $\alpha\text{-}PbO_2$ facilitates the possibility of displacement of Pb^{4+} ions.

The mechanism of cathodic reduction of lead dioxide

Cathodic reduction of lead dioxide at the discharge of the positive electrode of a lead acid battery represents a quite complex process, the kinetics of which have not yet been sufficiently studied.

This process, expressed by the summary equation (2.20), can occur, in principle, both in the solution and in the solid phase. In the first case it is assumed that the electrode reaction takes place on the electrode/electrolyte interface, where on discharge there takes place the reduction $Pb^{4+}_{(solid)}$ $Pb^{2+}_{(soln)}$ with simultaneous transfer of the reduced lead ions to the solution. The following stage is the formation of $PbSO_4$, as a result of the interaction of the Pb^{2+} ions with the sulphate ions.

The charge process, in accordance with the scheme of the liquid-phase mechanism, assumes the oxidation of the Pb^{2+} ions in the solution at the surface of the electrode with subsequent transfer of the Pb (IV) ions to the crystal lattice of the dioxide. The presence of Pb^{2+} ions in the solution is determined by the final solubility of the $PbSO_4$.

With regard to the state of the Pb (IV) in the solution innumerable hypotheses have been propounded. Thus, in the well known theory of Leblanc[48]) participation in the electrode reactions of a Pb^{4+} ion is postulated. The discharge of the positive electrode from this point of view can be described by the following scheme

$$PbO_2 \xrightarrow{+4H^+} Pb^{4+} \xrightarrow{+2e} Pb^{2+} \xrightarrow{SO_4^{2-}} PbSO_4 \tag{4.42}$$

According to Liebenow's ideas, the given process occurs with the intermediate formation of PbO_2^{2-} ions

$$PbO_2 \xrightarrow{+2e} PbO_2^{2-} \xrightarrow{+4H^+} Pb^{2+} \xrightarrow{SO_4^{2-}} PbSO_4 \qquad (4.43)$$

The authors of ref.[45]) come to the conclusion about the existence of $PbO(OH)^+$ ions in the sulphuric acid electrolyte, the reduction of which can occur according to the reaction

$$PbO(OH)^+ + 3H^+ + 2e \rightarrow Pb^{2+} + 2H_2O \qquad (4.44)$$

Finally, according to the data of Bode and Voss[49]) compounds of quadrivalent lead exist in the sulphuric acid electrolyte in the form of ions of $[Pb(OH)_2(SO_4)_2]^{2-}$, forming as a result of oxidation of Pb^{2+} at the charge. These authors also allow the possibility of formation of sulphate of quadrivalent lead $Pb(SO_4)_2$, hydrolysis of which leads to the obtaining of PbO_2. The discharge process can be, from the point of view of Bode and Voss, written down in the following form:

$$\left[Pb(OH)_2(SO_4)_2\right]^{2-} + 4H^+ + 2e \rightarrow Pb^{2+} + 2HSO_4^- + 2H_2O \qquad (4.45)$$

or

$$Pb(SO_4)_2 + 2H^+ + 2e \rightarrow Pb^{2+} + 2HSO_4^- \qquad (4.46)$$

The solid-phase mechanism of the charge-discharge process obtained considerable development in the works of Japanese researchers [50])[51]). According to these authors, the reduction of lead dioxide occurs through formation of a number of intermediate oxides, similar to thermal decomposition, the degree of oxidation of which gradually decreases in the discharge process. The active mass at any moment of time is considered as a solid solution containing ions of Pb^{4+}, Pb^{2+} and O^{2-} (or OH^-) in varying relationship. The formation of $PbSO_4$ is treated in this case as a process of interaction of the intermediate oxides with the sulphuric acid on the surface of the electrode. On charge, according to the given mechanism, the degree of oxidation gradually rises (the concentration of Pb^{4+} ions in the solid phase increases) as a result of oxidation of the intermediate oxides PbO_n. According to the data of Gensi[52]) in the Pb-O system zones of solid solutions exist with a degree of oxidation lying within the limits of $1.33 < n < 1.57$ and $1.87 < n < 2$.

In recent years in a number of works experimental confirmation has been obtained of the important role of solid-phase reactions in the kinetics of the cathodic reduction of lead dioxide. Thus, the results of electron microscope examination of a lead dioxide electrode, quoted by B N Kabanov[53]), show that PbO_2 crystals form aggregates, reproducing the form of crystals of the $PbSO_4$ from which they were formed as a result of anodic polarisation.

In work carried out under the leadership of K M Gorbunova[54–55]) experimental proof was given of the formation of intermediate oxides with electro-chemical reduction of α and β-PbO_2 in a solution of K_2SO_4 and KOH. These oxides are characterised by a highly disordered lattice of initial type and have a composition described by the formulae, respectively, $PbO_{1.34}$ and $PbO_{1.26}$. The appearance of intermediate oxides is accompanied by the appearance of considerable internal tension[55]).

In ref.[34]) a detailed study was made of the cathodic reduction of β-PbO_2 in $10N \cdot H_2SO_4$ solution. In fig. 4.10 a typical dependence of the potential of β-PbO_2 on time with cathodic reduction (discharge graph) is shown, and also the corresponding time dependence of the impedance of the electrode at ν = 100Hz. For convenience of analysis of these graphs they are broken down into 5 and 4 sections respectively. Section I of the discharge graph corresponds to a sharp drop in potential, after starting up cathodic polarisation, from the stationary value to the minimum. Then the potential increases a little, after which for a long time the graph is characterised by a slight slope towards the axis of the abscissae (section II). The value of the slope of the graph (φ, τ) on this section increases with an increase in the discharge current. A new fall of the discharge graph (III) is replaced by a second holding of the potential (IV), after which a sharp drop in the potential of the electrode is observed.

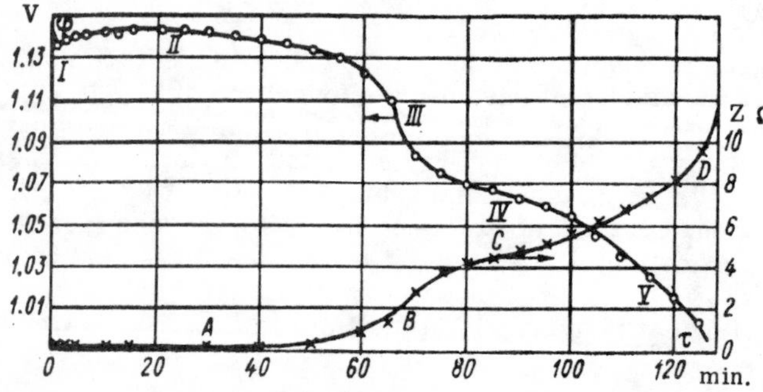

Fig.4.10 Dependence of potential and impedance (at ν = 100Hz) of β-PbO_2 on time in the process of cathodic reduction in $10N \cdot H_2SO_4$ at $j = 10^{-4}$ A/cm^2.

In the graph (Z, τ) section A corresponds to sections I-II of the discharge graph. The further course of graph (Z, τ), as can be seen from fig. 4.10, reproduces the character of the change of potential with this important difference, that a fall in the potential is paralleled by a rise in the impedance. The potential of the cathodic reduction can be written down in the form

$$\varphi = \varphi_{PbO_2/PbSO_4} - \eta_d \tag{4.47}$$

where η_d is the overvoltage of the discharge process, which is composed of the overvoltage of the reaction of reduction of the oxide (η_r) and ohmic potential drop (η_{om}).

Taking into account the possible participation in the discharge process of the ions of quadrivalent lead, which are to be found both in the crystal lattice of the PbO_2 and in the solution, it is possible to write down the process occurring on a lead dioxide electrode in the form

$$\alpha_T Pb^{4+}_{(sol)} + \alpha_d Pb^{4+}_{(soln)} + 2e = Pb^{2+} \tag{4.48}$$

Here α_T and α_d represent the stoichiometric coefficients $(\alpha_T + \alpha_d = 1)$, characterising the proportion of participation of the oxidant in the oxide phase (Pb^{4+}_{solid}) and in the electrolyte $(Pb^{4+}_{soln.})$. According to (4.47) and (4.48), the discharge potential of the lead dioxide electrode is equal to

$$\varphi = \varphi^{\circ} + \frac{\nu}{2} \lg \frac{a^{\alpha_T}_{Pb^{4+}(sol)} \; a^{\alpha_d}_{Pb^{4+}(soln)}}{a_{Pb^{2+}}} - \eta_B - \eta_{OM} \tag{4.49}$$

Equation (4.49) makes it possible to explain qualitatively the relationship observed (φ, τ). The initial potential drop (I fig. 4.10), is caused by an increase in the concentration of Pb^{2+} ions in the solution. At the minimum of the graph (φ, τ) the value $a_{Pb^{2+}}$ has, obviously, its maximum value, sufficient for the appearance of centres of crystallisation of $PbSO_4$. The formation of lead sulphate crystals leads to the decrease of $a_{Pb^{2+}}$ to the equilibrium value determined by the solubility of the $PbSO_4$ and to the increase in potential at the beginning of section II of the discharge graph under consideration.

Obviously, the subsequent slow fall in potential in section II is explained by the gradual decrease in the value of $a_{Pb^{4+}(solid)}$ as a result of a decrease in the degree of oxidation of the lead dioxide. The ohmic potential drop in sections I-II, is probably small, as is evidenced by the comparatively small changes in the impedance in section A of graph (Z, τ). At the maximum value of the potential in section II of graph (φ, τ) the value of a Pb^{4+}(solid), obviously, is close to the equilibrium value. Therefore it can be reckoned that the difference in φ from the equilibrium value in this area of the discharge graph is caused by the overvoltage of the process of reduction of β-PbO_2 (η_r). The values of η_r calculated from these ideas at different densities of discharge current ($j_d = 10^{-4}/3\cdot10^{-3}$ A/cm²) are shown in fig. 4.11.

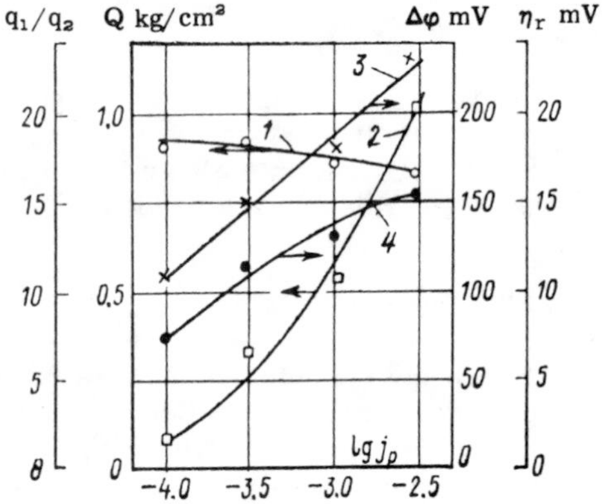

Fig.4.11 Discharge characteristics of β-PbO_2 in 10N·H_2SO_4. 1 Capacity Q/kg/cm²; 2 Relationship of capacities corresponding to the 1st and 2nd stages of discharge q_1/q_2; 3 Overvoltage of cathode reduction η_r (mV); 4 Difference in potentials corresponding to 1st and 2nd stages of discharge $\Delta\varphi$(mV).

According to the data obtained, the value of η_r varies within the limits ~10 to 20mV, rising with an increase in discharge current. The coefficient of slope of the straight line (η_r, lg j_d) constitutes ~8 to 10mV. Let us note that such low values of the pre-logarithmic coefficient of the Tafel straight line are possible in the case when the speed of the process is limited by the stage of disproportionality of dissociation of the oxide[56]).

The potential drop in section III of the discharge graph (fig. 4.10), and the corresponding rise in impedance in section B of the graph (Z, τ), is shown, obviously, to be the result of a substantial decrease in the activity of the Pb^{4+} ions in the electrode phase. The known influence can also be shown by the rise in ohmic potential drop and in overvoltage of the reduction process as a result of the formation on the surface of the electrode of a sulphate film.

The second plateau of the potential in the discharge graph and the corresponding inflection in the graph (Z, τ) are evidence of the fact that in the process of deep discharge of β-PbO_2 as a result of considerable decrease in the oxygen content in the oxide phase a definite intermediate compound is formed with a lower degree of oxidation. The nature of this compound can be explained by comparing the value of the potential (fig. 4.10) corresponding to section IV of graph (φ, τ) with the corresponding thermodynamic values examined in chapter 2 (see table 2.3).

Below we give the calculated values of the differences in equilibrium potentials ($\Delta\varphi_e$) corresponding to the process $PbO_2 \rightleftarrows PbSO_4$ and to other possible equilibria occurring at lower potentials (in $10N \cdot H_2SO_4$).

Table 4.2: Calculated values of differences in equilibrium potentials

Equilibria	$\Delta\varphi_e$ V
$PbO_2 \rightleftarrows Pb^{2+}$	0.036
$Pb_3O_4 \rightleftarrows 3PbO \cdot PbSO_4 \cdot H_2O$	0.095
$Pb_2O_3 \rightleftarrows 3PbO \cdot PbSO_4 \cdot H_2O$	0.232
$PbO_2 \rightleftarrows PbO \cdot PbSO_4$	0.287
$PbO_2 \rightleftarrows 3PbO \cdot PbSO_4 \cdot H_2O$	0.417

According to experimental data obtained by us, the difference in the potentials corresponding to the averages of sections II and IV of graph (φ, τ) changes within the limits 70-150mV, rising with a decrease in discharge current (fig. 4.11). Comparison of this value with the calculated values of $\Delta\varphi_e$ quoted above (table 4.2) shows that a most probable stage of cathodic reduction of β-PbO_2 with deep discharge is the formation of minium, which is then reduced to tribasic lead sulphate. In other words, the second plateau of the potential in the discharge graph obviously corresponds to the process

$$4Pb_3O_4 + 3HSO_4^- + 11H^+ + 8e \rightleftarrows 3\ 3PbO \cdot PbSO_4 \cdot H_2O + 4H_2O \qquad (4.50)$$

The increase in overvoltage of this process in time as a result of a further decrease in the degree of oxidation and passivation of the surface causes a considerable slope in section IV of the discharge graph towards the axis of the abscissae.

It is characteristic that the formation of minium takes place with thermal decomposition of the tetragonal modification of lead dioxide[57]). This fact, with account being taken of the above-mentioned analogy between thermal decomposition and cathodic reduction of PbO_2, can be considered as a known confirmation of the likelihood of intermediate formation of Pb_2O_4 at deep discharge of β-PbO_2 as a result of a solid phase reaction. The data quoted permit us to put forward the following scheme of cathodic reduction of β-PbO_2.

$$\beta\text{-}PbO_2 \rightarrow PbO_x \rightarrow Pb_3O_4 \rightarrow 3PbO \cdot PbSO_4 \cdot H_2O \rightarrow PbSO_4$$

where $2 > x > 1.33$.

As can be seen from fig. 4.11, the discharge capacity Q of the electrode under consideration changes comparatively little with a change in density of the discharge current j_d, decreasing a little with a rise in j_d. The relationship of the capacities corresponding to the 1st and 2nd degree of discharge (q_1/q_2) increases markedly with an increase in current. In other words, in proportion to the increase in j_d the amount of the intermediate compound appearing in the process of deep discharge of β-PbO_2 decreases. This can be explained by the increase in the density of the sulphate layer, forming at the first stage of the discharge, with an increase in current.

With the presence in the composition of the electrode of noticeable quantities of the rhombic modification of PbO_2 the second stage of discharge completely vanishes. This phenomenon is also explained, obviously, by the increase in the density of the sulphate layer[58])[59]). A characteristic feature of the discharge graphs taken at cathodic reduction of α-PbO_2 is the absence of the minimum in the initial period of discharge[58]). This result can be explained by the well-known isomorphy of α-PbO_2 and $PbSO_4$, which facilitates the formation of centres of crystallisation of sulphate on the surface of the given electrode. In the process of cycling of α-PbO_2 (after completion of 10-12 cycles) the minimum in the graph (φ, τ), however, appears as a result of the phase conversion $\alpha \rightarrow \beta$-PbO_2.

The processes occurring in the lead dioxide phase on discharge can be described by the equations of reactions

$$PbO_2 + 2(2-n)e \rightarrow PbO_n + (2-n)O^{2-} \tag{4.51}$$

$$PbO_2 + (2-n)H^+ + 2(2-n)e \rightarrow PbO_n + (2-n)OH^- \tag{4.52}$$

or

$$PbO_2 + 2(2-n)H^+ + 2(2-n)e \rightarrow PbO_n + (2-n)H_2O \tag{4.53}$$

where $n < 2$ is the degree of oxidation of the intermediate oxide. Reactions (4.51)-(4.53) represent the aggregate of a number of consecutive stages of decreasing the degree of oxidation of the initial compound

$$PbO_{n_i} \rightarrow PbO_{n_{i-1}} + (n_i - n_{i-1})\,O \qquad (4.54)$$

$$PbO_{n_i} + (n_i - n_{i-1})H^+ + 2(n_i - n_{i-1})e \rightarrow PbO_{n_{i-1}} + (n_i - n_{i-1})\,OH \qquad (4.55)$$

or

$$PbO_{n_i} + 2(n_i - n_{i-1})H^+ + 2(n_i - n_{i-1})e \rightarrow (n_i - n_{i-1})\,H_2O + PbO_{n_{i-1}} \qquad (4.56)$$

Here the values of n_i and n_{i-1} may differ only slightly. Let us remark that the equation of the reaction, analogous to (4.52) and (4.55), is used in ref. [60]) for describing the process of reduction of oxides by protons diffusing from the solution into the solid phase. It is possible to represent this process also as a result of the diffusion of O^{2-} ions towards the oxide-solution interface, where they react with the H^+ ions of the solution according to the scheme

$$O^{2-}_{(sol)} + H^+_{(soln)} \rightarrow OH^-_{(soln)} \qquad (4.57)$$

Judging by the data quoted above, anodic oxidation of lead sulphate at the charge also, at any rate partially, occurs through the stages of formation of intermediate oxides with a gradually increasing degree of oxidation

$$PbSO_4 + n_j\,H_2O \rightarrow PbO_{n_j} + (2n_j - 1)H^+ + HSO_4^- + 2(n_j - 1)e \qquad (4.58)$$

Discharge characteristics of a lead dioxide electrode

As is shown by numerous data from literature, the discharge characteristics of lead dioxide essentially depend on its phase composition. The specific weight discharge capacity of the tetragonal modification of PbO_2 (Q_β) exceeds by 1.5-3 times the capacity of the rhombic modification (Q_α). Experimental data obtained by Dodson in the study of coated electrodes of α and β-PbO_2 [12]) show that the dependence of discharge capacity (Q A·hr/g) on current density (j mA/cm^2) in the interval j = 17.4-174mA/cm^2 can be expressed by Peukert's equations:

$$Q_\alpha = 0.18 j^{-0.31} \qquad (4.59)$$

$$Q_\beta = 0.26 j^{-0.28} \qquad (4.60)$$

As far as concerns the reason for the substantial difference in the values of Q_α and Q_β there are different hypotheses in literature. First of all, an important role may be played by the value of the true surface of the electrodes, which in electrodes of β-PbO_2, as a rule, exceeds the corresponding value for α-PbO_2, even with uniform dimension of crystallites (see beginning of this chapter). In this connection ref.[61]) is of interest, the results of which show that in the calculation of discharge capacity per unit of true surface of the electrode the specific capacity of α-PbO_2 is shown to be somewhat higher than the capacity of β-PbO_2.

According to the data of refs.[58])[59]) an important reason for the difference in the capacities of α and β-PbO_2 is the character of the passivation of the electrode in the discharge process. On the surface of α-PbO_2 lead sulphate crystallises in the form of a dense, thin layer, quickly insulating the basic part of the active surface of the electrode. This fact is connected with the presence of a definite crystallo-chemical affinity of the lattices of α-PbO_2 and $PbSO_4$. Discharge of β-PbO_2 in the same conditions leads to the formation of a more macro-crystalline and loose film, the thickness of which, necessary for the passivation of the electrode, must be fairly large.

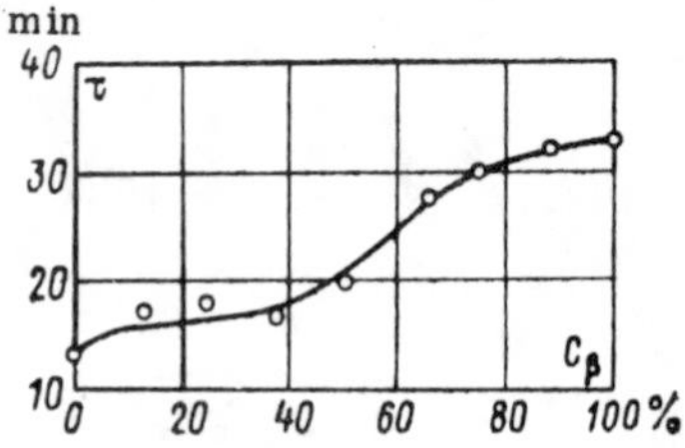

Fig.4.12 Dependence of time of discharge of a two-phase lead dioxide electrode on β-PbO_2 content. Discharge current 63mA/g.

A study of the discharge of two-phase electrodes with different proportion of α and β-PbO_2 showed that an increase in the concentrations of β-PbO_2 (C_β) to ~50% has comparatively little influence on the capacity and only at $C_\beta > 50\%$ does the capacity begin to increase markedly[62]) (fig. 4.12). The authors explain the dependence obtained by the fact that the dimension of particles of the β-PbO_2 preparation used in the work is considerably smaller than the dimension of the α-PbO_2 particles, therefore the influence of the β-PbO_2 on the discharge capacity shows up only in the case when the summary volume of β-PbO_2 exceeds the volume of the cavities between the α-PbO_2 particles. This idea can be confirmed with the aid of the following elementary calculation[32]).

Let us designate r_α and r_β the effective radii, and N_α and N_β the number of particles of α- and β-PbO_2 respectively. If we represent approximately the large particles of α-PbO_2 in the form of spheres situated in the volume of the electrode, then the volume remaining free will be equal to $\left[(2r_\alpha)^3 - \frac{4}{3}\pi r_\alpha^3\right]N_\alpha$, and the volume of β-PbO_2 particles will be equal to $\frac{4}{3}\pi r_\beta^3 N_\beta$. It can be assumed that if the value or r_β is small in comparison with r_α, then the influence of the β-PbO_2 on the discharge capacity of the electrode under consideration begins to show up substantially on the condition

$$\frac{4}{3}\pi r_\beta^3 N_\beta \geqslant \left[(2r_\alpha)^3 - \frac{4}{3}\pi r_\alpha^3\right]N_\alpha \qquad (4.61)$$

Let us further designate d_α and d_β the specific weights of α- and β-PbO_2, and m_α and m_β the weight quantities of these components. Obviously

$$m_\beta = \frac{4}{3}\pi r_\beta^3 N_\beta d_\beta \text{ and } m_\alpha = \frac{4}{3}\pi r_\alpha^3 N_\alpha d_\alpha \qquad (4.62)$$

Taking into account formulae (4.62), it is possible to rewrite the inequality (4.61) in the form

$$\frac{m_\beta}{d_\beta} \geqslant \left(\frac{6}{\pi} - 1\right)\frac{m_\alpha}{d_\alpha} \text{ and } \frac{m_\beta}{d_\beta} \geqslant 0.91\,\frac{m_\alpha}{d_\alpha} \qquad (4.63)$$

when it follows that

$$C_\beta \geqslant \frac{91 d_\alpha}{d_\alpha + 0.91 d_\beta} \qquad (4.64)$$

where $C_\beta = 100 m_\beta/(m_\alpha + m_\beta)$ %. Substituting in the inequality (4.64) the numerical values of d_α and d_β, we obtain $C_\beta \geqslant 48\%$, which is in conformity with the experimental data quoted above.

Taking into account the ideas put forward, it is possible to infer that the linear proportional dependence of discharge capacity of a coated electrode on the β-PbO_2 content in the active mass, described in the work of Dodson[12], is evidence of the absence of any marked difference in the dimensions of the crystallites of α- and β-PbO_2 in the positive electrode of a lead acid battery. This result is in conformity with the data of the X-ray phase analysis of the active mass, according to which the positive active mass represents a tight uniform mixture of α- and β-PbO_2. The dimensions of the crystals of both modifications of PbO_2 in the active mass do not differ substantially[14]).

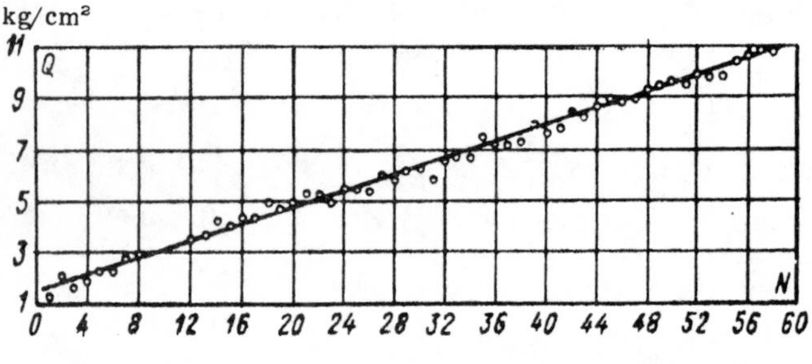

Fig.4.13 Dependence of the discharge capacity of $\alpha + \beta$-PbO_2 on the number of cycles N at $j_d = 10 mA/cm^2$.

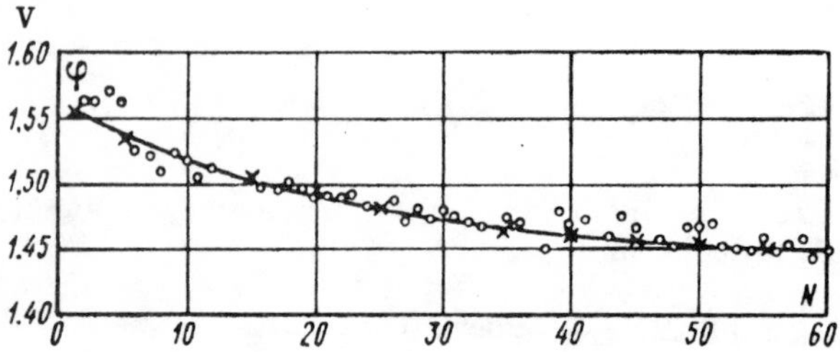

Fig.4.14 Dependence of final charge potential (in relation to Hg/Hg_2SO_4) of $\alpha + \beta$-PbO_2 on the number of cycles N.

For explanation of the respective influences of crystalline structure and dimensions of the true surface on the discharge capacity of a lead dioxide electrode, the data obtained in the cycling of a smooth electrode are of considerable interest. Change in capacity and in final charge potential of lead dioxide electro-deposited from a nitric acid solution

(α + β-PbO_2) with an increase in the number of charge-discharge cycles N is represented in figs. 4.13 and 4.14. This deposit represents, as has already been shown, a mixture of approximately equal quantities of α- and β-PbO_2, i.e. it is similar in composition to the active masses of the positive electrode, which generally contain 50-60% of β-PbO_2 after forming. The crystals of both modifications in this case (α + β-PbO_2) are characterised by practically uniform dimensions.

In the process of cycling an electro-chemical recrystallisation of PbO_2 occurs according to the scheme (2.31). As a result of this the amount of α-PbO_2 continuously decreases, converting into β-PbO_2.

If we designate the original content of α-PbO_2 in the active mass m_α and the coefficient of utilisation Θ_α, then the amount of α-PbO_2 remaining after the first cycle

$$m_\alpha^{(1)} = m_\alpha - m_\alpha \Theta_\alpha = m_\alpha(1 - \Theta_\alpha) \qquad (4.65)$$

and after the second cycle

$$m_\alpha^{(2)} = m_\alpha^{(1)} (1 - \Theta_\alpha) = m_\alpha (1 - \Theta_\alpha)^2 \qquad (4.66)$$

In a similar way it is not difficult to show that the content of the rhombic modification in the active mass after the Nth cycle constitutes

$$m_\alpha^{(N)} = m_\alpha(1 - \Theta_\alpha)^N \qquad (4.67)$$

Assuming that Θ_α = 0.3 [63]) at the end of the thirteenth cycle only 1% of the original quantity of α-PbO_2 should remain. In fact, as is shown by the data of phase analysis, α-PbO_2 remains in small quantities in the active mass after a large number of discharges and charges. This result can be formally interpreted by a decrease in the value of Θ_α in formula (4.67) with an increase in the number of cycles and it is evidence of the small degree of participation of the rhombic modification of PbO_2 situated in the depth of the active mass in the charge-discharge process. It is thus possible to infer that after a few initial cycles the capacity of the positive electrode is determined basically by the reduction of β-PbO_2.

The results of the impedance measurements (fig. 4.15) are evidence of the fact that in the process of cycling there occurs a considerable development of the active surface of the electrode. In fact, as follows from fig. 4.15, with an increase in the number of cycles, a substantial fall in impedance is observed. In this there is a decrease both in the slope of the graphs $(Z, \nu^{-1/2})$, i.e. the value of λ, and also in the extrapolated value of Z at $\nu \rightarrow \infty$, i.e. r_0. According to formulae (4.31) and (4.32), this is caused by an increase in the true surface of the electrode.

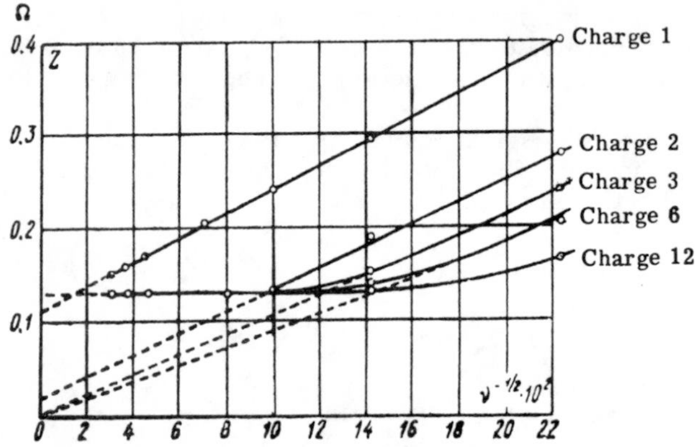

Fig.4.15 Dependence of the impedance of $\alpha + \beta$-PbO_2 on the frequency of the alternating current and the number of charge-discharge cycles.

In proportion to the cycling there is a decrease in the frequency dependence of the impedance, especially in the field of relatively high frequencies. After the carrying out of 10-15 charge-discharge cycles the impedance of the charged electrode in practice does not depend on the frequency of the alternating current. Obviously, this phenomenon, is connected with the appearance on the surface of the electrode of a porous layer. The resistance of the electrolyte in the pores of this layer (R_p) begins to show, in proportion to the cycling, an ever greater influence on the value being measured, Z, i.e. with an increase in the number of cycles (N) $Z \rightarrow R_p$.

It is not difficult to show that this very process of development of the surface of the electrode S determines the increase which has been observed in the discharge capacity. This is confirmed by the character of the change of final charge potential $\varphi_{f.c.}$ in the cycling process.

The value of $\varphi_{f.c.}$ can be identified (with the corresponding selection of reference potential) with the oxygen overvoltage on the surface of the electrode. Therefore the dependence of $\varphi_{f.c.}$ on S at constant charge current (I = const) can be written down in the form

$$\varphi_{f.c.} = a + b\lg j = a + b\lg I - b\lg S = C_1 - b\lg S \tag{4.68}$$

where a and b are constants in Tafel's equation, and $C_1 = a + b \lg I$. If we accept further that the discharge capacity of the electrode is directly proportional to its true surface

$$Q = fS \tag{4.69}$$

then, according to (4.68) and (4.69)

$$\varphi_{f.c.} = C_2 - b \lg Q \tag{4.70}$$

where $C_2 + C_1 + b \lg f = a + b \lg I + b \lg f$, and f is a constant coefficient.

Thus, as follows from equation (4.70), in the process of cycling the final charge potential $\varphi_{f.c.}$ should decrease with an increase in capacity according to the logarithmic law.

From fig. 4.13 it can be seen that the dependence of capacity Q on the number of cycles N can be expressed within a known interval of N by the linear equation

$$Q = G + PN \tag{4.71}$$

Substituting (4.71) in equation (4.70), it is possible to write down the dependence of $\varphi_{f.c.}$ on N in the form

$$\varphi_{f.c.} = C_2 - b \lg (G + PN) \tag{4.72}$$

According to data quoted in fig. 4.13, G = 1.5 Kl, P = 0.16 Kl/cycle, from equation (4.17) it follows that b = 0.12V. The value of C_2, determined by graphic extrapolation of the graph ($\varphi_{f.c}$, N) to the value N = 0, becomes 1.58V. Substituting all these values in equation (4.72) we shall have

$$\varphi_{f.c.} = 1.58 - 0.12 \lg (1.5 + 0.16N) \tag{4.73}$$

The graph of the dependence of $\varphi_{f.c.}$ on N, calculated according to formula (4.73), and the experimental values of $\varphi_{f.c.}$ (in relation to a mercury-mercurous sulphate electrode) is shown in fig. 4.14. As can be seen from the diagram, equation (4.73) completely satisfactorily describes the experimental dependence ($\varphi_{f.c.}$, N), which confirms the decisive role of the development of the surface of the electrode, which causes an increase in discharge capacity.

It must be noted that the phase conversion α-$PbO_2 \rightarrow \beta$-PbO_2, taking place in the cycling process, shows a known influence on the values of the final charge potential. This process causes an increase in the values of $\varphi_{f.c.}$ after the first 4-5 cycles (the corresponding points in fig. 4.14 deviate markedly from the calculation graph). The increase in $\varphi_{f.c.}$ is shown to be a result of the increased value of the oxygen overvoltage on β-PbO_2.

An increase in capacity and a drop in final charge potential are also observed in the process of cycling an electrode composed of the tetragonal modification of PbO_2, obtained by the method of electro-deposition from a perchloric acid electrolyte. Naturally, in this case only the development of the active surface of the electrode can serve as a reason for the change of the characteristics mentioned.

The discharge capacity of a smooth lead dioxide electrode is limited by the passivation of its surface by lead sulphate. According to the data of B N Kabanov and others [64]), passivation follows at the moment when more than 90% of the surface of the electrode is covered by a sulphate film. An increase in the concentration of sulphuric acid leads to an earlier passivation of PbO_2 owing to the formation of a denser layer of $PbSO_4$. This, obviously, is connected with the decrease in the solubility of the sulphate in proportion to the increase in the concentration of H_2SO_4.

For a porous lead dioxide electrode, together with passivation, a considerable role is played by diffusion limitations of capacity (see chapter 3). Therefore, the decrease in discharge capacity observed in the conditions of a real battery with the lowering of the concentration of the electrolyte is connected with the sharp decrease in the H_2SO_4 content in the pores of the active mass and in the pores of the sulphate layer which partially covers the surface of the electrode [64]). It must be noted that also in the case of a smooth electrode passivation causes a substantial decrease in the concentration of H_2SO_4 on the PbO_2-$PbSO_4$ interface, which serves as one of the important reasons for the drop in discharge potential. What has been said can be illustrated by the results of the impedance measurements shown in fig. 4.16.

The values of impedance increase substantially during the discharge This, naturally, is caused by the sharp decrease in the capacity of the double layer owing to screening of the surface of the electrode by $PbSO_4$ crystals, and to some extent also by the increase in the ohmic resistance

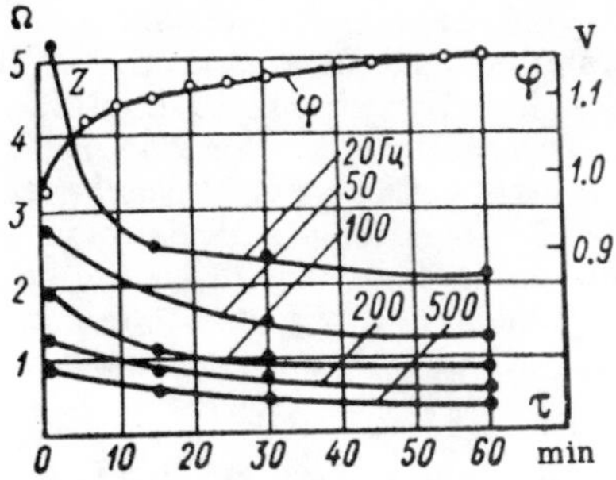

Fig.4.16 Dependence of impedance Z and potential φ (in relation to Hg/Hg_2SO_4) of α + β-PbO_2 in the discharge state on time (after completion of the discharge).

of the sulphate film. After the completion of the discharge and switching off the current, the impedance of the electrode decreases over a long time (fig. 4.16). The potential of the electrode at the same time increases, gradually approaching the equilibrium value. This phenomenon is obviously explained by the gradual increase in the concentration of the sulphuric acid on the PbO_2-$PbSO_4$ boundary surface as a result of the diffusion of H_2SO_4 into the pores of the sulphate film. The change in the values of φ and Z occurs over a longer period, the lower the discharge current, which is linked with an increase in thickness of the layer of $PbSO_4$ (discharge capacity) in proportion to the decrease in current[35]).

The relationship of the concentration of α and β modifications in the active mass depends on the conditions of preparation of the positive electrode. Changing these conditions, it is possible to increase the β-PbO_2 content, which leads to an increase in the initial value of the specific discharge capacity or, in other words, to a shortening of the number of practice charge-discharge cycles which it is necessary to carry out for attaining the necessary capacity value.

As was shown by Dodson[12]), an increase in the concentration of β-PbO_2 in the positive active mass is caused by a decrease in the density of the electrode paste, an increase in the concentration of H_2SO_4 and a lowering of the temperature.

The mechanism of deterioration of the active mass of a positive electrode

Deterioration and shedding of the active mass of the positive electrode is one of the basic reasons causing current lead acid batteries to become non-operational. The essence of this phenomenon generally consists of fine crystals of lead dioxide falling off from the battery plates. This leads especially to a decrease in the capacity of the positive electrode as a result of the decrease in the supply of active matter. In addition, the electrophoretic transfer of particles of PbO_2 to the plates of the negative electrode often leads to the appearance of short circuits along the edges of the plates and through the separators. Finally, baring of the grids of the positive plates, as a result of the shedding of the active mass, causes their more rapid corrosion.

At the present time a number of papers have been published on the mechanism of the deterioration of the positive active mass. A comprehensive study of the dependence of the rate of shedding of the active mass on the operating conditions of the positive electrode, undertaken by E I Krepakova and B N Kabanov[65]), showed that the rate of the process increases sharply with increase in the concentration of the electrolyte in which the discharge of the electrode is realised. The dependence of the shedding on the concentration of the acid during charging is an inverse relationship and is considerably less clearly defined. Deterioration of the active mass slows down with an increase in the temperature of the electrolyte and a decrease in the density of the discharge current. The density of the discharge current has no noticeable influence of the rate of the process under consideration. The decisive influence of the conditions of discharge, especially the final stage of it, on the service life of the active mass of the positive electrode led the authors[65]) to the conclusion that the rate of the shedding process depends on the structure of the lead sulphate forming at the discharge. With the formation of a loose, macro-crystalline sulphate subsequent charge leads to the production of a fairly strong layer of lead sulphate. If at the discharge a dense, fine-crystalline sulphate forms (discharge in an electrolyte of high concentration, at low temperatures and high current densities), then this leads to the formation on the charge of a loose layer of dioxide, tending to shed.

The crystallisation mechanism of the deterioration of the positive active mass obtained confirmation in the study of the influence of the addition of barium sulphate on the rate of this process. The introduction of $BaSO_4$ into the active mass, which is isomorphic to lead sulphate, causes a dispersion of the $PbSO_4$ crystals. At the same time $BaSO_4$ causes a sharp increase in the rate of shedding of the active mass. According to the data of the work[66]) the service life of a positive electrode is inversely proportional to the logarithm of the concentration of $BaSO_4$ in the active mass. A similar influence is shown by $SrSO_4$, which is also isomorphic to lead sulphate, while $CaSO_4$, the structure of the crystals of which differs substantially from the structure of $PbSO_4$, does not cause a more rapid shedding of the active mass.

It must be mentioned that, although the influence of the conditions of crystallisation of $PbSO_4$ on the rate of deterioration of the active mass of the positive electrode does not give rise to any doubts, the mechanism of shedding set out above is not the only one possible. A known influence on the service life of the active mass can be exerted by the material of the grid. As was shown in ref.[67]) the character of the oxide film forming on the surface of the grids to a great extent determines the bonding strength of the active mass with the grid and consequently the electrical characteristics and service life of the electrode. With the manufacture of the grid from pure lead, which forms a quite loose oxide film on anodic corrosion, or with the lead plating of grids of lead antimony alloy, the contact of the active mass with the grid deteriorates considerably, which leads to the shortening of the service life of the electrode. The mechanical properties of the anode alloy also to a known extent determine the strength of the active mass of the positive electrode. Deformation of the grids exceeding 5% of the original dimensions leads to rapid deterioration of the active mass[68]).

In recent years in a number of papers[8])[69])[72]) a proposition has been enunciated regarding the influence of phase composition and of the morphology of the particles of the active mass of the positive electrode, on the rate of its shedding in the process of utilisation of the battery. As has been shown above, deposits of α-PbO_2 are generally distinguished by a greater mechanical strength than those of β-PbO_2. As a rule the latter oxide is formed in the shape of fine needle-like crystals weakly linked together, which is caused by the considerable irreversible adsorption on β-PbO_2 of sulphuric acid. In the literature the opinion has more than once been expressed that the presence of the rhombic modification of lead dioxide in the active mass is necessary for increasing its strength. In ref.[72]) it is shown that in determined conditions the crystals of α-PbO_2 form a strong cellular structure inside the active mass, which does not change much in the process of cycling. This structure plays the role of a spatial lattice, in the cells of which the β-PbO_2 particles are retained. The conditions of formation of the structure described, however, have not been studied.

The deterioration of the positive active mass during the working of the battery may be caused by volume changes in the periodic charges and discharges of the electrode. Together with this a change in the form of the crystals also may play a well-known role. An attempt at quantitative calculation of these factors was undertaken in ref.[71]). Here it was shown that the smallest volumetric and morphological changes occur with the oxidation of quadribasic sulphate $4PbO \cdot PbSO_4$ in β-PbO_2 (table 4.3). Burbank[71] suggests that the space lattice causing the retention of the active mass may consist of this compound.

Table 4.3: Volumetric changes at the anode oxidation of compounds of lead in β-PbO_2

Compound	Density g/cm^3	Volume 1 g-mol cm^3	Number of mols of PbO_2 from 1 mol	Change of volume from 1g-at. Pb
Pb	11.311	18.28	1	+6.56
$PbSO_4$	6.323	47.96	1	-23.12
$PbO_{yell.}$	9.642	23.15	1	+1.69
PbO_{red}	9.355	23.88	1	+0.96
Pb_3O_4	8.925	76.79	3	-0.72
$PbO \cdot PbSO_4$	7.02	75.0	2	-12.66
$3PbO \cdot PbSO_4 \cdot H_2O$	6.05	152.0	4	-13.0
$4PbO \cdot PbSO_4$	8.15	146.76	5	-4.51
β-PbO_2	9.63	24.84	-	0.0

Let us note that according to the data of X-ray examinations tetrabasic sulphate is formed in the process of manufacture of the electrode mass, particularly at high temperatures (>70-80°C).

A definite role in the kinetics of the process of shedding of the active mass of the positive electrode is obviously played, by colloido-chemical laws. In ref.[73] hypotheses are propounded to the effect that in the charge of the positive electrode water-repellent positively charged PbO_2 particles are formed. Mutual electrostatic repulsion of these particles causes softening and shedding of the active mass. The carrying out of periodic discharges and long-lasting charges concentrates this effect on the grid-active mass interface, causing the deterioration of the active mass. It must be mentioned that in the process of cycling periodic changes of sign of the charge of the surface of the lead dioxide occur with transition through the point of zero charge. The change in the mechanical properties of the lead dioxide which accompanies this transition may cause the deterioration of the active mass of the electrode under consideration.

A radio-chemical study[74] of the transfer of lead ions in the positive active mass showed that in the process of cycling there is observed a migration of lead from the thickness of the active mass to the outer surface. In the opinion of the authors of ref.[74] this phenomenon is caused by the diffusion of the saturated $PbSO_4$ solution, which may produce an increase in the dendrites of PbO_2 during the charge as a result of current and diffusion, also causing shedding of the active mass.

In the process of charging the battery, particularly near the end of charge, the positive electrode works in conditions which are in many ways similar to the conditions of work of the insoluble anodes. Therefore, in order to explain the mechanism of shedding of the positive active mass, the data obtained in the study of the kinetics of the deterioration of the electrolytic deposits of lead dioxide in the process of anodic polarisation are of interest[75]. The basic form of deterioration of the electrolytic deposits of lead dioxide is dispersion or erosion, i.e. continuous transfer of fine particles of PbO_2 to the solution. The rate of this process in H_2SO_4 solution increases with an increase in the concentration of the acid and falls with an increase in temperature. It is not difficult to see that the influence of the conditions of electrolysis on the rate of dispersal of the PbO_2 is similar to the influence of the conditions of work of the positive electrode of a battery on the rate of shedding of the active mass.

In regard to the mechanism of the erosion of a lead dioxide anode, a hypothesis has been propounded to the effect that this process is caused by chemical interaction of PbO_2 with hydrogen peroxide forming with anodic oxidation of the H_2SO_4 solution. Another reason for this phenomenon may be catalytic corrosion of the lead dioxide[35], i.e. an increase in the mobility of the particles situated on the surface of the electrode owing to the energy of the radicals (OH or O) which appear as intermediate products in the process of liberation of oxygen. A direct result of catalytic corrosion, obviously, is the development of the surface of the PbO_2, causing a decrease in potential and impedance of the double layer in the process of anodic polarisation of lead dioxide electrodes[28][34][35].

Examining the solid-phase mechanism of electrolytic reduction of lead dioxide, we have pointed to the possibility of intermediate formation of not very oxidised compounds of lead at the discharge of the positive electrode of a battery. Such compounds, which are characterised by an amorphous structure, are found in the composition of the positive active mass. In ref.[35] a study was made of electrode behaviour of a similar oxide, the composition of which corresponds to the formula $PbO_{1.66}$.

In the process of anodic polarisation in $10N \cdot H_2SO_4$ a considerable loosening of the material of the electrode was observed. As a result a loose porous layer was formed on the originally smooth surface, weakly bound to the electrode and partially falling to the bottom of the tank. The presence of the loosened layer determined the practical independence of the double layer on the frequency of the alternating current over a wide interval of its change (ν = 20-2000Hz). The measured values of Z represent in this case basically the ohmic resistance of the electrolyte. The reactive components of the impedance are very small owing to the considerable magnitude of the true surface of the electrode. Radiographic study of the electrode under consideration showed that the cause of the loosening of the surface on anodic polarisation is oxidation, accompanied by considerable reconstruction of the crystal lattice of the initial oxide.

As can be seen from fig. 4.17, an X-ray amorphous phase, as a result of anodic polarisation is converted into a fine-dispersion tetragonal modification of lead dioxide. This conversion $PbO_{1\cdot 66} \rightarrow \beta\text{-}PbO_{n\beta}$ must naturally be treated as anodic oxidation. The complex character of the graphs (φ, lg j) in the initial period of polarisation (fig. 4.18), obviously, is connected with the process of oxidation of the material of the electrode occurring parallel to the process of liberation of oxygen. After the completion of the first process the whole current, obviously, is spent on the discharge of the oxygen, which causes a rectilinear dependence of the potential on the logarithm of the current density.

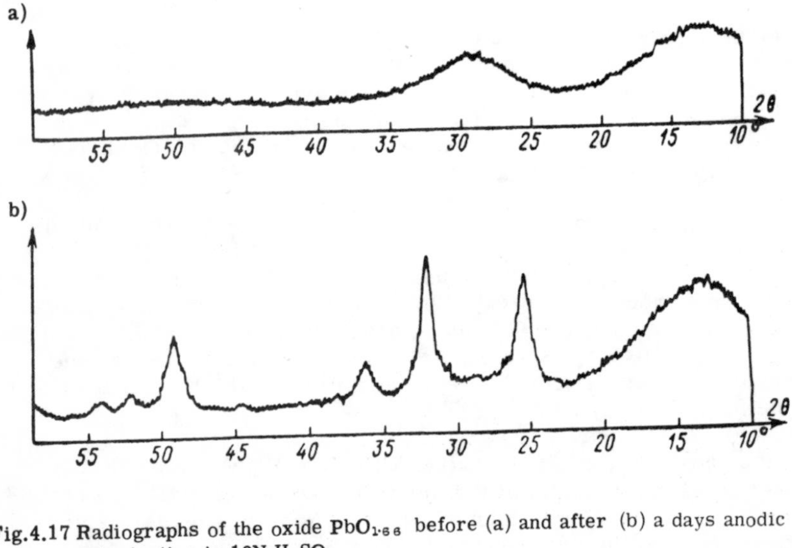

Fig.4.17 Radiographs of the oxide $PbO_{1\cdot 66}$ before (a) and after (b) a days anodic polarisation in $10N\cdot H_2SO_4$.

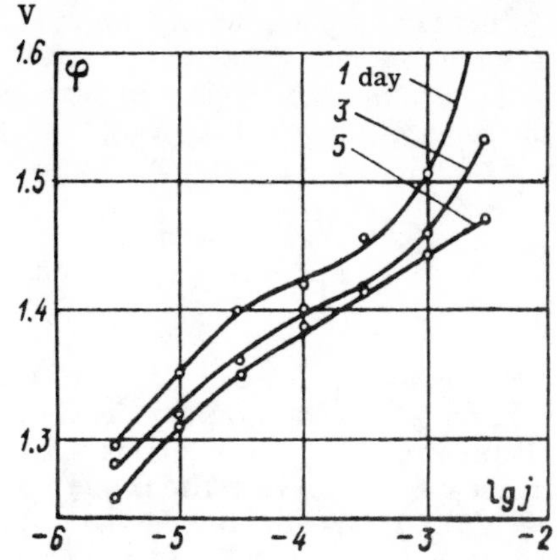

Fig.4.18 Dependence of the anode potential of $PbO_{1.66}$ on the density of current and time of polarisation in $10N{\cdot}H_2SO_4$ at 25^oC.

It can be assumed that in the process of discharge of the positive electrode of a lead acid battery a loosening of the active mass occurs similar to what has been described here. This process is connected with the reconstruction of the crystal lattice taking place on anodic oxidation of the intermediate phases appearing at the discharge of the electrode, and it may serve as one of the important causes of the deterioration of the active mass of the positive electrode.

It must be noted that analytical determination of the intermediate not very oxidised phases in the active mass of a discharge electrode, even in the case of relative stability of these compounds, is connected with considerable difficulties. The X-ray amorphosity of these oxides does not permit us to use the radiographic method for analysis. The presence also of basic sulphates in the active mass, along with the oxides under consideration as well as basic sulphates, hinders the interpretation of the results of chemical analysis.

A survey of current data on the question of the causes and the mechanism of the deterioration of the active mass of the positive electrode makes it possible to draw the following conclusions:

1. In the process of the work of the electrode different forms of deterioration of the active mass are possible (break-away of PbO_2 particles as a result of the looseness of the structure, electrolytic

erosion, separation of the active mass from the grid etc.).

2. Deterioration of the active mass may be caused by a number of factors and occurs according to different mechanisms (crystallisation of PbO_2 in the form of loose structures, transfer of lead to the outer surface of the electrode, volumetric and morphological changes in the active mass etc.).

3. Many factors causing deterioration of the active mass are connected in principle with the basic processes occurring in the work of the positive electrode.

In principle the character of the causes of deterioration of the active mass of the positive electrode of a lead acid battery essentially limit the possibilities of effectively combating this phenomenon. In order to increase the service life of the positive active mass, measures directed at improving the design of the battery take on a special significance. Here we must principally point to a rational selection of the material and design of the separators which, as is well known, play quite an important role in the lowering of the rate of shedding of the active mass. A change in the construction of the grids of the positive plates may have a definite significance, as also a change in the inter-electrode distances and other design elements of the battery. Finally, inert additive-binding agents, specially introduced for this purpose into the active mass, may serve as an effective means of combating the shedding of the active mass (see 'Ways of improvement of the characteristics of the active mass of the positive electrode': p. 170).

Self-discharge of the positive electrode

Self-discharge of a lead acid battery leads to a daily loss of up to 2% of capacity. This phenomenon is connected with the oxidation reduction processes occurring spontaneously both on the negative and also on the positive electrode of the battery.

The study of the processes occurring in an inactive battery on the positive electrode has been paid comparatively little attention in literature. The majority of researchers reckons that the rate of self-discharge of the positive electrode is so low (in comparison with the rate of self-discharge of the negative electrode) that it can, in practice, be disregarded. Vinal, according to whose data the self-discharge of the positive plates of the battery occurs with remarkable speed, is of the opposite opinion. Vinal established that, if the negative plates sulphate more quickly with an increase in the concentration of the acid, then self-discharge of the positive plates decreases with an increase in the concentration. Vinal considers the self-discharge of the positive plate as a result of the reaction of the metal of the grid with the active mass, which is like the reaction occurring in a lead acid battery according to the theory of double sulphation.

In the opinion of Lander[76]) self-discharge of the positive electrode of a battery occurs mainly owing to oxidation of the antimony used in the composition of the grid. It is also mentioned in the literature that self-discharge of the positive plates decreases with an increase in the temperature of forming of the plates. The liberation of oxygen from an inactive battery is explained differently by different authors. Elbs and Schoner explain this phenomenon by the action on the lead dioxide of persulphuric acid forming at an overcharge. This point of view is disproved by analytical data, which show that the amount of persulphuric acid formed is very small, even with long overcharges. whilst oxygen, although also in small quantities, is liberated from the battery over a long time. For the same reason the opinion of Robertson and Hume, who reckon that after the cessation of the charge the oxygen is liberated as a result of the interaction of the lead dioxide and hydrogen peroxide, is not valid.

A proposition has also been put forward according to which after the charge only the oxygen that has accumulated in the pores of the active mass is liberated from the battery. This proposition is disproved by measurement of the volume of the oxygen liberated, which considerably exceeds the total volume of the pores in the active mass.

It has been mentioned in the literature that the reason for the liberation of oxygen after the switching off of the charge current is the work of the concentration cell, which appears as a result of the difference in the concentrations of sulphuric acid in the depth of the pores and on the external surface of the positive plates. Finally, one of the reasons for the liberation of oxygen after the completion of the charge may be the direct action of the sulphuric acid solutions on the lead dioxide.

These and other data from literature were analysed in the works of B A Kosobryukhov, and also Rüetschi and Angstadt[77]), Ruetschi and Angstadt studied the self-discharge of the positive electrode of a battery depending on the composition of the alloy of the grid of this electrode, on the concentration of the electrolyte and other factors. Here it was established that the rate of self-discharge of the positive electrode essentially depends on the concentration of the acid and has a sharply expressed maximum, the situation of which is different for different alloys (fig. 4.19).

For plates with grids of lead-antimony alloys (with different alloying additions) the position of the maximum shown corresponds to the specific gravity of the electrolyte, equal to ~1.1, while with an increase in the antimony content in the grid the maximum shifts in the direction of higher concentrations of H_2SO_4. For plates with a grid of alloys containing calcium (0.07-0.082%) and aluminium (0.006-0.01%), corresponding to the maximum of self-discharge, the specific gravity of the electrolyte constitutes approximately 1.025.

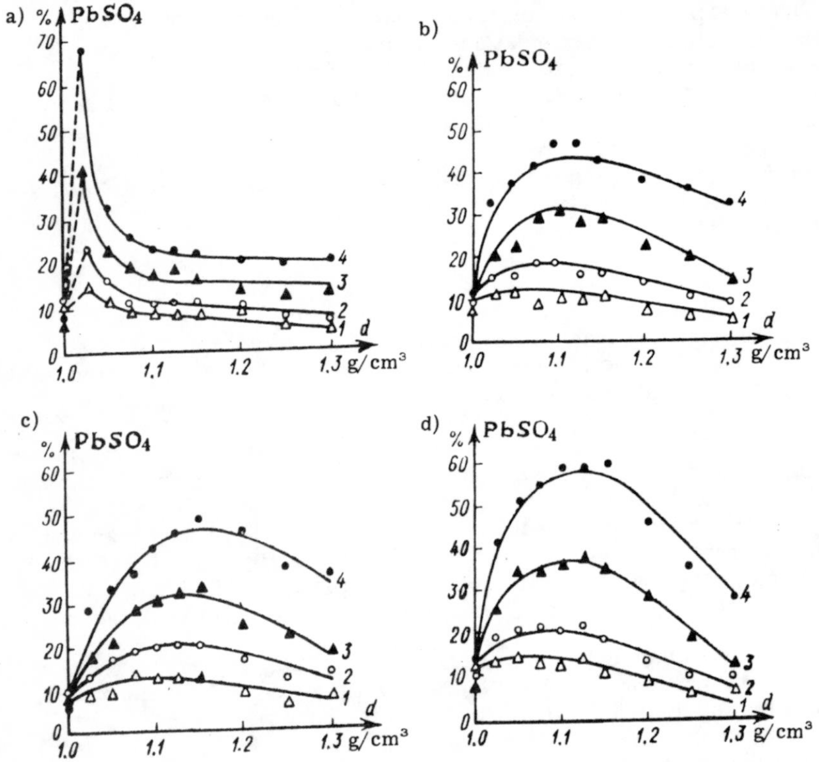

Fig.4.19 Dependence of the rate of sulphation of positive plates on the material of the grid, the density of the electrolyte d and the holding time (temperature +35°C). Holding time 1 (Δ) - 2 weeks; 2 (O) - 4 weeks; 3 (▲) - 8 weeks; (●) - 16 weeks. Composition of the alloy: a - Pb+0.082%Ca+0.006%Al; b - Pb+4.26%Sb+0.47% As+0.51%Sn+0.106%Ag+0.005%Cu; c - Pb+5.76%Sb+0.48%As+0.51%Sn+0.122%Ag+0.003%Cu; d - Pb+2.58%Sb+0.045%As+0.004%Ag+0.01%Cu.

Further, as can be seen from fig. 4.19, the maximum of self-discharge with an increase in the length of time of the experiment slowly shifts in the direction of higher concentrations of the electrolyte. For the range of concentrations of the acid used in lead acid batteries, self-discharge of the positive plates increases with a decrease in the specific gravity of the acid.

Self-discharge of insulated lead dioxide is caused by the reaction

$$PbO_2 + H_2SO_4 \rightarrow PbSO_4 + H_2O + (\tfrac{1}{2})O_2 \qquad (4.74)$$

the rate of which increases with an increase in the concentration of H_2SO_4. It must also be borne in mind that since reaction (4.74) occurs with the liberation of oxygen, to a considerable extent its speed is determined by the value of the oxygen overvoltage. Additives lowering the potential of liberation of oxygen (e.g. antimony, cobalt or silver) should cause an increase in the rate of this reaction. The characteristics of spontaneous reduction of α and β-PbO_2 are quoted in table 4.4[62]) whence it follows that the rate of self-discharge of α-PbO_2 considerably exceeds the similar value for β-PbO_2, which is explained naturally by the above described difference in the oxygen overvoltage.

Table 4.4: Self-discharge of α + β-PbO_2

Form of modification	Density of H_2SO_4 solution g/cm^3	Density of current of self-discharge A/cm^2	Rate of decomposition % per annum
α-PbO_2	1.140	$2.1 \cdot 10^{-10}$	3.9
	1.240	$1.3 \cdot 10^{-9}$	24
	1.340	$2.9 \cdot 10^{-9}$	54
β-PbO_2	1.140	$6.8 \cdot 10^{-12}$	2.5
	1.240	$3.4 \cdot 10^{-11}$	13
	1.340	$1.1 \cdot 10^{-10}$	41

The contact of the positive active mass with the grid may cause the occurrence of self-discharge according to the reaction (2.34) and

$$5PbO_2 + 2Sb + 6H_2SO_4 = (SbO_2)SO + 5PbSO_4 + 6H_2O \qquad (4.75)$$

Since the electrolyte has limited access to the grid, the formation of lead sulphate substantially impedes the occurrence of reactions (2.34) and (4.75). With a decrease in concentration of the acid the solubility of the lead sulphate increases and consequently the rate of the reactions under consideration increases.

It must be noted that the solubility of the salts of tri- and quinquivalent antimony rises with an increase in the concentration of the electrolyte. Therefore, in dilute acid solutions, passivation can be caused by antimony salts to a considerable degree. The different character of the dependence of the solubility of sulphates of lead and antimony on the concentration of the acid causes an extreme dependence of the rate of self-discharge of the positive electrode on the density of the solution.

The presence of silver in the composition of the anode alloy, also obviously shows influence on the self-discharge of the positive electrode as a result of the reaction

$$PbO_2 + 2Ag + 2H_2SO_4 = PbSO_4 + Ag_2SO_4 + 2H_2O \qquad (4.76)$$

Self-discharge of the positive plates generally speaking can be connected with the oxidation of the material of the separator[77]). However, in present day lead acid batteries, separators are used which are made from materials which, in practice, are not oxidised under the working conditions of the positive electrode. Therefore, due to the separators, the reduction of lead dioxide does not occur in practice.

Finally, it must be noted that hydrogen separating out on the negative electrode and diffusing towards the positive electrode can, in principle, cause the reduction of lead dioxide according to the reaction

$$PbO_2 + H_2 + H_2SO_4 = PbSO_4 + 2H_2O \qquad (4.77)$$

This reaction, however, plays no essential role as a result of the negligible solubility of hydrogen in sulphuric acid electrolytes. Adsorption of HSO_4^- ions on the PbO_2 causes a slowing down of reaction (4.77).

The kinetics of the liberation of oxygen from a battery were studied in detail by B A Kosobryukhov. In the investigation of the direct action of sulphuric acid on PbO_2 the determination was carried out by two methods; by means of chemical analysis of the initial specimens of lead dioxide after two months' action of sulphuric acid solutions of different concentrations and with the aid of the determination of the volume of oxygen evolving from the positive plate of a battery. It was found that marked liberation of oxygen begins in acid with a density of 1.10, and in acid with a density of 1.30 it increases five times, and in acid with a density of 1.70 many tens of times. This result corresponds to the data of ref.[62]). The rate of reduction of PbO_2, calculated according to the data of the chemical analysis, was greater than that determined by measurements of the volume of the evolving gas. The author explains this by the fact that, in the first case, the surface of the charged PbO_2 was considerably larger than the surface of the positive active mass. The process of liberation of oxygen, as a result of the action of the concentration couple, was investigated by B A Kosobryukhov. Two well-charged positive plates in electrolytes of a density of 1.10 and 1.30 were connected electrically and closed through an ammeter. In this the amount of oxygen evolution increased 3-4 times on the negative pole of the couple being formed. The action of the concentration couple in the positive plate was also demonstrated by B A Kosobryukhov with the aid of the following experiment. A dry positive plate was soaked in a solution of H_2SO_4 of high concentration and then plunged into water. Here, at the same time, evolution of oxygen is observed. The concentration couple in the pores of the positive electrode operates both on charge and discharge. Towards the end of the charge a higher concentration of the electrolyte is maintained in the depth of the pores of the active mass and consequently the outer layers of the active mass will serve as a negative pole on which the oxygen evolves. In the initial stage of discharge the concentration of the electrolyte in the depth of the active mass and in the outer electrolyte evens out, the emf of the concentration couple decreases and consequently the quantity of oxygen evolving should decrease. After the levelling out of the concentrations the liberation of oxygen, depending on the action of the couple under consideration, should cease. Obviously, this period should be of very short duration, since as a result of the continuous consumption of acid at the discharge in the thickness of the electrode a lower concentration is established, and therefore the negative pole of the couple, on which the oxygen evolves, shifts into the internal layers of the active mass.

If after the charge there was a sufficiently long pause, in the course of which the concentration of the acid in the depth of the pores and in the outer electrolyte levelled out, then in the discharge, the liberation of oxygen commences immediately with the second stage, increasing in proportion as the gradient of graphs of liberation of oyxgen illustrating the law mentioned are shown in fig. 4.20. These graphs were obtained in testing of plates of thickness 6.3mm. However, with smaller electrode thicknesses, too, similar graphs were obtained with some modifications, which are explained by the conditions of formation of the concentration cell.

In table 4.5 data are shown which were obtained by B A Kosobryukhov in a study of the influence of overcharge on the rate of liberation of oxygen.

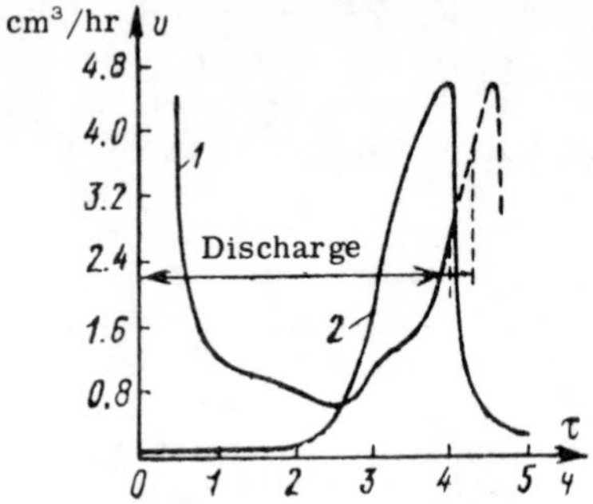

Fig.4.20 Kinetics of liberation of oxygen in the process of discharge of a positive plate 1 - Switch-over from charge to discharge; 2 - discharge after pause.

Table 4.5: Liberation of oxygen after charge

Density of electrolyte g/cm^3	Volume of evolved oxygen cm^3		Difference of volumes cm^3
	after normal charge	after overcharge	
1.1	3.05	4.55	1.40
1.2	6.4	8.75	2.35
1.3	15.3	19.0	3.80

Obviously the surplus volume of oxygen, caused by overcharge, should be fully removed owing to the gas absorbed by the active mass. As is suggested by E V Krivolapova, E S Weissberg and B N Kabanov[78]), in anodic polarisation (in the recharge process) of a coated lead dioxide electrode, part of the oxygen manages to diffuse into the crystal lattice of the PbO_2. After switching off the current the diffusion of the oxygen goes in the opposite direction. In this initial period the volume of oxygen evolving is observed to vary linearly with the square root of the time. Such a relationship, as is well known, is peculiar to non-stationary diffusion.

After removal from the active mass of the surplus oxygen the rate of liberation of O_2 decreases with time according to the linear law. The formation of oxygen appears in this period as a result of spontaneous reduction of PbO_2 according to scheme (4.74). The rate of this process increases with an increase in temperature and concentration of the H_2SO_4.

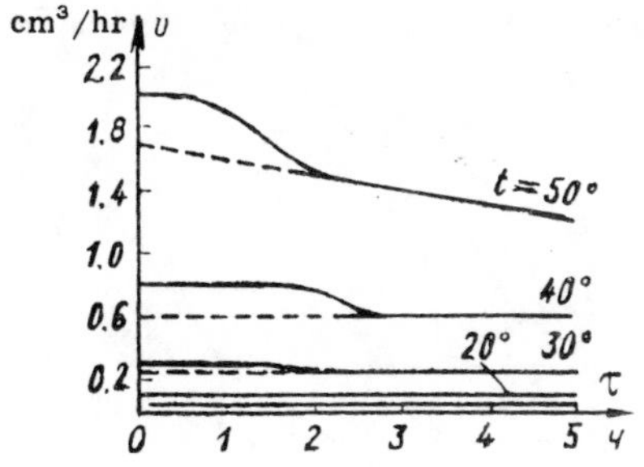

Fig.4.21 Dependence of rate σ of liberation of oxygen on time τ and temperature t.

It was also established by the authors[78]) that the amount of "diffusion" oxygen does not depend on the density of the discharge current (with a uniform amount of electricity). Consequently, the rate of diffusion of oxygen into the PbO_2 lattice increases proportionally with increase in the current density, and this is possible if the formation of O_2 molecules is slowed down. Oxygen is also released during discharge. This results both from the functioning of the concentration cell and from the diffusion of O_2 from the active mass.

The influence of temperature on the rate of liberation of oxygen from the positive electrode of a battery is shown in fig. 4.21. As can be seen from the diagram, for low temperatures the rate of liberation of the gas does not change during the experiment. Starting with 30°C, the rate of liberation of O_2 decreases in time and that all the more so, the higher the temperature. In experiments carried out at high temperatures (>30°C), after the lapse of some time, the rate of liberation of the gas decreases according to the linear law. In this stage, of course, the liberation of oxygen from the PbO_2 lattice ceases and a decrease in the speed of this occurs as a result of the passivation of the active mass.

Continuing the rectilinear sections up to the intersection with the axis of the ordinates (fig. 4.21), we obtain on the graph the region delimited by the curve of liberation and the dotted line. This region, obviously, should be completely removed owing to liberation of absorbed oxygen.

The temperature dependency of the rate of liberation of oxygen is subject to Arrhenius' equation (fig. 4.22). The activation energy constitutes ~4kcal/g-mol. This value is peculiar to the processes controlled by the diffusion stage.

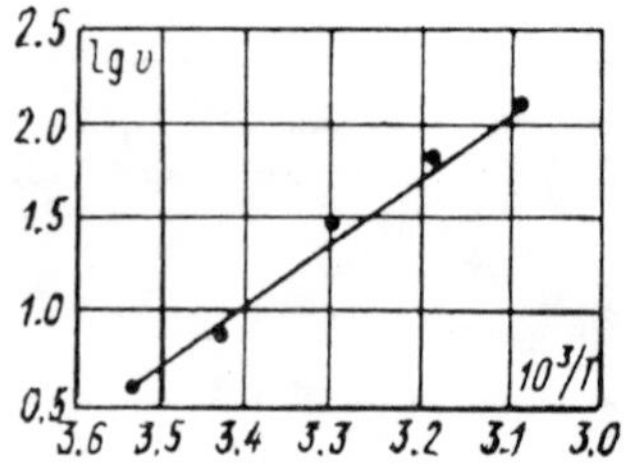

Fig.4.22 Temperature dependence of the logarithm of the rate of liberation of oxygen.

Let us note that in the active mass of the positive electrode, besides the marked quantities of oxygen, a certain quantity of hydrogen is also retained. The presence of the hydrogen in the crystal lattice of the PbO_2 is characterised only for dioxide obtained by the electro-chemical method[79]). In ref.[79]) a hypothesis is propounded of the PbO_2 at its reduction (discharge). In the process of cycling the hydrogen content gradually decreases, which leads to a lowering of the electro-chemical activity of the PbO_2 and of the discharge capacity of the positive electrode.

Ways of improvement of the characteristics of the active mass of the positive electrode

Prospects of increasing the capacity of the electrode

The coefficient of utilisation of the active mass of the positive electrode in current lead acid batteries does not exceed 45-50%. This fact points to the greater potential possibilities for increasing the capacity of the electrode by means of activating additives.

During recent years a large number of such additives introduced into the active mass, into the grid alloy, or into the electrolyte of the finished battery have been studied. The majority of these substances have been patented. The mechanism of influence of the additives on the work capacity of the positive electrode is quite varied. It seems appropriate to carry out some classification of the additives according to the character of their effect on the electrode. Analysis of data in literature in existence on this question permits us to differentiate substances influencing the structure of the corrosion film, the morphology of the lead dioxide, and also the volumetric porosity and structure of the pores of the active mass.

Additives of the first type are intended to affect the structure of the transitional layer on the grid-active mass interface. It is known that the structure of the film forming on the surface of the grid in anodic polarisation of the electrode has a marked influence on the capacity of the electrode. Thus the transient electrical resistance in the case of formation of loose films is higher than on the appearance of dense films. The resistance of the films substantially depends on their phase and chemical fusion.

As an example, let us mention that attempts to lead-plate grids of a lead-antimony alloy with the aim of delaying the dissolution of the antimony on anodic polarisation of the electrode lead to a marked decrease in the discharge capacity. A similar decrease in capacity is observed also in the testing of batteries the positive grids of which are made of pure lead[80]). It can be assumed that the loose film forming on anodic polarisation of the lead hinders the formation of a good contact of the grid with the active mass, which leads to an increase in ohmic voltage drop on the electrode.

It is further known that the use of lead-calcium alloys causes the formation of a sulphate film with high electrical resistance on the grid-active mass interface, which is not oxidised to lead dioxide even with a long charge. This fault with lead-calcium alloys can be eliminated by the addition to the electrolyte of a certain quantity of phosphoric acid[73]).

Cobalt sulphate may be numbered among the effective additives influencing the structure of the film. It is suggested that the Co^{3+} ions oxidise the lead in the pores of the lead dioxide film, at the same time increasing its density. The mechanism of the action of cobalt ions has been studied in a number of papers[81-83]) and explained in sufficient detail in the review[84]).

As a rule the action of additives influencing the morphology of the active mass has an adsorption character. Adsorbed on PbO_2 crystals, these additives lead to the formation of dispersion deposits, which in the end increases the active surface of the electrode and decreases the true density of the current.

It must be noted that the selection of additives introduced into the active mass of the positive electrode of a lead acid battery is extremely limited, since organic substances at the potentials obtaining on the positive electrode, as a rule, are oxidised, while many inorganic substances are either useless or have quite a considerable deleterious effect ($BaSO_4$, $SrSO_4$). Among the additives influencing the morphology of the active mass must be numbered the salts of a number of metals (arsenic, antimony, cobalt, etc.). A similar influence is shown also by many components of the anode alloy, in particular antimony. The presence of antimony in the positive active mass was shown in[69]). Later it was found that after several charge-discharge cycles the charged active mass of the positive electrode contains 0.03-0.04% of antimony. The adsorption of antimony causes a dispersion of the structure of the lead dioxide and a marked increase in its active surface[15])[80]). Thus the use of a lead-antimony anode alloy in batteries not only causes a decrease in contact resistance on the boundary of the grid with the active mass, owing to a consolidation of the structure of the lead dioxide film, but also improves the morphology of the crystallites forming the active mass.

By specially introducing antimony into the active mass, it is possible to increase somewhat the capacity of the electrode in the initial cycles. It is proposed to introduce antimony either into the paste - in the form of oxides, or into the lead powder - in the form of an alloy of antimony with lead.

According to patent data, the increase in the dispersibility of the PbO_2 formed on charging is also brought about by the presence of persulphonic acid or its salt in a compound which contains in a molecule 5-10 atoms of carbon. This additive is also useful, as it improves the conditions of saturation of the electrodes with electrolyte, as well as decreasing their internal resistance.

A considerable amount of research has been devoted to the action of additives of the third type, which influence the volumetric porosity and the structure of the pores. These additives (which often are called porophorous) are introduced as a rule into the electrode paste. In the process of forming the plate, and also in the initial period of utilisation of the battery they transfer to the electrolyte, thereby increasing the volumetric porosity of the active mass. The size of the pores here substantially depends on the dispersibility of the substances introduced. Among the additives increasing porosity of the active mass may be numbered, e.g. $Al_2(SO_4)_3 \cdot 18H_2O$, $MgSO_4 \cdot 7H_2O$, diatomite, soda, granite, kaolin etc. An increase in porosity is also caused by an increased sulphuric acid content in the paste. A substantial influence on the capacity stock of the positive electrode in the initial period of cycling is exerted by the PbO_2 content (especially the β-modification) in the active mass, which may vary within fairly wide limits, depending on the technology of manufacture of the electrodes. As has already been shown above, the conditions of forming to a large extent determines the composition of the active mass of the positive electrode. In particular, the preliminary maintenance of the plates in the forming electrolyte until the switching on of the current, in the process of which interaction of the oxides and the basic sulphates of lead and sulphuric acid takes place and leads to an increased β-PbO_2 content in the active mass [85]).

Influence of phosphoric acid on the characteristics of the lead dioxide electrode

A special place among additives improving the work of the positive electrode is occupied by phosphoric acid, to which great attention has been paid in the literature in recent years. In connection with this, we considered it necessary to go into both the evidence in literature on this additive and the results of our own research.

In literature [73]) it is mentioned that the addition of H_3PO_4 to the battery electrolyte decreases the sulphation of the active mass, , lowers the rate of its dissolution, and also decreases the rate of corrosion of the grid. The addition of phosphoric acid (5-7%) makes it possible to use grids of lead-calcium alloys in batteries discharged at considerable currents. This additive causes oxidation of the sulphate layer forming on the surface of the grids.

The introduction of phosphoric acid and some of its derivatives to the positive active mass leads to some improvement of the discharge characteristics, at any rate in the initial period of utilisation of the battery. The positive influence of H_3PO_4 on the strength of the active mass is explained in literature by the following reasons: increase in the viscosity of the active mass, a decrease of volumetric changes in the process of cycling as a result of the formation of phosphate compounds of lead and of the adsorption of multi-valent PO_4^{3-} ions on positively charged PbO_2 particles, thanks to which there is a decrease in electrostatic repulsion, which is one of the reasons for the dissolution of the active mass. It must be noted that this last hypothesis is not very probable owing to the extremely low concentration of ions of PO_4^{3-} in the solution (according to our calculations one ion falls to 20 000m^2 of surface of PbO_2).

In the paper of Tudor, Weisstuch and Davant[73]) it was established that in the process of charge of a battery containing in the electrolyte an addition of phosphoric acid the concentration of the H_3PO_4 decreases, but during discharge it increases. The change in concentration of H_3PO_4 with time bears a long-term character.

The nature of the compounds forming on the positive electrode of a battery in the presence of phosphoric acid was studied by Bode and Voss[49]). These authors observed the formation of two compounds. The composition of one of these may be expressed by the formula $2PbO_2 \cdot P_2O_5 \cdot xH_2O$ (x = 2.5-3). This compound possesses considerable solubility in the electrolyte. The other, insoluble compound is characterised by a composition described by the formula $PbO_2 \cdot$ $\cdot P_2O_5 \cdot xH_2O$. The formation of this compound is particularly characteristic for solutions containing considerable quantities of phosphoric acid. A study of some physico-chemical properties of the compounds mentioned permitted the authors of the work under consideration[49]) to propose for the soluble matter the formula $H[Pb(OH)_2PO_4]$, according to which quadrivalent lead comes into the composition of the complex anion. For the insoluble compound, characterised by colloidal properties, the formula $\{H_2[Pb(PO_4)_2]\}_n$ was proposed.

Let us note that the results mentioned were used by Bode and Voss for working out a scheme of the charge-discharge process described by the equations of reactions (4.45)-(4.46). The formation and decomposition (reduction of phosphates of quadrivalent lead) cause changes in the concentration of H_3PO_4 in the electrolyte in the process of charge and discharge of a lead dioxide electrode. In ref.[86]) it is shown that on discharge of a lead dioxide electrode in phosphoric acid there is no formation of insoluble compounds which are capable of passivating the electrode.

As object of research we used electrodes obtained by deposition of lead dioxide from a nitric acid electrolyte (α- + β-PbO_2) and from a perchloric acid solution (β-PbO_2). Measurements were carried out in 10N·H_2SO_4 solution, to which was added from 2.5 to 20% (volume) 10N·H_3PO_4 [87]). It was established that phosphoric acid shows comparatively little influence on the anodic behaviour of a lead dioxide electrode. The introduction into the solution of 10-20% H_3PO_4 causes a decrease in the anode potential of an electrode of $\alpha + \beta$-PbO_2 by 10-20mV, while this effect was strengthened in the field of low polarisation. The last fact can be explained by the known influence of phosphoric acid on the equilibrium value of the potential $\varphi_{PbO_2/PbSO_4}$ as a result of a decrease in the activity of the sulphuric acid.

A small decrease in the oxygen overvoltage on an electrode of a mixture of $\alpha + \beta$-PbO_2, obviously, is caused by the adsorption of the phosphoric acid, which is accompanied by a shift of the ψ_1 potential to the negative side. Here, judging by the values of the constants of dissociation of H_3PO_4 ($K_1 = 7.52 \cdot 10^{-3}$; $K_2 = 6.23 \cdot 10^{-8}$; $K_3 = 9.20 \cdot 10^{-12}$) it may be probably only a question of the adsorption of single-charge ions of $H_2PO_4^-$ or even of molecules of H_3PO_4. The comparatively small effect observed with the introduction of phosphoric acid, is obviously explained by the considerable concentration in the double layer of the electrode of specifically adsorbed sulphate ions.

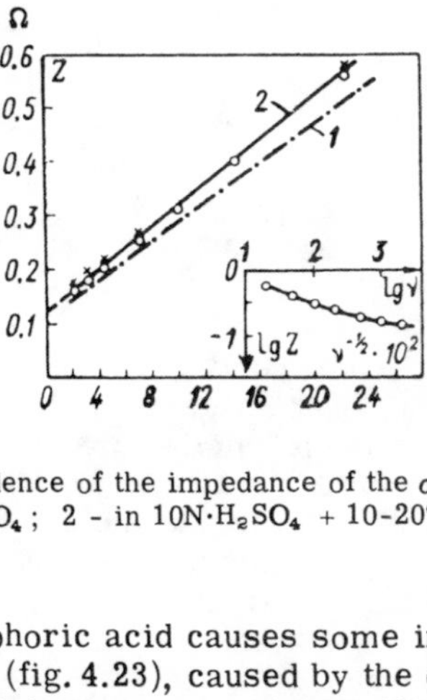

Fig.4.23 Frequency dependence of the impedance of the $\alpha + \beta$-PbO_2 on current density j j. 1 - in $10N \cdot H_2SO_4$; 2 - in $10N \cdot H_2SO_4$ + 10-20% $10N \cdot H_3PO_4$.

The addition of phosphoric acid causes some increase in the impedance of the electrode (fig. 4.23), caused by the decrease in the capacity of the double electrical layer, as calculation shows. In solutions containing 10-20% H_3PO_4 this value averages $C_d \approx 100 \mu m/cm^2$ of visible surface. The decrease in C_d, is connected, obviously, with the adsorption of phosphoric acid on the electrode.

Passing on to an examination of the above behaviour of β-PbO_2 in solutions containing H_3PO_4, it must be said that in this case the influence of the phosphoric acid shows more noticeably. The introduction into the electrolyte of 5-10% H_3PO_4 causes some increase in the stationary values of oxygen overvoltage on the tetragonal modification of PbO_2 (fig. 4.24). The increase in overvoltage of the liberation of oxygen cannot, of course, be caused by the shift of the ψ_1 potential to the negative side. This suggests that adsorption of H_3PO_4 on β-PbO_2 hinders the discharge of the water molecules without causing any noticeable change in the charge of the electrode surface. The difference in the behaviour of an electrode of a mixture of α + β-PbO_2 and one of β-PbO_2 characterises the influence of the rhombic modification of the dioxide on the adsorption properties of the electrode.

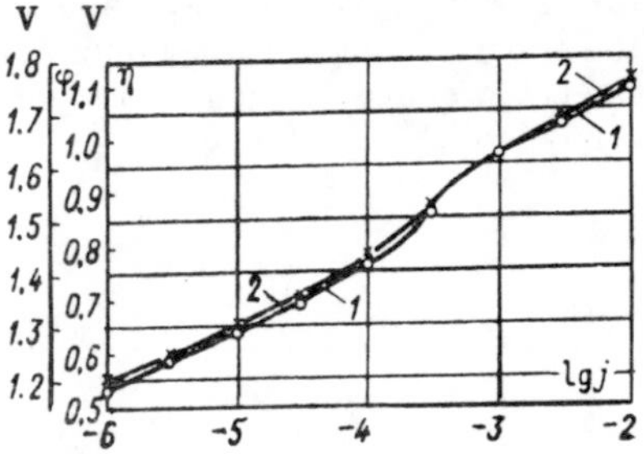

Fig.4.24 Dependence of the oxygen overvoltage on β-PbO_2 on density of current j. 1 - in 10N·H_2SO_4 ; 2 - in 10N·H_2SO_4 +10% 10N·H_3PO_4 .

The introduction of the H_3PO_4 additive causes a marked decrease in the established values of the impedance of β-PbO_2, caused by an increase in the capacity of the double layer and fall in the polarisation resistance and of Warburg's coefficient of diffusion resistance. The relationship of the double layer parameters mentioned, measured in a H_2SO_4 solution and in the same solution with the addition of H_3PO_4, constitutes on average (over the range $j = 10^{-6}$ to 10^{-2} A/cm^2):

$$\frac{C_{d(H_3PO_4)}}{C_d} \approx 1.70; \quad \frac{r_0}{r_{0\,(H_3PO_4)}} \approx 1.45; \quad \frac{\lambda}{\lambda_{(H_3PO_4)}} \approx 1.46$$

The data obtained point to the fact that the addition of phosphoric acid causes more intensive development on the surface of the β-PbO_2 in the process of anodic polarisation. Setting out from the above-mentioned relationships, it can be assumed that the value of the true surface of the electrode in a solution containing H_3PO_4, established as a result of long polarisation, is 1.5-1.7 times greater than the corresponding value in a "pure" H_2SO_4 solution. The increase in the true surface may mask to a known extent an increase in oxygen overvoltage, since the increase in the surface by 1.6 times causes a decrease in potential by $0.12 \cdot \lg 1.6 = 0.024V$.

The action of the H_3PO_4 addition described, is caused, obviously by the influence of the adsorbed molecules or ions of phosphoric acid on the process of catalytic corrosion of β-PbO_2 at the liberation of oxygen. The increase in catalytic corrosion is connected with the hindering of the process of liberation of oxygen, which can be considered as an increase in the time of the intermediate radicals remaining on the surface of the electrode, up to their recombination into oxygen molecules.

Comparison of the influence of phosphoric acid on the value of the impedance and potential of electrodes of $\alpha + \beta$-PbO_2 and of β-PbO_2 shows that the presence of α-PbO_2 causes an increase in resistance of the electrode surface to catalytic corrosion in solutions of $H_2SO_4 + H_3PO_4$, causing simultaneously a decrease in the overvoltage of the liberation of oxygen.

The introduction into the electrolyte of the phosphoric acid addition exerts a considerable influence on the character of the discharge graphs of a lead dioxide electrode. This effect is particularly noticeable in the case of a β-PbO_2 electrode. The discharge graphs of β-PbO_2, taken in the interval of current densities $j = 10^{-4}$ -3.10^{-3} A/cm^2, are characterised principally by the absence of the minimum in the initial period if the discharge is carried out in a solution containing >5% H_3PO_4. In a solution with a concentration of H_3PO_4 <5% the minimum on the graphs (φ, τ) is observed, but its depth is less than in "pure" sulphuric acid. This phenomenon is evidence of the fact that the presence of the additive H_3PO_4 facilitates the formation of centres of crystallisation of $PbSO_4$ in the process of cathodic reduction of lead dioxide. It is possible that a definite role is here played by the finer crystals of lead phosphate, the solubility of which is almost two orders lower than the solubility of $PbSO_4$. It must be noted that according to X-ray analysis data only lead sulphate is found on the surface of a discharged lead dioxide electrode, even if the discharge was carried out in a solution containing 50% H_3PO_4. Therefore $Pb_3(PO_4)_2$ may be found only in the depth of the sulphate film or be present in quantities that are beyond the sensitivity of X-ray analysis.

A typical discharge graph of β-PbO_2 and the corresponding time dependency of the impedance at $\nu = 100$Hz in a solution upon the addition of H_3PO_4 are shown in fig. 4.25. The graphs (φ, τ) and (Z, τ) have, in the initial period of discharge, a noticeable plateau. This phenomenon appears plainly at all discharge conditions investigated. An exception is the first discharge, in which the graphs have only one plateau according to the basic discharge process.

It can be assumed that the presence of an additional holding of the potential, preceding the base plateau, is linked with the participation in the discharge of phosphatic compounds of quadrivalent lead. The first discharge occurs, of course, according to the normal scheme

$$PbO_2 + HSO_4^- + 3H^+ + 2e \rightarrow PbSO_4 + 2H_2O \qquad (4.78)$$

The subsequent charge can be described by the equations

$$PbSO_4 + 2H_2O - 2e \rightarrow PbO_2 + HSO_4^- + 3H^+ \qquad (4.79)$$

and

$$PbSO_4 + H_2PO_4^- + 2H_2O - 2e \rightarrow [Pb(OH)_2PO_4]^- + HSO_4^- + 3H^+ \qquad (4.80)$$

In the period of the second and subsequent discharges the processes (4.79) and (4.80) occur in the reverse direction, with reaction (4.80) obviously going on at a more positive value of the potential.

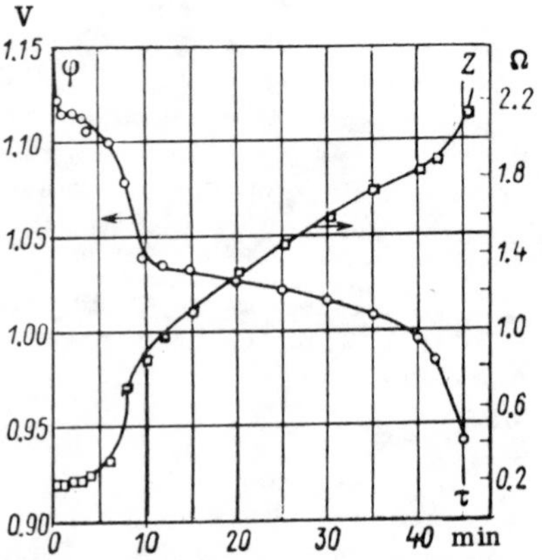

Fig.4.25 Dependence of the potential φ and impedance Z (ν = 100Hz) of β-PbO_2 in $10N \cdot H_2SO_4 + 10\% \; 10N \cdot H_3PO_4$ on time τ at discharge $j_d = 3 \cdot 10^{-4}$ A/cm^2.

The relationship of the amounts of electricity transmitted through the electrode in the periods corresponding to the 1st and 2nd plateaus, in practice, does not depend on the current and changes symbiotically with the concentration of H_3PO_4 in the solution. In an electrolyte containing 10% of phosphoric acid this relationship is approximately 0.15 and with 5% content of H_3PO_4 ~0.13. This means that in the first case ~13% and in the second ~11% of the electrode capacity is caused by the supplementary discharge process.

In the testing of an electrode representing a mixture of α and β-PbO_2 the above-mentioned properties of the discharge graphs (absence of initial minimum, and supplementary plateau in the potential curve) were only noticed at fairly high densities of discharge current: $j_d \geqslant 10^{-3}$ A/cm². In the reduction of $\alpha + \beta$-PbO_2 at low current densities the presence in the solution of the additive phosphoric acid did not influence the character of the change in potential in practice. This difference, caused by the effect of the rhombic modification of PbO_2, probably is connected with the consolidation of the sulphate film forming at the beginning of the discharge.

The potential corresponding to the middle of the 1st plateau varies within the limits φ_1 = 1.05-1.15V (in relation to a Hg/Hg_2SO_4 electrode in 10N·H_2SO_4), and the potential in the middle of the second plateau φ_2 = 0.98-1.05V. Both values (φ_1 and φ_2) decrease somewhat with an increase in discharge current which, of course, is connected with the increase in the overvoltages of the corresponding processes. The difference in the potentials $\varphi_1 - \varphi_2$ increases with an increase in current, i.e. φ_1 shows a smaller dependence on current than φ_2.

A comparison of the values of the potential corresponding to the 2nd plateau in the graph (φ, τ) with equilibrium potential of $PbO_2 \rightleftarrows PbSO_4$ (10N·H_2SO_4) shows that φ_2 is situated more on the negative side than $\varphi_{PbO_2/PbSO_4}$, at approximately 100mV. This difference is characteristic also for the value of the discharge potential in the first discharge, there is only one plateau in the graph (φ, τ). Probably, along with the overvoltage of the reduction processes, a known role is played here also by the decrease in the activity of the H_2SO_4, in the layer next to the electrode, with the introduction into the solution of phosphoric acid. A decrease in discharge potential on the introduction of H_3PO_4 into the solution causes the absence of a potential plateau on the graph (φ, τ), which is connected with the reduction of the intermediate oxide on deep discharge of β-PbO_2.

As was mentioned above, in the process of cycling a lead dioxide electrode in a H_2SO_4 solution with the addition of H_3PO_4, insoluble colloidal phosphates are formed of the type $\{H_2[Pb(PO_4)_2]\}_n$. The formation of these compounds may be described by the equations of the reactions

$$PbSO_4 + 2H_2PO_4^- \rightarrow [Pb(PO_4)_2]^{2-} + HSO_4^- + 3H^+ + 2e \qquad (4.81)$$

$$n[Pb(PO_4)_2]^{2-} + 2nH^+ \rightarrow \{H_2[Pb(PO_4)_2]\}_n \qquad (4.82)$$

Obviously, reactions (4.81) and (4.82) occur to a considerable degree irreversibly, which leads to the accumulation of insoluble compounds on the surface of the electrode. This phenomenon causes a pronounced character of the dependence of the impedance of the electrode on the number of cycles (fig. 4.26).

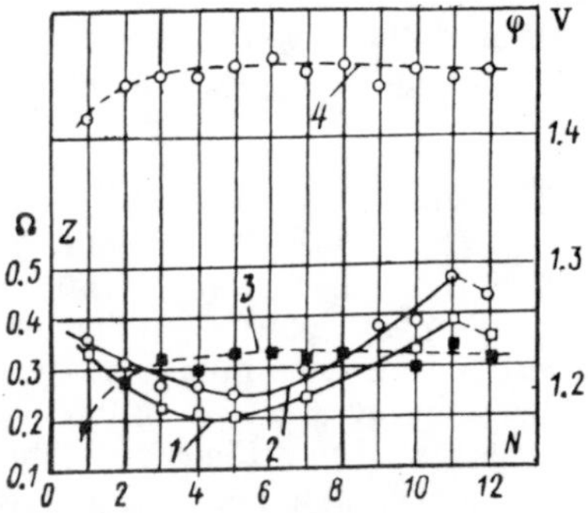

Fig.4.26 Change of impedance Z (ν = 100Hz) and potential φ in the process of cycling β-PbO_2 in 10N·H_2SO_4 + 10% 10N·H_3PO_4. 1 - Z at I = 0; 2 - Z at I = 0.3mA; 3 - φ at I = 0; 4 - φ at I = 0.3mA.

The initial fall in impedance is caused by the development of the surface of the electrode (as happens also in a "pure" solution of H_2SO_4). The subsequent raising of the value of Z (after 4-5 cycles) can be explained by an increase in ohmic resistance of the layer next to the electrode as a result of the formation and growth of the phosphate film *). This film in the form of a semi-transparent white

---

*) An increase in the values of final discharge and stationary potential (fig. 4.26) in the initial period of cycling can be explained by an increase in the concentration of ions of Pb^{4+} in the solution.

layer is visible on the surface of an electrode withdrawn from an electrolyte containing the H_3PO_4 additive after long-term cycling.

A detailed examination of the oscillogram of the initial section of the discharge graphs taken at low current density (10^{-4} A/cm^2) shows that the first stage of the discharge, caused by the introduction into the electrolyte of phosphoric acid, has a small inflection. This points to the complex character of the process, in which several different compounds possibly participate.

In fig. 4.27 a comparison is made of the values of discharge capacity of β-PbO_2 in solutions with different H_3PO_4 contents. As can be seen from the diagram, the addition of H_3PO_4 leads to a marked increase in the capacity of the β-PbO_2 at low densities of discharge current j_d. At high current densities in the presence of H_3PO_4 a sharp decrease in the capacity of the electrode is observed. Both effects increase with an increase in concentration of the H_3PO_4 in the solution. The increase in capacity at low densities is connected, obviously, with the increase in the active surface of the electrode, and also with the occurrence of supplementary discharge processes of reduction of the phosphates of quadrivalent lead. At high current densities when an important role is played by the ohmic component of the potential, the formation on the electrode of a phosphate film, of course, determines the sharp drop in discharge capacity.

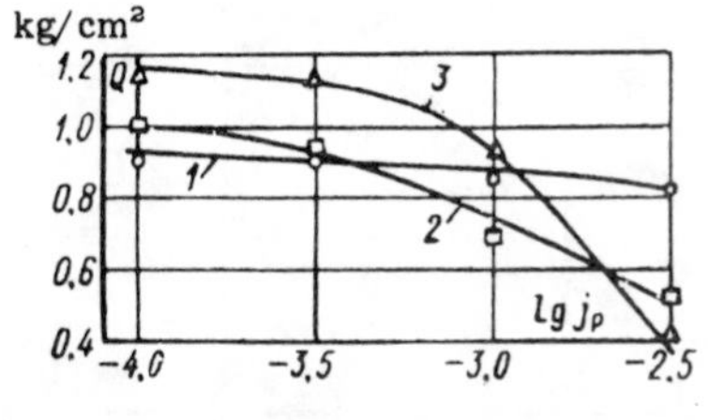

Fig.4.27 Dependency of discharge capacity of β-PbO_2 on current density. 1 - 10N·H_2SO_4; 2 - 10N·H_2SO_4 + 5% 10N·H_3PO_4; 3 - 10N·H_2SO_4 + 10% 10N·H_3PO_4.

Thus, the positive influence of the addition of H_3PO_4 on the discharge characteristics of β-PbO_2 shows up only at fairly low currents. In the case of electrodes representing a mixture of α- and β-PbO_2 the supplementary discharge processes occur to a marked degree only at high currents, when an essential role is played by ohmic potential drop, and the area of the true surface of an α + β-PbO_2 electrode does not generally change markedly.

The results described permit us to explain the known contradictions in data obtained in the testing of the H_3PO_4 addition and of phosphate salts in lead acid batteries. The influence of this additive substantially depends on the phase composition of the electrode. The addition of H_3PO_4 can be successfully used only at quite small concentrations. Here it is desirable that the active mass of the positive electrode should represent, basically, the tetragonal modification of lead dioxide. It seems appropriate to introduce the H_3PO_4 additive into the battery electrolyte after completion of the practice cycles, when basically the process of recrystallisation $\alpha \rightarrow \beta$-PbO_2 is completed.

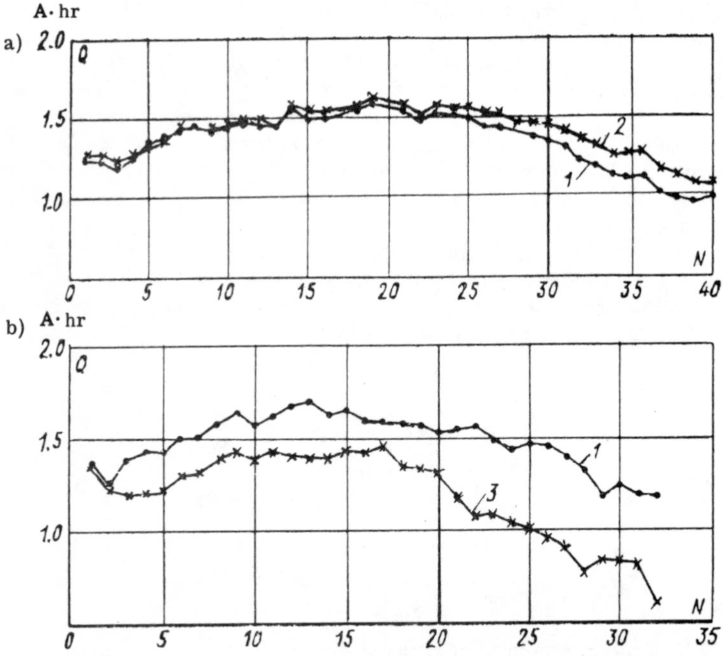

Fig.4.28 Change in capacity of the RG positive plates in the process of cycling. 1 - in a solution of H_2SO_4 (SG 1.32); 2 - in the same H_2SO_4 solution with addition of 1% H_3PO_4 ; 3 - in the same H_2SO_4 solution with addition of 2.5% H_3PO_4 .

The results obtained were verified by us by testing of positive plates of the RG type (in surplus electrolyte), and also batteries of the ZST-70 type. Up to 5% H_3PO_4 was introduced into the electrolyte. It was established that, if 2.5-5% H_3PO_4 is introduced into electrolyte with a density of 1.32, then this leads to a decrease in capacity of the positive electrode (fig. 4.28b), whilst an addition of up to 1% H_3PO_4 causes a slight increase in capacity (fig. 4.28a). With cycling of RG plates in an electrolyte containing 5% H_3PO_4 an impeding of the charge process was observed, which was evidenced by the appearance of the maximum on the graph of change of potential in time at the beginning of the charge. The final charge potential of the electrodes investigated did not depend, in practice, on the presence in the electrolyte of the additive under investigation. All these data are in conformity with the results described above.

As was shown by bench tests, batteries containing 0.2-0.3% H_3PO_4 in the electrolyte did not differ in capacity from normal batteries at practically all discharge regimes. At the same time the service life of the batteries with the addition of phosphoric acid, determined by the method of a "live test", exceeded the service life of a normal battery by approximately 10-15%.

a)

b)

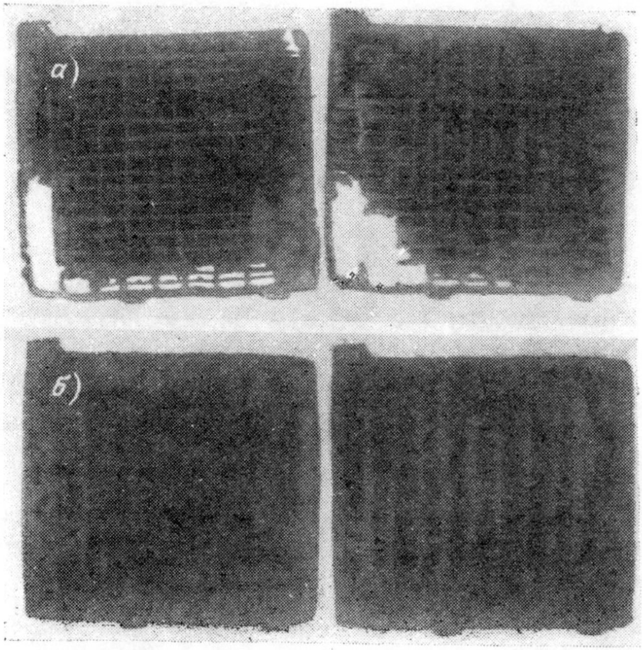

Fig.4.29 External view of the positive plates after testing for service life; a - electrolyte is a solution of H_2SO_4 of SG 1.27; b - the electrolyte is the same solution with the addition of 0.5% H_3PO_4.

In batteries with the H_3PO_4 addition practically no shedding of the active mass of the positive electrode is observed (fig. 4.29). Increased H_3PO_4 content led to phenomena similar to those noted in the testing of separate positive plates (decrease in capacity and impeding of the charge process). It was also noted that the presence in the battery of the H_3PO_4 addition, causes the formation of sponge on the negative plates, particularly on the bottom edge of the plates. In the case of low separator height (in comparison with the dimensions of the plates) this sponge may lead to the appearance of short circuits. The reason for this phenomenon is, of course, the increase in concentration of the soluble compounds of lead under the influence of the phosphoric acid. Thus, the use in batteries of an electrolyte with the addition of phosphoric acid requires a particularly careful selection of material and design of the separators.

An effective way of increasing the service life of a lead acid battery is also the introduction into the electrolyte, along with phosphoric acid, of cobaltic sulphate. The presence of 0.05-0.3% of this additive markedly depresses the rate of shedding of the positive active mass and corrosion of the grids. Thus, simultaneous introduction into the battery electrolyte of the additives H_3PO_4 and $CoSO_4$ or $Co_3(PO_4)_2$ can cause an increase in the service life of storage batteries both owing to an increase in the corrosion resistance of the grids and also as a result of the consolidation of the positive active mass.

Ways of increasing the service life of the active mass of a positive electrode

The most important utilisation characteristic of the positive electrode of a lead acid battery is the service life which, as a rule, determines the service life of the source of current as a whole. The positive plates of a battery becoming non-operational is caused mainly by corrosion of the grids and shedding of the active mass, with the proportion of both these reasons at the present time being approximately the same. In this chapter an examination will be made of data in literature and experimental and production data on the combating of the shedding of the active mass of the positive electrode.

One of the possibilities of affecting the process of crystallisation of the lead sulphate in the direction of an increase in the service life of the active mass consists in the introduction into the electrolyte of special additives. The influence of a large quantity of different substances on the electro-crystallisation of PbO_2 was investigated by A K Lorenz. He established that metavanadate and bichromate of ammonia (0.03mol/l) increase the service life of the active mass. Some other admixtures, particularly barium sulphate, have a sharp negative effect. The exclusion of the possibility of $BaSO_4$ reaching the positive active mass in its time played quite an important role, causing an increase in the service life of lead acid batteries.

Since the shedding of the active mass can be caused, to a known extent, by electrostatic repulsion of positively charged particles of lead dioxide, the use of additives of multi-charge anions, causing discharge of the surface of the PbO_2 particles, is of interest. It is possible to increase the service life of the active mass by introducing organic reducing agents (for example hydroxylamine sulphate) in the quantity of 0.5-1.0%[88]). The effect of such substances leads to chemical reduction of the lead dioxide with the formation of macrocrystalline lead sulphate, from which, as was mentioned above, in the following charge there is formed an active mass of strong structure.

As binding materials which are often introduced simultaneously with a pore-former the patent literature recommends the use of the copolymers vinylidene chloride, acrylonitryl, polyvinyl spirit, polyethylene terepthalate, alginic, polyacrylic and polysytrenic acids. These substances are also recommended to be applied to the surface of the plates in the form of a film. If the film is applied by spraying, then the quantity of solvent is selected by calculation to ensure that the mass is ejected in the form of inter-crossing filaments. It is also possible to apply the surface layer to the electrode by dipping the electrode in the liquid and then drying it. Such a layer may also play the part of a separator.

The majority of patents recommend the combination of different additives (as a rule, oxides and salts of metals). Among such additives are Ag_2SO_4 and Al_2O_3, $Al_2(SO_4)_3$ and $C_{16}H_{16}N_3SCl$ and other combinations. The bonding additives considered must be the ones with the best prospects. Some of these substances have already found industrial application, such as fluorinated plastics and polyvinyl chloride fibre.

The influence of fluorinated plastics on the work of the positive electrode has been studied in recent years by N M Yemelyanov, A I Trepalin, G E Demin and others. As a result suggestions were made for an acidless paste with the solution of 'Fluoroplast 42' on acetone (Yemelyanov), a paste with 'Fluoroplast 4B' or '4D' in powder form (Trepalin) and a paste with the addition of an aqueous suspension of 'Fluoroplast 4D' (Demin).

Comparative testing of the pastes mentioned was carried out in the following way. Mock-ups of cells were assembled from one positive and two negative electrodes without separators (free assembly).

In order to shorten the duration of the tests, a regime of cycling was adopted which caused more pronounced shedding of the active mass. After taking the initial characteristics in the first 10 cycles the electrodes were cycled with a current corresponding to a 5-hour discharge regime. Duration of the discharge was 3 hours (50% of capacity was removed), charges were carried out with the same current for 4 hours. Full capacity of the electrode was determined at every 10th cycle. The high density of the electrolyte at the end of the discharge (1.25-1.27g/cm^3) the comparatively low temperature of the electrolyte in the process of testing (+22 - +30°C) and the systematic undercharges caused more pronounced shedding of the active mass.

Tests of the control electrodes (with the addition of 'Fluoroplast' to the paste) by this method are generally possible up to 60-70 cycles, after which the plates become non-operational as a result of the loss of a considerable amount of the active mass and of short circuits through sludge on the bottom of the cells. In order to prevent short circuits high knife-edge supports were installed in the cell with the control electrode, and this made it possible to carry out cycling until almost complete shedding of the active mass of the positive electrode has occurred.

The results of the testing come to the following. Acidless paste shows the best discharge characteristics and the longest service life (fig. 4.30). However, this recipe for paste cannot be recommended at the present time for wide industrial application owing to the considerable volatility and explosion danger of the solvent coming into its composition. Besides, acidless pastes are very complex in their manufacture because of their quick setting.

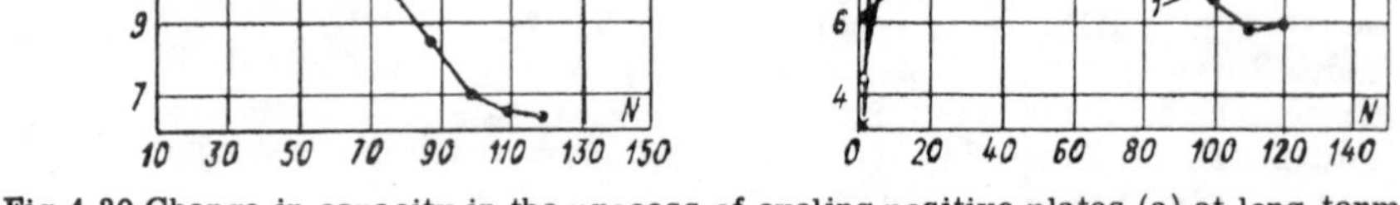

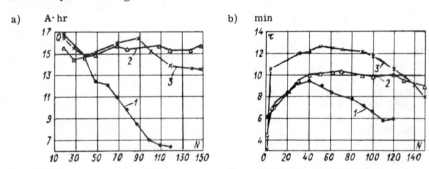

Fig.4.30 Change in capacity in the process of cycling positive plates (a) at long-term regime and (b) at short-term regime.
1 - control plates (without additives); 2 - plates containing in the paste "Fluoroplast F-42" and $NaHCO_3$; 3 - plates containing in the paste "Fluoroplas F-42" and KMC.

Pastes with fluorine plastic in powder form have already found practical application and shown good results. Thus the use of a paste with 'Fluoroplast 4D' made it possible to increase the service life of starter batteries by more than 50%. In comparative tests, control batteries of the ZST-70 type underwent 340 cycles on the bench, and the experimental ones with the addition to the paste of 1% of fluorinated plastic endured 500 cycles in the same conditions. Production diesel locomotive batteries in their utilisation in the southern regions of the U.S.S.R. served 20 months and were removed owing to the fall in capacity to below 45%, the experimental batteries with fluorinated plastic in the same conditions after 30 months of utilisation still had a capacity equal to 75% of the nominal.

Finally, traction batteries of the EN-200 type, assembled with coated plates and with side grooves hindering the appearance of short circuits along the edge, in a bench test endured 800 cycles, and the experimental ones with fluorinated plastic 1250 cycles. On the control batteries the nominal capacity was maintained only in the first 200 cycles, and on the experimental ones for a duration of 750 cycles. The increase in service life due to the addition of fluorinated plastic is explained by the consolidation of the active mass of the positive electrode as a result of the formation of an inner structure (skeleton) which keeps the PbO_2 particles from shedding. According to the data of G E Demin, good results in the consolidation of the active mass and the increasing of the capacity characteristics of the electrode can be obtained with the introduction into the paste of 'Fluoroplast 4D' in the form of an aqueous suspension.

Quite promising results were also obtained in the study of the influence of the addition of fibrous substances on the characteristics of the positive electrode. In the works of B S Klyazin and his collaborators additives (0.05-0.1% of fibres) quoted in table 4.6, were investigated. The control and experimental batteries with the addition of fibre were manufactured under production conditions and were tested by the MEK system. The results of these tests are shown in figs. 4.31 and 4.32. The comparatively low service life in variants with LN (see table 4.6) is explained by the formation of short circuits in the lower part of the blocks through lead sponge. The authors reckon that the use of PVC fibre is undesirable as a result of its low heat resistance, which makes difficult industrial preparation for introduction into the paste; 'Fluorolon' fibre cannot be recommended as a result of its high cost. Better results were obtained with PVC and polypropylene fibres, which were recommended for practical application. However, after taking into account availability, production capacity and cost, production of these two PVC fibres was put in hand.

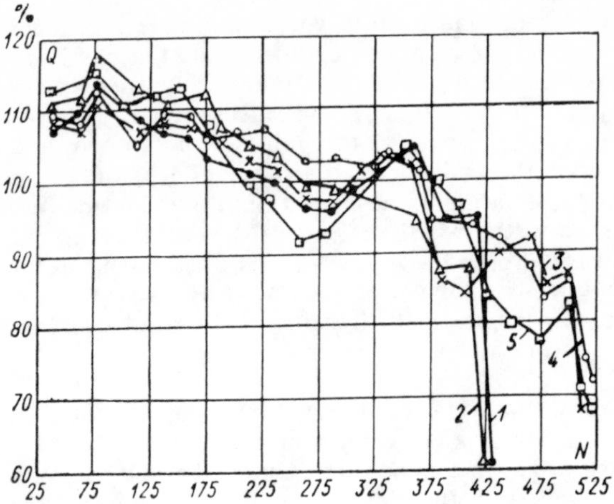

Fig.4.31 Change in capacity in the process of cycling experimental batteries with different additives in the positive active mass. 1 - control variant (without additives 2 - with the LN additive; 3 - with PVC additive; 4 - with PVC additive; 5 - with polypropylene additive.

Table 4.6: Comparative characteristics of acid-resistant fibres[89])

No. of preparation	Designation of the fibre	Chemical composition	Density g/cm^3	Thermal property	Chemical properties
1	Chlorinated (PClV)	Perchlorvinyl resin	1.40	Softening temperature 100-105°C. Utilisation limit - up to 85°C.	Chlorine content 65-68%. Resistant against the action of strong acids and alkalis up to 50°C. Water-repellent. Above 140°C decomposes with liberation of HCl.
2	Polyvinyl chloride (PVC)	Polyvinyl chloride	1.38	Softening temperature over 140°C, decomposition temperature 140-170°C. Lead compounds are thermal stabilisers of decomposition.	Chlorine content 56.8%. Close to chlorinated type in its properties. Chemical stability somewhat higher.
3	Lausanne (LN)	Polyethylene terephalate	1.38	Working temperature up to 175°C. Melts at 250-255°C.	Chemically resistance against the action of acids and alkalis; even stable at boiling point.
4	Poly-propylene (PP)	Polypropylene	0.91	Softening temperature 123-126°C, melting temperature 163-166°C, decomposition temperature 268°C.	Chemically inert. Subject to thermo-oxidising destruction.
5	Fluorolon (F)	Polytetrafluor-ethylene	2.3	Working interval of temperatures from -150 to +260°C. Temperature of decomposition 400°C.	Chemically resistant against the action of acids and alkalis; stable even at boiling point.

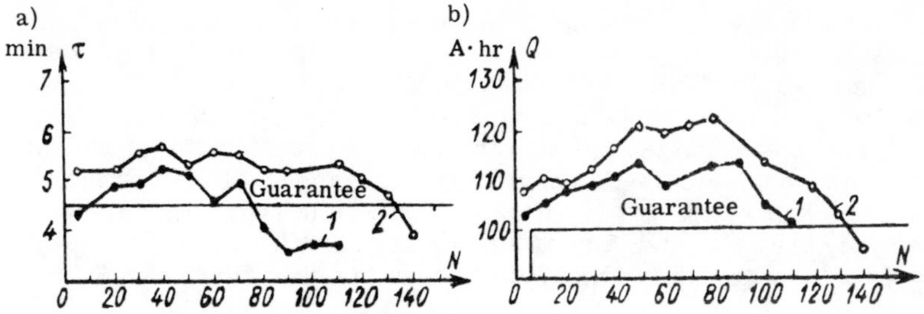

Fig.4.32 Influence of the addition of PVC on the service life of 6STM-128MC batteries; a - starter regime; b - 10-hour regime.
1 - battery without additives; 2 - battery with the addition of PVC.

A technology of preparation of the fibre was worked out by B S Klyazin and others, which ensured evenness of its distribution in the paste, and also production equipment was designed and manufactured for cutting the fibre. The length of the cut fibre should constitute 4-5mm. The fibres obtained are introduced into the lead powder and are thoroughly mixed in mixers before the addition of the remaining components of the paste. As a result of this work they succeeded in obtaining plates with high mechanical properties with simultaneous saving of lead used of up to 5-8%.

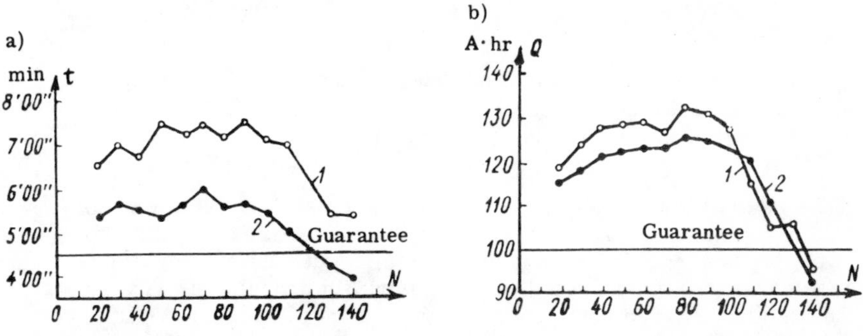

Fig.4.33 Influence of the form of separator on the service life of 6STM-128 batteries with the addition of PVC; a - starter regime; b - 10-hour regime.
1 - battery with single separation (miplast 2.4mm); 2 - battery with dual separation (miplast 1.7mm + glass wool 0.4-0.6mm).

As is well known, to decrease the shedding of the active mass in some types of starter batteries glass wool is also used in addition to the synthetic separator of the miplast type. However, the use of glass wool decreases the electrical performances of the batteries, especially in starter discharges. In connection with the introduction of PVC fibres into the active mass a study was made of the possibility of giving up using glass wool. Investigations showed that with the presence in the paste of the fibre the service life of the batteries with dual and single separation was comparable. Here the capacity characteristics in batteries with single separation are considerably higher, especially at starter regime (fig. 4.33). The service life of both batteries is alike and exceeds the guarantee by about 50%.

It must be noted that with the use of the 'Fluoroplast' additive the necessity for the use of dual separation also disappears. The removal from production of the glass wool opens up the possibilities of mechanisation of the assembly of lead acid batteries and gives great savings in labour costs.

Corrosion of the grids of the positive electrode

The mechanism of lead anode corrosion

Corrosion of the positive electrode grids is the most important reason for lead acid storage batteries becoming non-operational. This phenomenon is caused by the thermodynamic instability of lead and lead alloys in the field of potentials occurring on a lead dioxide electrode. In principle, the basic reason for the corrosion deterioration of positive grids greatly hinders the possibilities of an effective fight against corrosion in a lead acid battery.

A large number of investigations has been devoted to the study of the mechanism of the corrosion of lead and lead alloys in sulphuric acid solutions. The basic results of this work are reflected in refs.[32][84][90][91].

Theoretical interpretation of the experimental data on anodic corrosion of lead differs substantially in the works of different authors. In the papers by B N Kabanov and his colleagues the viewpoint has been developed that lead anode corrosion is a process of oxidation of the metal by oxygen separating on the surface of the lead dioxide film[92]. It is suggested that the oxygen partially comes into the crystal lattice of the lead dioxide in the form of "superstoichiometric" atoms and is diffused towards the metal-oxide film interface, where there occurs oxidation of the lead into the tetragonal modification of PbO *)

---

*) Lead oxide is an amphoteric semi-conductor, the character of the conductivity of which depends on the external conditions, and the composition always differs to a greater or lesser degree from the stoichiometric[18]).

and into α-PbO_2. The rhombic modification of PbO_2 can also be formed as a result of the disproportionation of the intermediate oxides according to the scheme

$$2PbO_{1.5} \rightarrow \alpha\text{-}PbO_2 + PbO \qquad (4.83)$$

The influence of the conditions of polarisation on the rate of anodic oxidation is treated as a result of the change in the rate of diffusion of oxygen in the lead dioxide lattice. The formation of β-PbO_2 in anodic corrosion of lead appears to be from this point of view a consequence of the anodic oxidation of $PbSO_4$ and also of the recrystallisation of α-PbO_2 according to the scheme (2.31) or (2.32).

The mechanism of anodic corrosion of lead described is thus based on the assumption that the oxidation products form as a result of the gradual penetration of oxygen into the crystal lattice of the metal according to the scheme

$$Pb \rightarrow PbO \rightarrow PbO_x \rightarrow \alpha\text{-}PbO_2 \ (2 > x > 1) \qquad (4.84)$$

with all the basic processes occurring in the solid phase. Certainly the authors admit also the possibility of partial oxidation of the metal as a result of the penetration of the electrolyte between the crystals or agglomerates of the PbO_2 [82]).

In the works of N F Razina and others, attention is drawn to the important role of catalytic corrosion in the kinetics of anodic oxidation of lead[93]). The lead dioxide film on the surface of a lead anode is considered as the catalyst of a process of liberation of oxygen on which 95-99% of the electricity is expended. The loosening of this film as a result of the recombination on it of the intermediate radicals (OH, O, HSO_4) facilitates the dissolution of the metal. The presence in the products of anodic oxidation of peroxide compounds (O_3, H_2O_2, and $H_2S_2O_8$), and also the change in the rate of corrosion of the lead depending on the brightness of its surface confirms the influence of catalytic reactions on the character of the course of the process under consideration.

The laws of the formation of peroxide compounds and their influence on the anodic corrosion of lead were studied in refs. [94]) [95]) by the potentio-static method. Here, in particular, the symbiotic change of rate of corrosion and rate of liberation of ozone over a wide interval of anode potentials was established. The rate of formation of $H_2S_2O_8$ passes through a narrow maximum at a lead anode potential equal to 2.3V (in relation to hydrogen zero). The formation of persulphuric acid is linked by the authors with the adsorption of the oxygen and of the radicals of HSO_4 on PbO_2 in conformity with the scheme

$$\left.\begin{array}{l} PbO_2(O)_x + HSO_4^- \rightarrow PbO_2(O)_x(HSO_4) + e \\ PbO_2(O)_x(HSO)_4 + HSO_4^- \rightarrow PbO_2(O_x) + H_2S_2O_8 + e \end{array}\right\} \quad (4.85)$$

The possibility is suggested of chemical interaction between the adsorption anion-radicals of HSO_4 and lead ions with the formation of surface compounds of the type $PbO(HSO_4)_2$ and $Pb(HSO_4)_4$. Hydrolysis of such compounds

$$PbO(HSO_4)_2 + H_2O \quad PbO_2 + 2H_2SO_4 \quad (4.86)$$

leads to the dispersion of lead dioxide on the surface of the lead anode.

In the works of Lander the important role of the oxidation reactions with the participation of water molecules in the kinetics of anodic corrosion of lead is observed[96][97]. These reactions occur on the metal-oxide film interface and lead to intermediate formation of hydrate of lead oxide

$$Pb + 2H_2O \rightarrow Pb(OH)_2 + 2H^+ + 2e \quad (4.87)$$

and also of oxide appearing as a result of the decomposition of hydroxide

$$Pb(OH)_2 \rightarrow PbO + H_2O \quad (4.88)$$

or as a result of electro-chemical oxidation of lead according to the scheme

$$Pb + H_2O \rightarrow PbO + 2H^+ + 2e \quad (4.89)$$

It is also observed that the formation of PbO can be the result of the reaction of co-proportionation occurring in the solid phase as a result of the migration of electrons from the Pb and PbO_2 inter- face.

$$Pb + PbO_2 \rightarrow 2PbO \quad (4.90)$$

Anodic oxidation of lead with the participation of water molecules may also lead to the formation of PbO_2

$$Pb + 2H_2O \rightarrow PbO_2 + 4H^+ + 4e \quad (4.91)$$

$$PbO + H_2O \rightarrow PbO_2 + 2H^+ + 2e \quad (4.92)$$

The equilibrium values of the potential, corresponding to processes (4.91) and (4.92), are at a considerably more negative figure than the equilibrium potential of $PbO_2 \rightleftarrows PbSO_4$. Therefore, if anode corrosion occurs at potentials less than $\varphi_{PbO_2/PbSO_4}$ lead dioxide may be formed only in the shape of an intermediate product which converts on the oxide film-solution boundary surface to $PbSO_4$, and on the metal-film interface to PbO according to the scheme (4.90).

It was shown by Lander that the rate of corrosion, which is determined by the weight of lead oxidised (ΔP_1) during a determined time of polarisation at a given potential $\varphi < \varphi_{PbO_2/PbSO_4}$, is a linear function of the square of the activity of water, and $\lg \Delta P_1$ a linear function of the potential. These relationships are considered by Lander[96]) as evidence of the intermediate formation of $Pb(OH)_2$ according to the equation of reaction (4.87).

The potentio-static study of the anodic corrosion of lead, and also of lead-antimony (6.5% Sb) and lead-antimony-silver alloys (6.5% Sb + 0.5% Ag), carried out by us[98]) showed that the rate of corrosion decreases with an increase in the concentration of H_2SO_4. This relationship remains correct over a wide range of potentials (1.31-2.11V in relation to hydrogen zero) and concentrations of the solution (2.5-14.3N$\cdot H_2SO_4$).

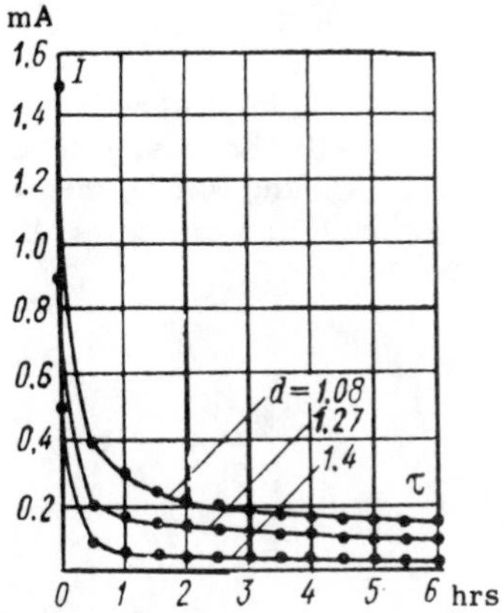

Fig. 4.34 Change of current I in time with potentio-static polarisation of the alloy Pb + 6.5% Sb, φ = 0.7V (in relation to Hg/Hg_2SO_4); d - densities of H_2SO_4 solutions.

In fig.4.34 typical graphs of the change of current in time with potential $\varphi < \varphi_{PbO_2/PbSO_4}$ are shown. At the beginning of potentiostatic polarisation a sharp fall in current I is observed. Then the rate of decrease of the current diminishes, and the dependence of the current on the time gradually approaches the linear. It can be assumed that the initial fall in current characterises the formation of $PbSO_4$ crystals and their rapid spread over the surface of the electrode. The further process obviously consists in gradual oxidation of the metal in the pores of the sulphate film. As follows from fig. 4.34, with a rise in the concentration of H_2SO_4 there is a decrease both in the current values and in the graph slope (I, τ) which is established as a result of fairly long polarisation. This means that increasing the concentration of the acid leads to a decrease in the rate of anodic oxidation of the metal and an increase in the density of the passivating sulphate film[98]).

The character of the graphs (I, τ) taken at values of potentials exceeding $\varphi_{PbO_2/PbSO_4}$ becomes considerably complicated, since along with the process of oxidation of the metal liberation of oxygen takes place at these potentials. The rate of the first process decreases in time owing to the decrease in the area of the unoxidised surface of the electrode, while the rate of liberation of oxygen increases since the surface of lead dioxide on which this process occurs increases. At fairly high anode potentials the current is basically characterised by the rate of liberation of oxygen. In this case (fig. 4.35) a decrease in the concentration of H_2SO_4 leads to a sharp increase in the slope of the graph (I, τ), which, of course, is evidence of the formation on the electrode in dilute acid solutions of quite a loose lead dioxide film with a rapidly increasing value of the active surface. If we assume that anodic corrosion occurs according to reactions of the type (4.87), (4.91) and (4.92), then the amount of electricity (Q) expended on the oxidation of the metal during the time t can be written in the form form

$$Q = \left[K_1 \exp\left(\frac{\beta_1 z_1 F\varphi}{RT}\right)\int_0^t \sigma_1 d\tau + K_2 \exp\left(\frac{\beta_2 z_2 F\varphi}{RT}\right)\int_0^t \sigma_2 d\tau\right] a^2_{H_2O} + \gamma_0 q_0 \tag{4.93}$$

where K_1 and K_2 are the specific rates and β_1 and β_2 the coefficients of transfer of the processes of oxidation of Pb and PbO into PbO_2 respectively, σ_1 and σ_2 the parts of the electrode on which processes of the type (4.87) and (4.91) occur, z_1 and z_2 the number of electrons participating in the electro-chemical stages limiting the rate of these processes, q_o the amount of electricity expended in the time t on the liberation of oxygen, γ_O a coefficient showing what part of the oxygen causes oxidation of the electrode.

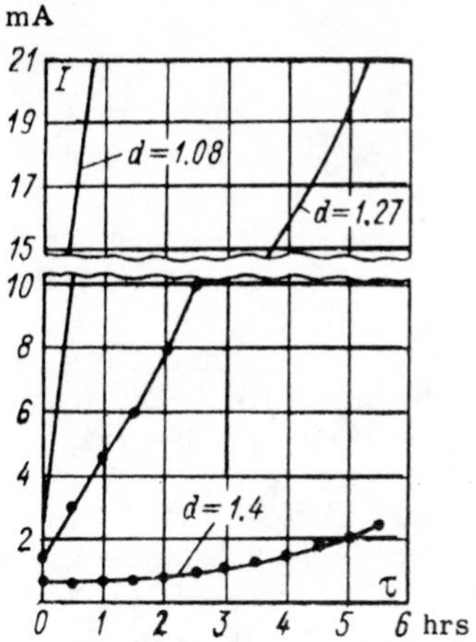

Fig.4.35 Change of current I in time with potentio-static polarisation of the alloy Pb + 6.5% Sb, $\varphi = 1.5V$ (in relation to Hg/Hg_2SO_4); d - densities of H_2SO_4 solutions.

From equation (4.93) it is clear that the value of Q which determines the rate of anodic corrosion with φ = const increases with an increase in α_{H_2O}, i.e. with a decrease in the concentration of H_2SO_4. This follows not only from the function $Q(\alpha_{H_2O})$, but also from the fact that, according to the data described above, a decrease in the concentration of H_2SO_4 leads to an increase in the porosity of the anode film, i.e. to an increase in the rate of change in time of σ_1 and σ_2, and also in the value of γ_O.

The mechanism of anodic corrosion of lead, based on the hypothesis of the essential role of the processes occurring in the pores of the oxide film at the metal-solution interface, received further development in refs.[62][99][101]. It is suggested that, along with reactions (4.87) and (4.90), at potentials $\varphi > 1.58V$ *) the subsequent occurrence

*) This value corresponds to the potential of the equilibrium $O_3 + 6H^+ + 6e \rightleftarrows 3H_2O$ ($\varphi^O = 1.51V$).

of the following processes is possible

$$H_2O \rightarrow O + 2H^+ + 2e \qquad (4.94)$$

$$PbO + O \rightarrow PbO_2 \qquad (4.95)$$

and also

$$(1 + y)PbO + yPbO_2 \rightarrow PbO_{y+1}, \quad (0.4 < y < 0.6) \qquad (4.96)$$

On the surface of the metal PbO (tetrag.), $Pb(OH)_2$ and α-PbO_2 are formed, and at the film interface with the solution a thin layer of β-PbO_2 appears as a result oxidation of $PbSO_4$. The formation of such compounds as PbO, $Pb(OH)_2$ and α-PbO_2 is explained by the low acidity in the pores of the anode film. The film of $PbSO_4$ or β-PbO_2 that originally appeared serves as a diaphragm carrying the positive charge. Such a film is penetrable for OH^- ions and H_2O molecules and does not let hydrogen ions through[102]). In the works of Pavlov, another mechanism is suggested for the alkalisation of the solution in the pores of the anode film[101]). This mechanism is based on taking account of the different mobility of ions of Pb^{2+} and H^+. Accelerated migration of H^+ ions into the thickness of the solution and the insufficient amount of sulphate ions in the pores of the film to maintain the electrical neutrality cause a dissociation of the water, i.e. an increase in the concentration of OH^- ions. The formation of α-PbO_2 can occur in the pores of the anode film according to the scheme

$$Pb + 2OH^- \rightarrow PbO + H_2O + 2e \qquad (4.97)$$

$$PbO + 2OH^- \rightarrow \alpha\text{-}PbO_2 + H_2O + 2e \qquad (4.98)$$

and the formation of intermediate oxides of the type PbO_{1+y} according to reaction

$$PbO + 2yOH^- \rightarrow PbO_{1+y} + yH_2O + 2ye \qquad (4.99)$$

The question of phase composition of the corrosion films will be considered in detail in the part concerning "The properties of oxide films forming in the process of anodic corrosion of lead alloys" (p. 231).

The influence of alloying additions on the anodic corrosion of lead and lead-antimony alloy

Work on the increasing of the corrosion resistance of the grids of the positive electrode is being carried out at the present time in several directions. Research is being carried out on new metals and alloys capable of replacing lead and its alloys. The possibilities are being studied of manufacturing grids from reinforced or metallised plastics, and also from metallo-ceramic compositions based on dispersion-hardened lead powder. Finally, research is being carried out on the alloying of lead and lead-antimony alloy with different additives. The method of alloying must be considered to have particularly good prospects.

The character of the influence of small additions of different elements on the anodic corrosion of lead up to the present time has been explained. This applies at any rate to elements that are fairly widely used in technology. Among the elements slowing down the rate of corrosion of lead and lead-antimony alloy are: Ag, Co, Tl, As; corrosion is intensified by alkaline metals and also Mg, Zn, Sb and Bi. A special case is calcium which, although it does not to any noticeable degree change the rate of corrosion of lead, nevertheless presents at the same time a definite interest, since the use of lead-calcium alloys substantially decreases self-discharge of the battery.

Alloys made up of silver, arsenic and calcium will be further examined in more detail, while special attention will be paid to lead-antimony alloys containing an addition of arsenic, since at the present time it is namely these alloys that constitute the basis of the production of mass-produced types of lead acid batteries in all the leading countries.

The mechanism of the influence of different additives on the corrosion resistance of lead and lead alloys can be quite different. There are, however, some general principles which make it possible to classify the alloying additives. Thus, in refs.[103][104] it was shown that the classification of small additions according to their effect on the rate of anodic corrosion of lead and its alloys can be carried out on the basis of the theory of modification. According to the hypotheses developed in these works, the alloying elements which do not show any influence on the structure of the alloy generally either do not change the rate of anodic oxidation of the alloy or cause intensification of corrosion. Additives/modifiers which régulate the process of crystallisation and cause marked dispersion of the grain dimension, as a rule also increase the corrosion resistance of the metal at the same time.

Such a link between the structure of the alloy and the corrosion resistance is especially characteristic for metals of which the corrosion occurs under the layer of oxide film. The essence of this link can be schematically explained in the following manner. Admixtures and additives which do not dissolve in crystals are concentrated on the boundary surface and form a so-called inter-crystalline layer (ICL). For a given amount of admixtures with a macro-crystalline ingot structure the ICL thickness is much greater than the thickness of the ICL in the dispersed sample (fig. 4.36). The special character of the bond of the atoms of the ICL makes it the most active zone in respect of the different physico-chemical processes. It can be assumed that the greater the thickness of the ICL, the more intensively corrosion should occur in it. Dispersion, leading to a decrease in thickness of the ICL with other conditions being equal, should increase the corrosion resistance of the metal.

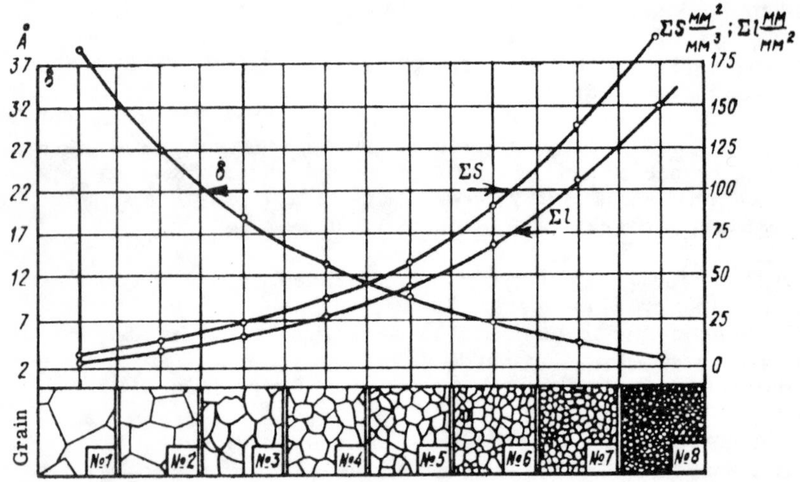

Fig. 4.36 Dependence of the thickness of the inter-crystalline layer δ, the extent of the boundaries Σl and the specific grain surface ΣS on the structure of the metal.

For metals protected by passivating films from the products of corrosion, this action can be explained in the following manner. Metal with macro-crystalline structure, when immersed in a corrosive medium, will decompose intensely as a result of the fact that the products of the corrosion of the mono-crystals are not capable of covering the whole surface of the metal, including also the ICL. The latter deteriorates under the influence of the medium, due to which the link between the crystals is weakened and there follows deterioration of the polycrystalline body. Metal with fine-crystalline structure decomposes more slowly since the corrosion products in this instance can practically completely cover the ICL which has a negligible thickness, causing passivation of the metal.

An increase in dispersibility of the structure thus ensures the formation of a denser protective film. Consequently, depending on the magnitude of the crystals there can be formed on one and the same metal either a porous film, which is not capable of markedly hindering corrosion, or a dense protective film. These ideas were confirmed in the selection and study of the modifiers of crystallisation of lead and lead-antimony alloy. In table 4.7 data are quoted which show that additions of Ag, Te, S and Ca which disperse the structure of the lead, also slow down its corrosion. Additions of Li, Na, K, Sn, Bi, Zn and Mg which show no marked effect on the course of crystallisation of lead, are either harmful or useless.

Table 4.7: Values of Σl and relative corrosion of lead alloys

Nature of alloying addition	-	Sn	Na	Bi	Li	K	Zn	Mg	Ca	S	Ag	Te
Σl mm	4.0	2.0	2.3	2.5	2.8	4.7	7.2	11.6	30.2	33.5	38.6	41.9
Relative corrosion %	100	137	109	122	104	111	116	$\gg$100	75	73	60	87

As a parameter characterising the structure, the total extent of the grain boundaries Σl corresponding to $1 mm^2$ of section was selected. This value was determined by S A Saltykov's method of arbitrary secants[108]). The rate of corrosion was determined by the weight method, with the rate of corrosion of pure lead being taken as 100%. The influence of some elements on the structure of the lead is shown in fig. 4.37.

Dispersion, leading to the formation of a compact and not very porous film, is shown to be an important factor causing an increase in corrosion resistance of the alloy. The latter can also be increased by means of additives which form chemically inert phases with the ICL which are distinguished by increased corrosion resistance in a given corrosive medium. The greatest ingot consolidation must be expected in those cases where the element added to the lead serves as a modifier of the structure and at the same time forms a chemically inert phase with the ICL. The modification theory thus makes it possible to predict the influence of one or another of the additives on the rate of corrosion.

The protective properties of oxide films obtained in anodic polarisation of samples of lead alloys can be to a known degree characterised by the dimensions of the particles forming the anode film. Obviously, the smaller the average size of these particles, the greater the density of the film, and also its capacity to protect the metal from further

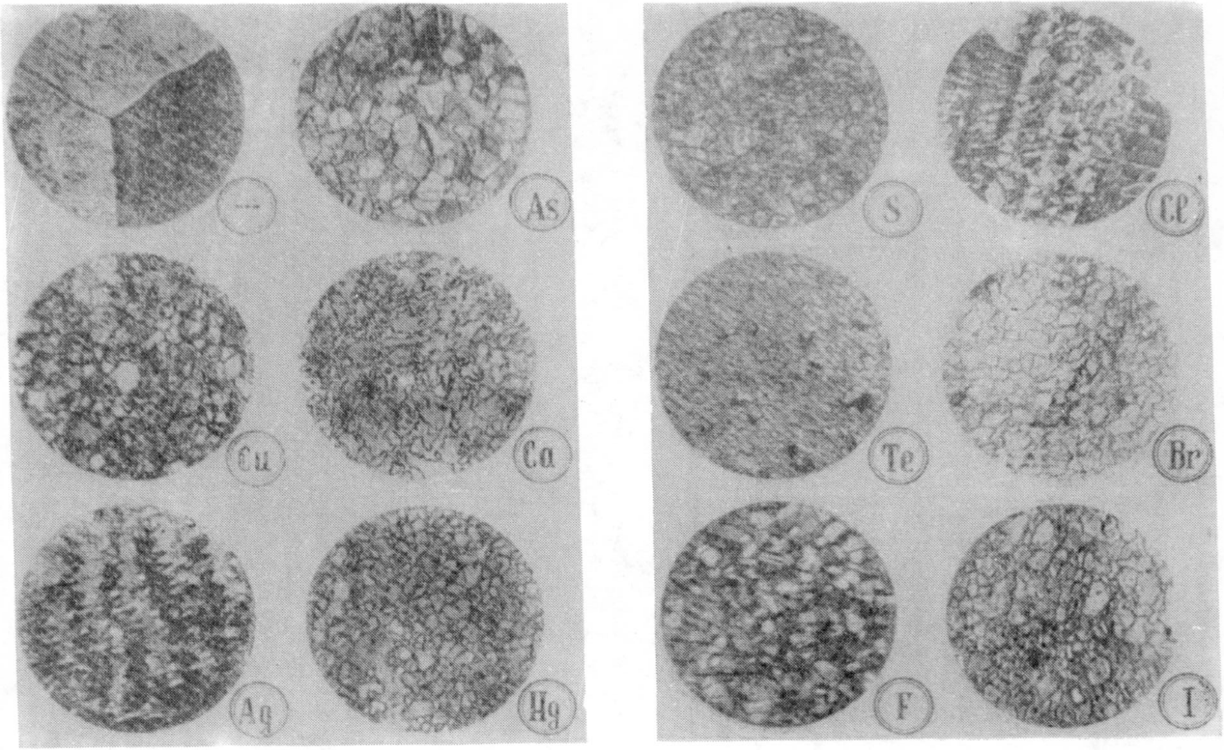

Fig. 4.37 Micro-photographs of sections of lead alloyed with different elements.

oxidation. As is shown by a comparison of the electron microscope photographs obtained at x 6000 magnification, the introduction of silver into a lead-antimony alloy causes considerable comminution of the particles composing the anode film (fig. 4.38). Obviously, this phenomenon is directly linked with the dispersing influence of the silver on the structure of the alloy.

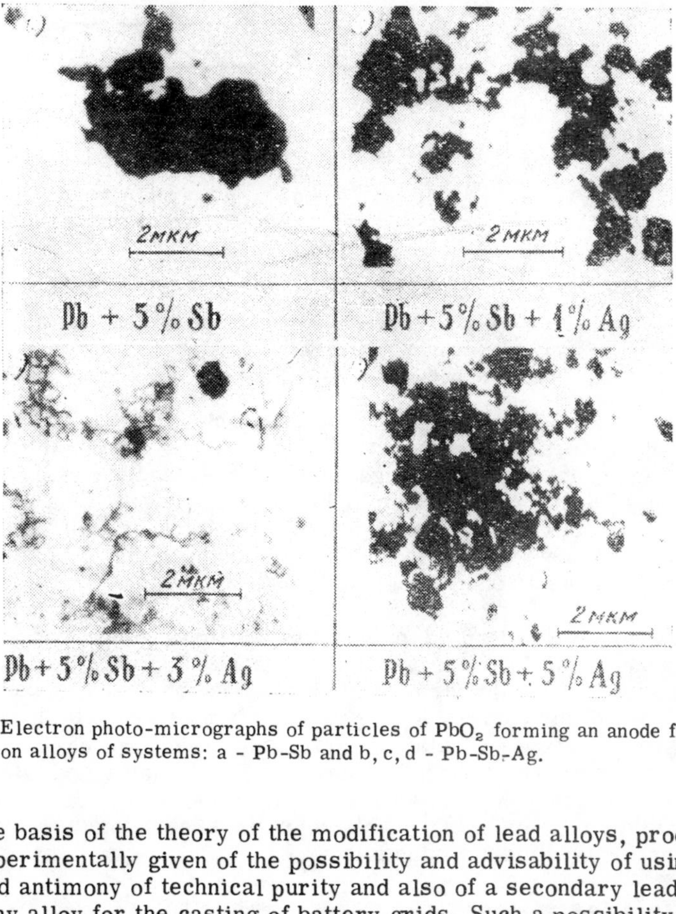

Fig. 4.38 Electron photo-micrographs of particles of PbO_2 forming an anode film on alloys of systems: a - Pb-Sb and b, c, d - Pb-Sb-Ag.

On the basis of the theory of the modification of lead alloys, proof was experimentally given of the possibility and advisability of using lead and antimony of technical purity and also of a secondary lead-antimony alloy for the casting of battery grids. Such a possibility is the result of the combined action on the physico-chemical properties of the alloy of other elements encountered in the lead and antimony. The action of the harmful additions (Mg, Zn, Bi etc.) is neutralised by the action of the useful additions (Ag, As, S, Ca, Co), the content of which is always somewhat greater in low-quality metals. The passivating influence of an Ag addition on the corrosion of an alloy containing added Zn, Mg and Bi is shown in fig. 4.39.

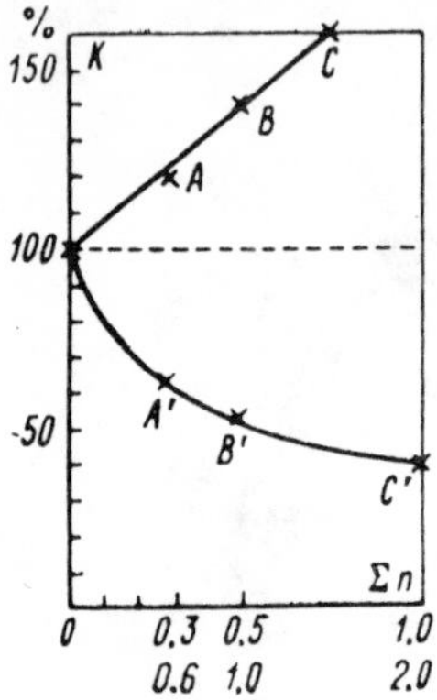

Points on the graphs	Added to the series alloy 6%				Σn
	Bi	Zn	Mg	Ag	
A	0.1	0.1	0.1	-	0.3
B	0.17	0.17	0.17	-	0.5
C	0.33	0.33	0.33	-	1.0
A'	0.1	0.1	0.1	0.3	0.6
B'	0.17	0.17	0.17	0.5	1.0
C'	0.33	0.33	0.33	1.0	2.0

Fig. 4.39 The passivating effect of silver additions on the corrosion of the alloy containing admixtures of Zn, Mg and Bi.

The realisation of the results of the research described has considerably broadened the raw material basis of our home battery industry, and enabled great savings of resources, since technical metals are 15-20% cheaper than higher quality metals. Finally, with the use of effective modifiers (Ag, As, Co, Ca, S etc.) alloys were evolved which possessed increased corrosion resistance. Some of these alloys have already found application in practice.

Let us note that according to the views developed in the works of G Z Kiryakov and Yu D Dunayev and summarised in ref.[90]), the anticorrosion effect of alloying metals is explained basically by the redistribution of the current under the oxide film as a result of the heterogeneity of the lead alloys. The conditions for increasing corrosion resistance under the influence of one or another of the alloying elements from this point of view is high corrosion resistance of the additive, a low oxygen overvoltage on the alloying metal and a considerable electrical conductivity.

Lead alloys compounded with arsenic

a) Physico-mechanical and technological parameters: The grids of the positive electrode experience considerable mechanical loads. The oxide film forming on the surface of the grid exerts pressure on the corroding metal, causing its deformation. In the process of preparation of the plates (coating, forming, cutting etc.) the grids also experience mechanical stresses. As a result of this an alloy intended for manufacture of the grids should possess a definite mechanical strength, which can be characterised by the values of breaking load σ_B and hardness H_B. A study of these parameters for a number of alloys showed that the addition of arsenic, both to lead and also to lead-antimony alloy, in the quantity of a few tenths of a percent increases the breaking strength and hardness (fig. 4.40).

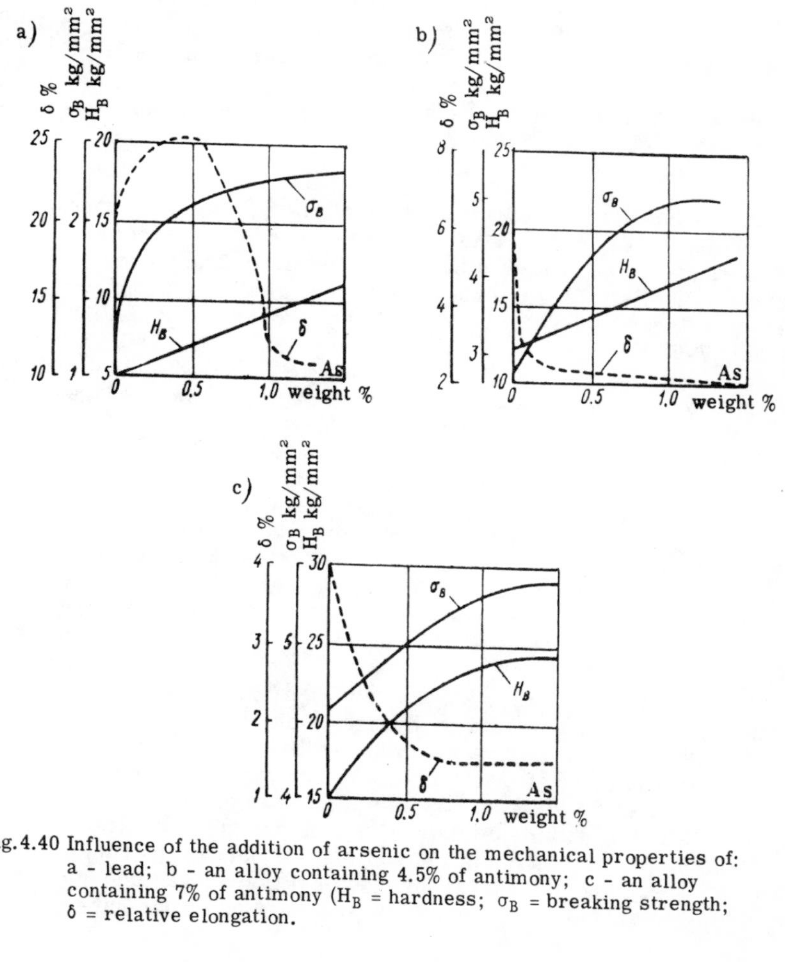

Fig.4.40 Influence of the addition of arsenic on the mechanical properties of: a - lead; b - an alloy containing 4.5% of antimony; c - an alloy containing 7% of antimony (H_B = hardness; σ_B = breaking strength; δ = relative elongation.

As can be seen from fig. 4.40, the addition of even ~0.1% As to an alloy containing 4.5% Sb makes this alloy comparable in mechanical properties with a normal alloy (6.5% Sb). This circumstance opens up the possibility of considerable reduction in the consumption of antimony in the casting of battery grids.

Considerable influence on the strength characteristics of arsenical alloys is shown by the temperature conditions of the casting; the temperature of the metal t_M and of the mould t_ϕ and also the conditions of cooling of the castings. In a study of the strength and hardness of Pb-Sb-As alloys the results were obtained which are quoted in fig. 4.41. An analysis of these data shows that the air-cooled alloys obtained are less strong than those quenched in water, but on the other hand, they are less subject to the formation of cracks. The optimum condition ensuring a sufficiently high hardness and the absence of cracks is some intermediate type of cooling, e.g. blowing with air. Here it is desirable to maintain the temperature of the mould around 150°C.

The data obtained are evidence of the fact that alloys compounded with arsenic are subject to faster dispersion hardening, especially if the castings are subjected to quenching in water. The mechanical properties of alloys with 4-6% of antimony and 0.1-0.2% of arsenic are comparable with the mechanical properties of an alloy containing 7-8% Sb.

The conditions of casting and the method of cooling show a marked influence also on such an important characteristic, in respect of technology, as the brittleness of grids manufactured from arsenical alloys[107]). In studying this question, the absence of cracks or fractures with bending at the roller, was taken as a criterion of the suitability of grids. Let us note that such an evaluation of the suitability of the grids is conditional, since in practice grids are not subjected to such severe testing either in the battery or in the process of production. Nevertheless, testing of this sort is used in the determination of the brittleness of a number of materials.

The results of the tests show that the addition of As to 6% Pb-Sb alloy at all casting temperature conditions studied and with slow cooling does not lead to a deterioration in the quality of the castings. This conclusion is correct also for 8% lead-antimony alloy only if the As content does not exceed 0.2%. An alloy with 4% of antimony makes it possible to obtain quality castings only with the addition to it of ~0.3% As. Rapid cooling of the castings substantially changes the properties of the grids cast from arsenical alloys, particularly if the tests are carried out after a day's keeping. The resistance of

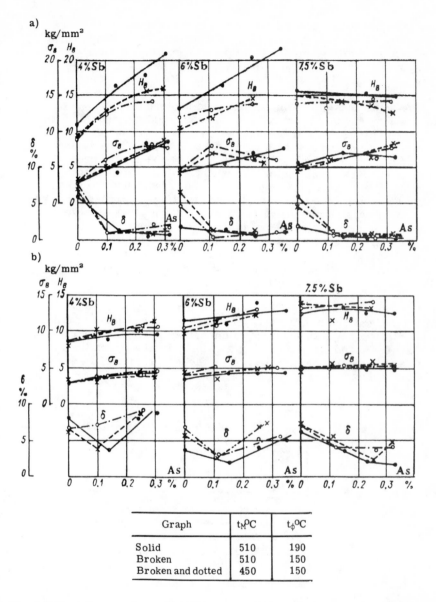

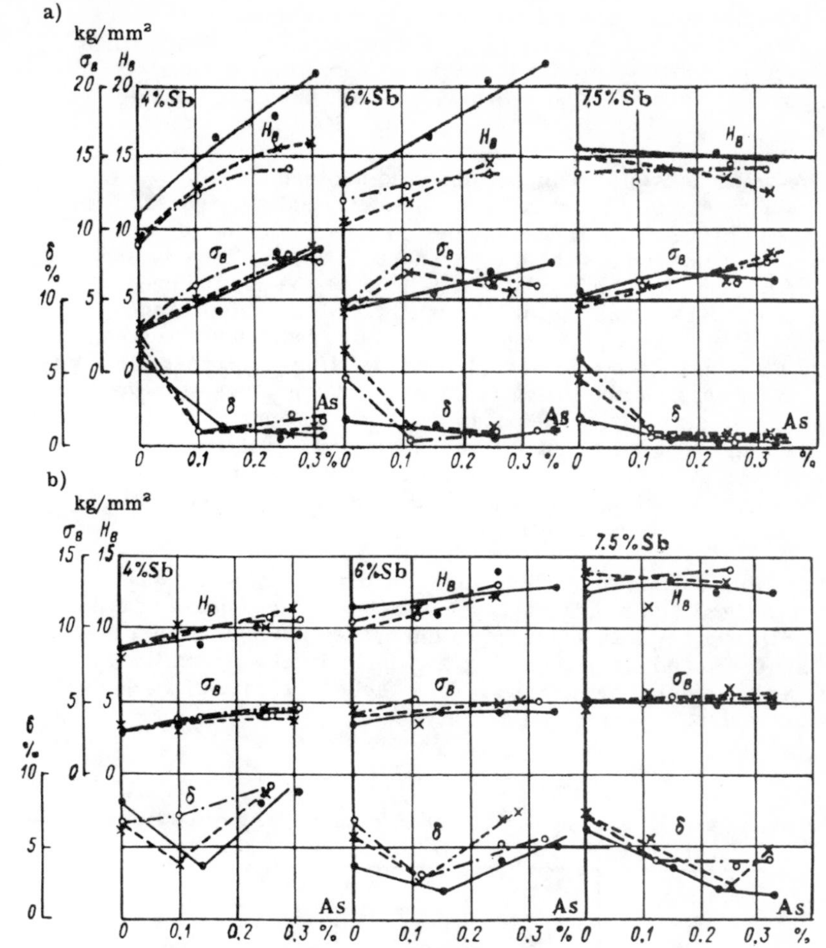

Graph	t_M°C	t_ϕ°C
Solid	510	190
Broken	510	150
Broken and dotted	450	150

Fig. 4.41 The influence of arsenic additions and of the conditions of casting on the mechanical properties of lead-antimony alloys quenched in water (a) and cooled in air (b)

the samples to bending is here decreased but the hardness is increased. Consequently alloying with arsenic and rapid cooling can be used in industry only for those parts from which a high level of hardness is required, and which will not be subjected to bending.

The brittleness of arsenical alloys and the tendency to the formation of cracks in the castings can be substantially decreased by means of proper selection of the design of the grid and of the foundry mould, and also by the introduction into the composition of the alloy of small additions which improve the casting properties of these alloys. Thus, it was established that the presence of thin members in the grid, together with thick frames and vertical members leads to uneven rate of cooling of the different parts of the casting, to uneven distribution of temperature and as a result to the appearance of residual internal tensions which are a cause of defects originating from deformation (crack formation, buckling etc.). Going over to flashless grids and the use of differential rates of cooling of the casting moulds will undoubtedly cause a decrease in the wastage due to cracks and brittleness.

According to data in the literature, the addition of small quantities of Cu and Sn to arsenious alloys also produces quality castings. The influence of these additives on the properties of an alloy containing 6% Sb and 0.2% As was studied using different conditions of casting and cooling of the grids. The results of the tests are quoted in table 4.8.

Table 4.8: Influence of the composition of the alloy and the casting conditions on the brittleness of battery grids

Composition of the alloy	Method of cooling	Suitability of grids		
		$t_\Phi = 150^oC$	$t_\Phi = 170^oC$	$t_\Phi = 190^oC$
Pb + 6% Sb	Air	100	100	-
	Water	100	90	-
Pb + 6% Sb + 0.2% As	Air	90	90	-
	Water	30	30	-
Pb + 6% Sb + 0.2% As + + 0.09% Cu	Air	100	90	100
	Water	90	70	40
Pb + 6% Sb + 0.2% As + + 0.05% Sn	Air	100	100	90
	Water	90	0	0

As can be seen from the data of table 4.8, the introduction of arsenic does not have much effect on the quality of the grids cooled in air, but the faster cooling of them in cold water sharply reduces the percentage of suitable grids. These data are in close conformity with the results of the testing of samples cast in definite temperature conditions but tested over a different period: starting from 3 hours after casting and up to 1-3 days. In the first case the introduction of arsenic has little influence on the quality of the grids, but already in the following day the introduction of arsenic leads to a substantial decrease in the quality of the grids.

From the same data the positive influence of a fourth component can be seen, especially copper, which decreases the brittleness of the grids and increases the percentage of their suitability. Additions would appear to broaden the temperature range in casting. However, with considerable overheating of the mould (~190°C) the brittleness of the grids (especially with subsequent sudden cooling) remains high, even with the presence of added copper.

With the aim of explaining the influence of the fourth component on the quality of the grids, a study was made of the effect of a number of alloying additions on other mechanical properties of arsenical alloys (fig.4.42). As can be seen from fig. 4.42, the influence of the fourth component was more marked on the hardened samples. With the introduction of copper and tin, the hardness of the alloy increases at the first, which is in conformity with data from literature.

Let us look at the influence of additions on the breaking strength and the relative elongation. Thanks to the presence of a fourth component, arsenical alloys approximate in these characteristics to antimony-free ones, i.e. they become more plastic, which obviously also explains the positive influence of the additions on the brittleness of the grids cast from arsenical alloys.

Among the measures aimed at decreasing the brittleness, which is characteristic of arsenic-containing alloys, an important place is taken by thermal treatment of the castings. It is well known that in alloys of the Pb-Sb system of hypoeutectic composition, thanks to the different solubility of antimony at different temperatures, decomposition of the solid solution occurs and a separation of the antimony into a finely dispersed state, which is the reason for dispersion hardening of the alloys. This process can be speeded up by keeping the alloys at high temperatures. In selection of the conditions of heat treatment of arsenic-containing alloys the annealing temperature varied within the limits 160-200°C, the time of annealing was varied from 1 to 12 hours. Grids were annealed which had been quen-

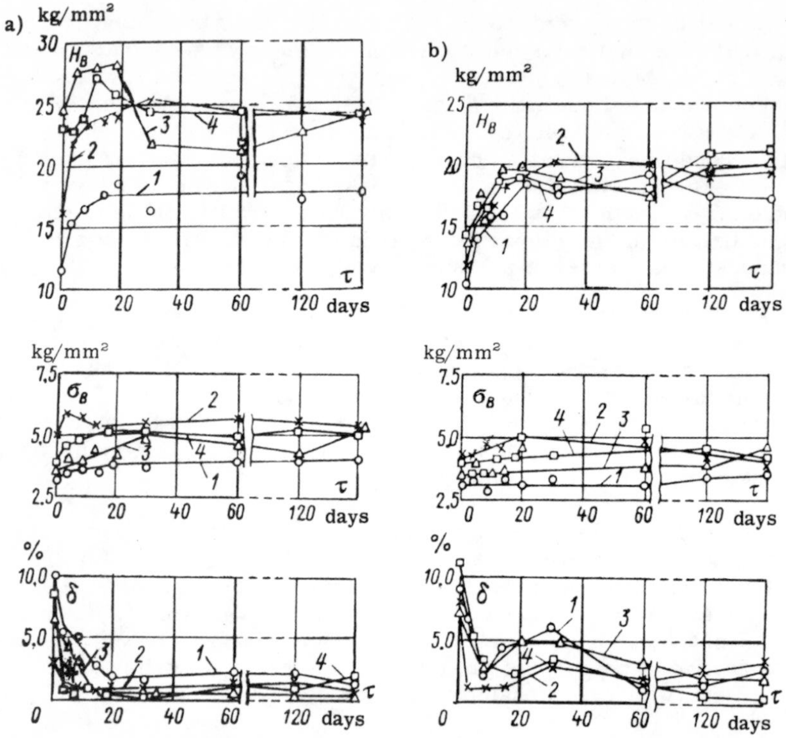

Fig.4.42 Influence of the fourth component on the properties of an arsenic-containing alloy: a) with hardening of the castings in water; b) with cooling of the castings in air.
1 (O) - Pb-Sb; 2 (X) - Pb-Sb-As; 3 (Δ) - Pb-Sb-As-Cu; 4 (□) - Pb-Sb-As-Sn.

ched in cold water and also cooled in air after casting. The annealing was carried out for up to a week after casting. In addition, part of the grids were annealed immediately after extraction from the mould. This was done with the aim of maintaining the supply of heat which the grid has after coming out of the mould and shortening the duration of annealing. It was established that in all the cases considered the annealing increases the percentage of suitability of the grids and makes them more plastic. The brittleness of the grids disappears and, as observations showed, in the course of a week it does not appear again. Even the most brittle (hardened) grids, having lain for a week before annealing, break easily in the bend test but do not break after annealing. In this case it is true that longer annealing is necessary. The optimum conditions of annealing can be reckoned to be approximately the following: 3 hours at 180-190°C and 4-6 hours at 150-160°C. With the annealing of grids that had lain a week after casting, annealing at 180°C over a period of 5-6 hours was necessary. If we anneal grids immediately after removal from the mould, then 15-30 minutes is sufficient.

The positive influence of annealing in reducing brittleness of grids is in conformity with the influence of annealing on other mechanical properties of the alloy. Annealed castings have a lower hardness and breaking strength, but a greater relative elongation. In annealed alloys these properties are practically unchanged with time, while in the unannealed alloys substantial changes in the properties are observed, especially in the first 5-6 days.

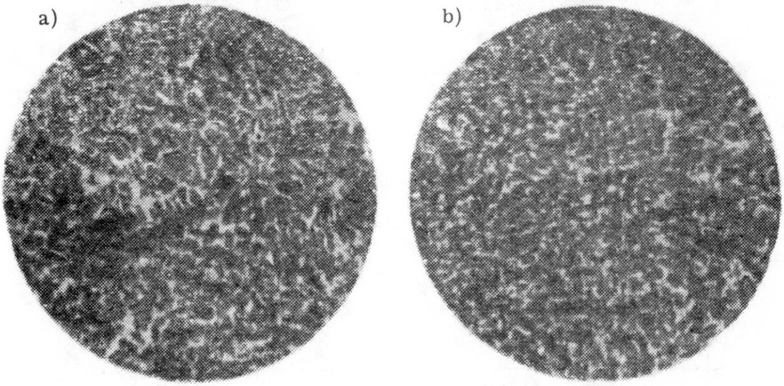

Fig.4.43 Micro-structure of a lead-antimony-arsenic alloy (magn. x300): a) unannealed sample; b) after undergoing annealing for 6 hrs at 180°C).

For an explanation of the nature of these differences a micro-structural analysis was carried out on annealed and unannealed samples, and this showed that after annealing the micro-structure does not change (fig. 4.43). The eutectics (the light parts on the section) in both cases have a banded structure and there is no concentration of the antimony phase after the annealing. The fact that the annealed samples do not change their properties with time is evidence of the completion of the processes of ageing, which at room temperature go on for a few days, but at annealing temperature for a few hours. The increase in hardness, which is characteristic of the processes of ageing, is not observed in this case, on the annealed samples, owing to the appearance of micro-segregations. The latter, which cause weakening of the alloy, at the same time show no noticeable influence on its structure. Thus, it was established that the suggested conditions of annealing ensures the necessary change in the mechanical properties of the alloy, whilst not taking the process as far as recrystallisation and change of temperature.

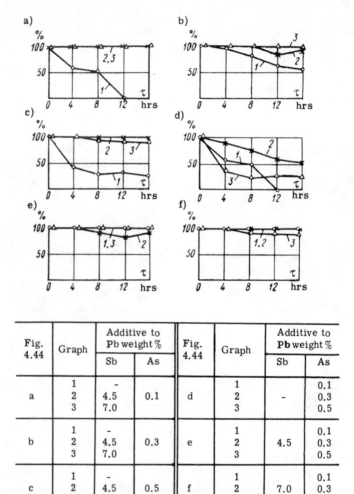

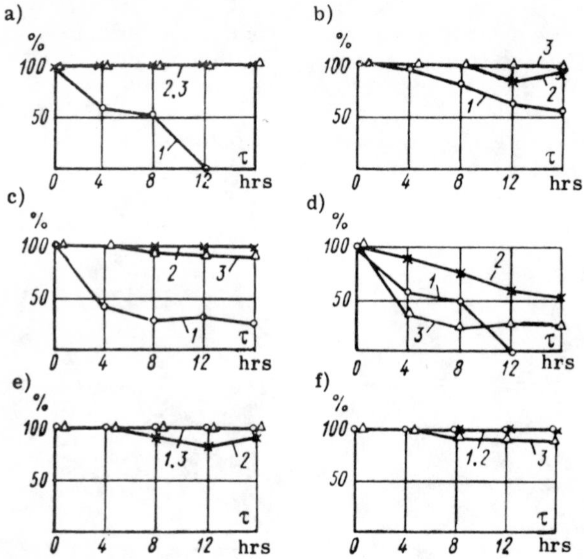

Fig. 4.44	Graph	Additive to Pb weight %		Fig. 4.44	Graph	Additive to Pb weight %	
		Sb	As			Sb	As
a	1 2 3	- 4.5 7.0	0.1	d	1 2 3	-	0.1 0.3 0.5
b	1 2 3	- 4.5 7.0	0.3	e	1 2 3	4.5	0.1 0.3 0.5
c	1 2 3	- 4.5 7.0	0.5	f	1 2 3	7.0	0.1 0.3 0.5

Fig.4.44 Change of concentration of arsenic in lead and in alloy in the process of heating at a temperature of 500 ± 15°C.

In work with arsenic-containing alloys an essentially important factor is the constancy of the composition of the alloy, since arsenic is subject to considerable melting loss. In connection with this, a study was made of its rate of burning up in an alloy with lead and a production alloy. For this purpose over a period of two shifts (16 hrs) samples of the alloy were analysed every 2 hrs. The data obtained are shown in fig. 4.44. Arsenic is characterised by a low temperature of sublimation and a high affinity for oxygen. Therefore it burns out of an alloy with lead fairly quickly. However, the composition of Pb-Sb-As alloys remains constant in time. This is caused, of course, by a decrease in the volatility of the arsenic as a result of the action of the antimony.

b) Corrosion properties: The first work of the authors of this book on the study of the influence of arsenic additions on anodic corrosion of lead was undertaken in the fifties. It was shown that arsenic belongs to the number of effective modifiers of lead and of lead-antimony alloys, and therefore, in principle, can exhibit a favourable influence on the corrosion behaviour of battery grids. However, at the same time, owing to the considerable scarcity and high cost of arsenic its use was obviously uneconomic; therefore, this research did not receive any further support.

The authors returned to a study of arsenic-containing alloys in the period when these alloys had already found practical application in the batteries of leading foreign firms and when a new, more economical method of introducing arsenic into battery alloys was found.

The first research of this period concerned explaining the corrosion resistance of the new alloys and a study of the kinetics of separation of gases on them. It was shown that lead and the production alloy corrode unevenly with long anodic polarisation. The surface of the samples decomposes strongly at definite places, as a result of which deep pits and cracks appear. Such intercrystallite character of the corrosion often is a basic reason for decomposition of the sample even with comparatively small total weight losses.

Arsenic-containing alloys corrode quite evenly[108]), although the rate of corrosion of these alloys, determined by the weight method, hardly differs at all from the rate of corrosion of the production lead-antimony alloy. The presence of arsenic in the alloy does not cause any noticeable changes in the anode potential of the sample either, nor in the phase composition of the oxide film. The reason for the anti-corrosion effect of arsenic in a battery is mainly the already mentioned evenness of the progress of the corrosion process. In the opinion of Mao and Larson[109]), such a character of the corrosion of arsenic-containing alloys is explained by the fact that the arsenic weakens the dendrite structure of the lead-antimony alloy and decreases the effect of the acid on the β-phase, which is rich in antimony. Similar observations were also made in refs.[106-108]).

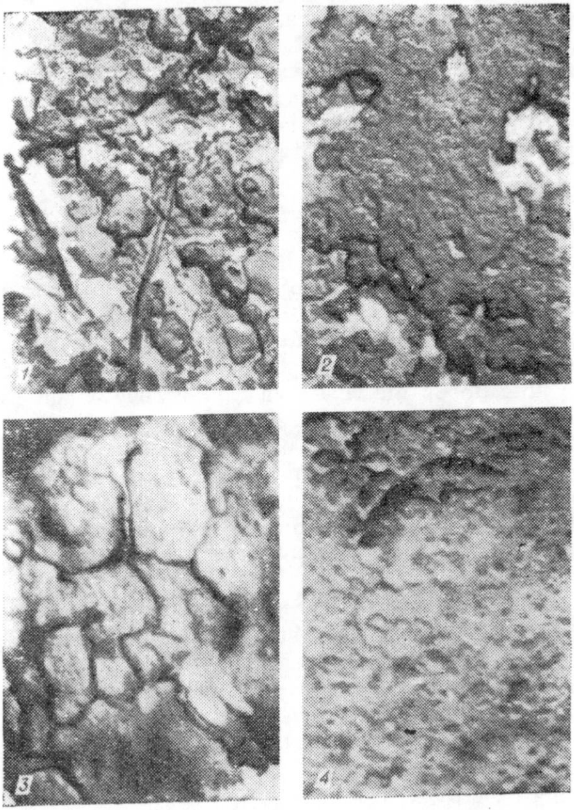

Fig.4.45 Structure of anode film formed at different potentials.
1 and 2) φ = 1.5V (nve); 3 and 4) φ 1 2.16V; 1 and 3) alloy without As; 2 and 4) alloy with As.

The anode films which formed on the experimental and on the production alloy were investigated with an electron microscope. Part of the photographs is shown in fig. 4.45. From the data obtained it follows that on electrodes of arsenic-containing alloy (2, 4) an anode film is obtained which is more dispersed and is distributed more evenly than on electrodes of alloys without arsenic (1, 3). This is in close conformity with the more even character of the corrosion of arsenic-containing alloys mentioned above. The character of the corrosion and the observed structure of the anode film are in their turn closely connected with the structure of the alloy, with the modifying influence of the arsenic.

Another important reason for the increased service life of grids of arsenic-containing alloy with the same (in comparison with production alloys) rate of anodic oxidation is the high mechanical strength (creep resistance) of this alloy, since corrosion of the grids is caused by their deformation. As will be shown below, research on the corrosion of alloys that are under mechanical stress confirmed the quite substantial role of this factor. The favourable influence of the additive arsenic on the corrosion behaviour of grids of the positive electrode obtained numerous experimental confirmations. Let us look at a few examples.

Production and experimental batteries with an electrolyte of density 1.28 were put on continuous charge at a current of 9A (2.35A/dm^2), for a period of one month. Tests showed that the production batteries had markedly corroded positive grids, while the grids of the experimental batteries remained almost complete.

In another series of experiments the control and the experimental batteries were tested both by the method of 30-day continuous polarisation and also by the method of "the live test". In both cases it was found that the reason for the control batteries becoming non-operational was the marked corrosion of the grids of the positive electrode, but the grids in the experimental batteries, which were cast from an arsenic-containing alloy, held out for 30% more cycles.

Batteries intended for different purposes (car, tractor, carriage lighting, stationary installations, etc.), assembled with grids of production lead-antimony alloy and of an alloy also containing arsenic, were bench tested by different methods, and also under conditions of use. As the results of these tests showed (table 4.9) the use of arsenic-containing alloy causes a quite substantial increase in the service life of all batteries, with this increase attaining 60-70% for different types of batteries.

The optimum concentration of arsenic in the alloy depends on the content of antimony in it. In ref.[109]) 0.10-0.14% As is recommended for a 4.5% Pb-Sb alloy, whilst 0.15-0.19% As is recommended for 7% Pb-Sb alloy. These recommendations are made with the idea of improving the dendrite structure of the alloy. However, the idea of effective or optimum concentration of arsenic in the alloy must not be limited by this one effect alone, since for industrial application of the alloy the techno-

Table 4.9: Dependence of service life of lead acid batteries on composition of the alloy for manufacture of grids

Type of batteries	Method of testing	Service life of batteries (cycles)		Increase in service life %
		Control (production alloy)	Experimental (alloy with addition of As)	
6ST-45	Live test	440	530	20
6ST-54	" "	409	483	18
6ST-81	" "	358	458	28
3ST-70	" "	366	441	20
3ST-70	" "	270	335	24
12ST-70	Cycling	110	145	32
6ST-140	" "	104	164	58
6ST-140	" "	130	209	60
6ST-128	" "	99	148	50
3TST-135	Live test	362	508	40
VNC-$\left(\frac{450}{500}\right)$	" "	210	360	70
SN-(7mm)	" "	1150	1600	40
SN-(5mm)	" "	520	730	40
6TST-120	Overcharge according to MEK	7 periods	11 periods	57
6ST-54	In conditions of utilisation	71.7thous. km	94.1thous. km.	31

logical properties of the alloy must also be taken into account. For this reason, the concentrations recommended by Mao and Larson differ somewhat from those which were made in our investigations.

According to our data the effective concentration of arsenic should be increased in proportion to the decrease in the antimony content in the alloy. Thus, if for an alloy with 5-6% of antimony the recommended concentration of arsenic amounts to 0.1-0.2%, then for a low-antimony alloy it should attain 0.15-0.3%.

c) Technico-economic aspects of the use of arsenical alloys: Industrial use of arsenical alloys in the production of lead acid batteries results in a positive solution to a number of problems, among which the most important are: increasing the service life of batteries and increasing their specific electrical characteristics. As has already been mentioned, the use of arsenic-containing alloys led to a real increase in the service life of starter batteries by 25-30% and of some other types of batteries by 60-70%. In connection with the strengthening of the grids of the positive electrode there was a steep drop in the number of cases where the battery became non-operational through corrosion of the grids. In the majority of cases, the service life of batteries with grids of Pb-Sb-As alloy is limited by the shedding of the active mass of the electrode. Therefore, what is of primary importance is the task of strengthening the active mass which, as has already been mentioned, can be solved by means of the introduction of fluorinated plastic, of fibrous substances, and the use of an electrolyte containing H_3PO_4 and $CoSO_4$. Experimental data existing at the present time show that the realisation of the technical means mentioned makes it possible to increase the service life of starter batteries to 400-600 cycles, and the service life of traction batteries with covered coated plates or with plates of tubular construction can be brought up to 1500-2000 cycles.

Not less important is the role of arsenic-containing alloys in improving the specific electrical characteristics of lead acid batteries. Experience of the work of many foreign firms may serve as proof of this, since as a result of using arsenic-containing alloys they have achieved greater successes in the modernisation of starter batteries which caused an increase in their specific characteristics and an increase in their service life.

As is shown by existing experimental data, redesign of starter batteries of our own home industry in connection with the use of arsenic-containing alloys in them will ensure the achievement of a specific energy of the order of 40A.hr/kg. This is dependent on the condition that this redesign covers not only a decrease in the thickness of the plates but also includes such important technical measures as the realisation in the new batteries of a method of joining the elements through monobloc bulkheads and the use of monoblocs of current polymers, e.g. polypropylene. Taking into account the scale of production of starter batteries in the U.S.S.R. and the prospects of its further development, it is hard to overestimate the value of these technical solutions.

A no less important question is the increasing of the profitability of the production of battery alloy compounded with arsenic. In arriving at the method of obtaining this alloy, the use of elementary arsenic was rejected, since this method inevitably would lead to a quite substantial increase in the cost of the alloy. A method was perfected, which is new in principle, for obtaining an arsenic-containing alloy, at the basis of which lies the use of arsenic contained in the by-products of lead factories. According to the method proposed, the initial materials (converter dust, secondary lead dust etc.) are mixed with a reducing agent and granulated fuming slag, and then melted at 800-1250°C. Coal and charcoal, coke, fuel oil etc. can be used as a reducing agent. The lead is reduced both by solid carbon and by carbon monoxide in proportion to the heating of the charge. The reduced lead forms numerous drops over the whole section of the charge, which causes the best contact of the lead and arsenic. The metallic lead dissolves the arsenic and flows down in the form of a lead-arsenic foundry alloy. After a number of improvements this method made it possible to obtain 7-10% foundry alloy, the cost of which is comparable with the cost of lead, and consequently does not cause an increase in the cost of the production alloy.

A further improvement in the method of obtaining an arsenic-containing alloy for the needs of the battery industry was the ending of its manufacture at each battery factory and the going over to centralised manufacture of the alloy at a specialised plant. This involved adding a calculated quantity of the lead-arsenic foundry alloy and antimony to the liquid secondary alloy ready for casting. This procedure for manufacturing the alloy is in current use. Finally, it is necessary, in the long term, also to solve the question of the use of the arsenic contained in rough antimony, which at present is removed in obtaining metallic antimony. A new technology is proposed, permitting the retention of this arsenic in the antimony and consequently cutting down the consumption of lead-arsenic foundry alloy in the manufacture of the battery alloy.

Lead alloys compounded with silver

Among the anti-corrosion alloying additives studied up to the present time, silver is worthy of particular attention. The influence of silver on the corrosion behaviour of lead alloys has been the subject of study of many researchers. Alloys compounded with silver find practical application as insoluble anodes and are also used for the manufacture of grids of the positive electrode of some types of lead acid batteries.

It was established that silver substantially increases the corrosion resistance of lead-antimony alloy even at comparatively low concentrations of this metal (~0.1%)[110-111]. Addition of silver considerably disperses the structure of the lead and of lead-antimony alloy and increases the compactness of the lead dioxide film. The papers [112][113] are devoted to a systematic study of the influence of silver (over a wide range of its concentration) on the anodic behaviour of lead and lead-antimony alloy. The basic results obtained by us in these works lead to the following:

In galvano-static polarisation of samples the anti-corrosion effect of silver shows up with the introduction into the alloy in a quantity not exceeding 1.5-2% (fig. 4.46). Further increasing the silver content in the alloy does not show any marked influence on the rate of anodic corrosion of alloys of the Pb-Ag and Pb-Sb-Ag systems. As can be seen from fig. 4.46, lead-antimony-silver alloys slightly surpass the two-component lead-silver alloys in corrosion resistance especially at low concentrations of silver, although the Pb + 5% Sb alloy corrodes more severely than pure lead. In this connection it is interesting to note that, as shown by the results of measurement of electrical conductivity and also by X-ray structural analysis, in alloys of the Pb-Sb-Ag system the silver, obviously, comes (at any rate partially) into the composition of intermetallic compound Ag_3Sb[113]. The presence of this compound can cause an increased mechanical strength and corrosion resistance of lead-antimony-silver alloys. The relationships quoted in fig. 4.46 (in the field of low concentrations of Ag) later obtained confirmation in the works of Pavlov and others[114].

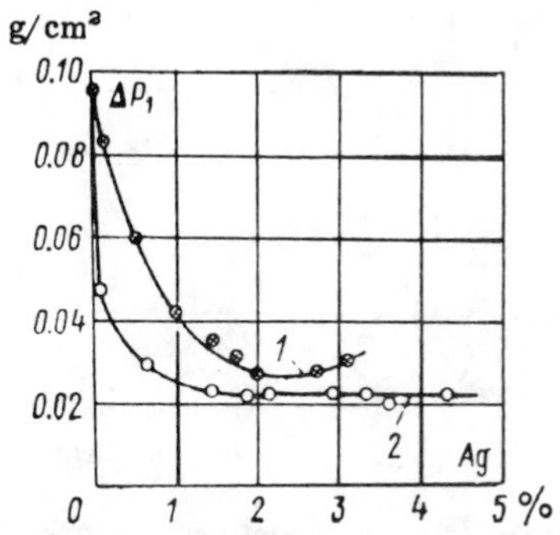

Fig.4.46 Dependence of weight losses in anodic corrosion of lead alloys on the silver content (Q = 100A·hr, i = 10mÅ/cm²). 1) Pb + Ag; 2) Pb + 5% Sb + Ag.

Potentio-static study of anodic behaviour of lead-silver and lead-antimony-silver alloys showed that the presence of silver in the alloy has an influence on the kinetics of the oxidation processes at potentials exceeding the potential of the equilibrium $PbO_2 \rightleftarrows PbSO_4$. In the field of potentials where the end product of anodic oxidation is lead sulphate, the introduction of silver does not cause any change in the character of the graphs (I, π), which are similar in this case to the graphs in fig. 4.34. In the graphs of change of current in time, taken at the potential of formation of PbO_2, in the case of alloys compounded with silver the maxima are observed in the initial period of polarisation (fig. 4.47). A similar phenomenon was found subsequently in ref. [100]) in potentio-static study of a lead-calcium alloy.

The origin of the maxima in graphs (I, τ) can be explained by the parallel occurrence of the processes of oxidation of the surface of the electrode and of liberation of oxygen, the rate of which changes differently with time. An important fact here is that the introduction into the alloy of silver causes a considerable decrease in oxygen overvoltage[115]. Therefore, even at relatively low values of the potential not differing much from the value corresponding to the equilibrium $PbO_2 \rightleftarrows PbSO_4$, the process of liberation of oxygen on alloys containing silver can play a marked role, especially in the initial period of polarisation.

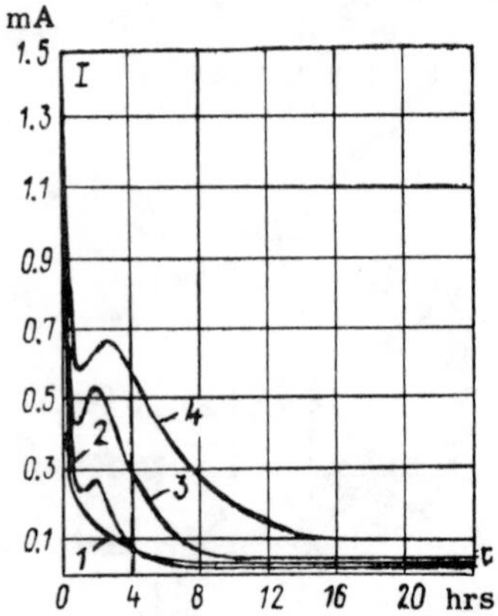

Fig.4.47 Change of current with time in potentio-static polarisation of lead-silver alloy at φ = 1.2V (in relation to Hg/Hg_2SO_4). 1) Pb; 2) Pb + 1.01% Ag; 3) Pb + 4.73% Ag; 4) Pb + 9.87% Ag.

In the work quoted[100] the origin of the maxima in the graphs (I, τ) is connected with the phase conversion $PbSO_4 \rightarrow \beta\text{-}PbO_2$. However, from the point of view of these ideas it is difficult to explain the specific influence of the silver on the course of the I-τ graphs and the absence of the maximum in the graph taken in the polarisation of pure lead (fig. 4.47).

The dependence of the corrosion rate of lead-silver and lead-antimony-silver alloys in potentio-static conditions on the concentration of silver is strong (fig. 4.48). The minimum corrosion, determined according to stationary value of current or to weight of oxidised metal, is observed with a content in the alloy of ~3% Ag. This concentration of silver approximately corresponds to the composition of the eutectics in the system Pb-Ag. Let us also mention that, as was shown by electron-microscope study of anodic films the formation of lead oxide in the anodic oxidation of a Pb-3% Ag alloy is distinguished by the most finely dispersed structure[113].

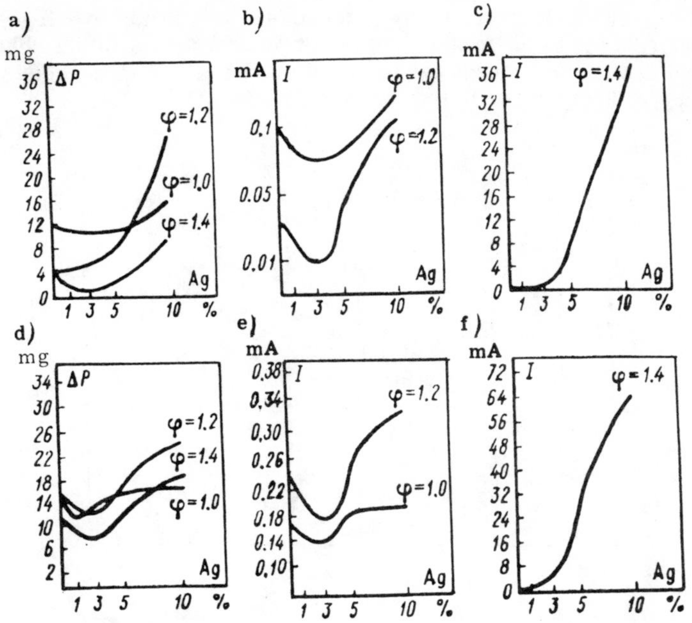

Fig. 4.48 Dependence of the corrosion of lead alloys on the concentration of silver at different potentials of polarisation a, b, c - Pb; d, e, f - Pb-Sb-Ag. ΔP - weight losses, I - stationary current after one day's polarisation.

At $\varphi = 1.4$V (Hg/Hg_2SO_4 electrode) an increase in the concentration of silver in the alloy to >3% causes a sharp increase in the value of the current I, i.e. in the rate of liberation of oxygen (fig. 4.48). Therefore, it is possible that a decrease in corrosion resistance of the alloys with a considerable content of silver is linked with the marked oxidation of the metal by oxygen in the mechanism examined above.

A study of the overvoltage of liberation of oxygen on a number of alloys of the systems Pb-Ag and Pb-Sb-Ag, previously oxidised during a day's polarisation at a current density $j = 10^{-3}$ A/cm^2, was carried out by us in ref.[115]). The results of the measurements are shown in fig. 4.49.

From this diagram it follows that the introduction of silver into the alloy causes a marked decrease in oxygen overvoltage (especially in the case of alloys without antimony). Alloys compounded with silver are characterised by a decreased coefficient of slope of the graphs (φ, lg j). In the field of low current densities a sharp potential drop is observed, caused by the process of spontaneous reduction of PbO_2 according to the scheme (4.74).

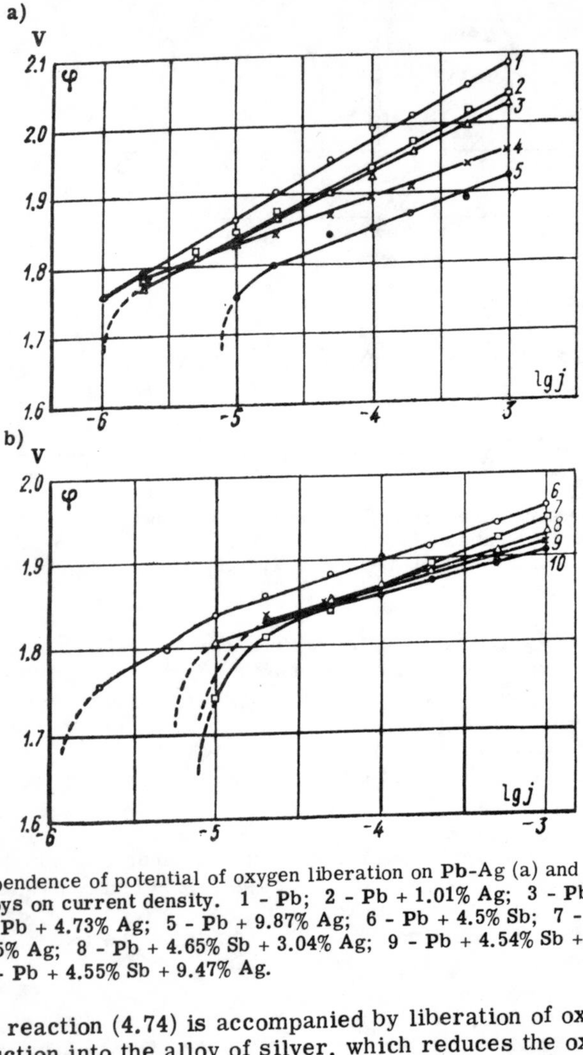

Fig.4.49 Dependence of potential of oxygen liberation on Pb-Ag (a) and Pb-Sb-Ag (b) alloys on current density. 1 - Pb; 2 - Pb + 1.01% Ag; 3 - Pb + 2.94% Ag; 4 - Pb + 4.73% Ag; 5 - Pb + 9.87% Ag; 6 - Pb + 4.5% Sb; 7 - Pb + 4.65% Sb + 0.95% Ag; 8 - Pb + 4.65% Sb + 3.04% Ag; 9 - Pb + 4.54% Sb + 4.94% Ag; 10 - Pb + 4.55% Sb + 9.47% Ag.

Since the reaction (4.74) is accompanied by liberation of oxygen, the introduction into the alloy of silver, which reduces the oxygen overvoltage, causes an acceleration of this process. Naturally the current density at which the voltage drop is observed increases with an increase in concentration of the silver.

The depolarisation effect of silver on the process of oxygen liberation may be partially linked with the course of the oxidation reactions with the participation of ions of Ag^{2+} or Ag^{+} [115][116]. These ions play the role of catalysts of the process of oxidation of the water. A possible reason for the reduction in oxygen overvoltage is also the displacement of the point of zero charge of lead dioxide and the rise in the negative potential of ψ_1 [113].

Testing of grids of the positive electrode cast from lead-antimony-silver alloys in batteries of different types showed that the presence of 0.5-1% Ag ensures good preservation of the grids over a long time both in conditions of continuous charge and with cycling. Production lead-antimony alloy (6.5% Sb) grids under these conditions turn out to be completely destroyed. The results obtained made it possible to state precisely the composition of the anode alloy used for the manufacture of positive electrode grids of several types of lead acid batteries.

Corrosion-resistance alloys compounded with silver continue to remain at the centre of the interest of researchers. In the recent work of Mao and Rao[117] a study was made by the method of electron microscope investigation of the mechanism of the protective effect of the silver addition (0.2%) on anodic corrosion of a lead-antimony alloy containing 4.5% of Sb. The main interest of the authors in this work was in the explanation given of the role of a number of metallurgical factors in the behaviour of an alloy compounded with silver. A study was made of samples that were freshly cast, normalised and quenched. The electron microprobe used in the work gave the possibility of investigating the distribution of the elements in the thin structure of the alloy (near the grain boundaries, in the inter-dendrite spaces, and also inside the grains).

The authors of the work arrived at the following conclusions: normalising increases the effectiveness of the additive silver. Corrosion of Pb-Sb alloys takes place mainly in the field of inter-dendrite boundaries and is brought about as a result of the selective decomposition of a phase rich in antimony. In normalised Pb-Sb-Ag alloys corrosion predominantly develops by way of selective oxidation of the grains of the matrix with a limited attack on the antimony phase. The difference noted in the mechanism of the corrosion behaviour of binary and ternary alloys grows with an increase in silver content in the alloy. Further, the authors established that the silver predominantly borders on the antimony phase. In a given field, the silver surrounds the antimony spheroids and thus prevents selective dissolution of the antimony phase from the corroding anode, which explains the increased corrosion resistance of the ternary alloys. On the other hand, microsonde analysis shows that only a relatively small amount of the antimony phase has a close link with the silver in freshly cast three-component alloys. The phase rich in antimony, not surrounded by silver, is subjected to the main corrosion, which causes faster corrosion of unnormalised Pb-Sb-Ag alloys.

The paper[117]) noticeably widens the ideas about the mechanism of the corrosion of alloys compounded with silver, complementing the electro-chemical research examined above. The conclusions reached by Mao and Rao are in close conformity with the theory of the modification of metals and, in particular, with the link which exists between the structure of the metal and the rate of corrosion of it.

Lead alloys compounded with calcium

In literature for many years consideration has been given to the problem of using in batteries grids made of lead alloys containing calcium. Alloys of the following composition have been proposed by different authors: Pb + (0.01-0.10)% Ca; Pb + (0.03-0.1)% Ca + (1-2)% Sn + (0.01-0.1)% Al; Pb + (0.03-0.1)% Ca + (0.1-1)% Ag; Pb + 0.2% Ca + 0.2% Ag + (0.3-3)% Sn; Pb + (2-7)% Sb + (0.01-0.1)% Ca etc. As can be seen from these data, lead-calcium was investigated over a fairly wide range of change of calcium concentrations. As far as the totality of properties is concerned, the optimum alloys are reckoned to be those containing 0.6-0.9% Ca, and also alloys containing together with Ca (0.03-0.1%) also silver (0.1%).

Lead-calcium alloys of the composition indicated are comparable in their mechanical properties with ordinary lead-antimony alloys: the hardness of Pb-Ca alloys after casting and cooling in air amounts to ~9kg/mm^2. The use of water cooling increases this characteristic to ~13kg/mm^2. The corrosion resistance of calcium alloys is evaluated quite contradictorily, which can be explained by insufficient control of the calcium content in the alloy. In addition, corrosion resistance of lead-calcium alloys is connected with the formation of the intermetallic compound Pb_3Ca. The appearance of this compound, which occurs in definite conditions of hardening of the alloy, depends on the temperature and rate of cooling.

The formation of a high-dispersion intermetallide causes an increase in the corrosion resistance of the alloy. According to the data in ref.[103]) calcium refines the structure of the lead and causes an increase in its corrosion resistance. V V Stender and G Z Kiryakov considers that the protective effect of calcium bears a temporary character and decreases in the process of anodic polarisation[90]. A feature peculiar to the alloys mentioned is the deterioration of the sample along the boundaries of the grains (intercrystalline corrosion).

On the basis of a large amount of experimental data it is possible to state that alloys of the Pb-Ca system do not differ much in corrosion resistance from normal battery alloys of the Pb-Sb system. In order to increase the corrosion resistance of lead-calcium alloys they must be compounded with silver (fig. 4.50).

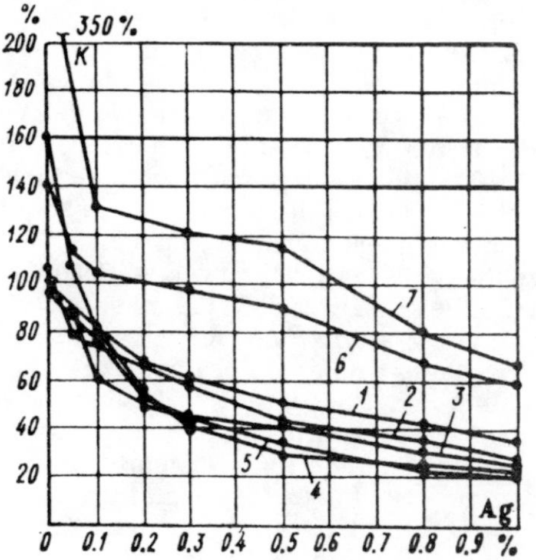

Fig.4.50 Dependence of corrosion of alloys of the Pb-Ca-Ag system in a solution of H_2SO_4 of density 1.25g/cm^3 on the composition of the alloy. 1 - without Ca; 2 - 0.01% Ca; 3 - 0.05% Ca; 4 - 0.1% Ca; 5 - 0.5% Ca; 6 - 1% Ca; 7 - 1.5% Ca.

Calcium alloys find some application in the battery industry[76]. They are successfully used in stationary batteries working at a constant recharge regime, in sealed lead acid batteries, and in some other cases, when what is primarily important is the maintenance of the charge with time, i.e. when the minimum rate of self-discharge is required of the batteries. A wider use of calcium alloys is hindered by the complexity of work with them, caused by rapid burning out of the calcium and the difficulty in obtaining castings with constant calcium content.

In order to remove these difficulties an electrolytic method of obtaining Pb-Ca alloys was proposed. According to this method the casting of grids into the casting mould is carried out directly from the electrolyser. An alloy is obtained on the molten lead cathode. The constancy of composition of the alloy is ensured by the presence of a layer of melted calcium salts ($CaCl_2$ + 13% CaF_2) which protect the alloy from oxidation and also by the regulating of the conditions of electrolysis. A method of obtaining Pb-Ca alloys which also clearly has prospects is that of obtaining them in sealed magneto-dynamic furnaces and casting the grids in an inert atmosphere which excludes oxidation of the alloy in the process of casting the grids.

Among the special points about the utilisation of batteries with Pb-Ca alloys we must refer to the difficulty of controlling the degree of charge according to the density of the electrolyte, since a weak charge current excludes "bubbling" of the electrolyte and the density inevitably "lags" behind the degree of charge. An excessive deformation of grids made of lead-calcium alloys was also noticed. The capacity of batteries with Pb-Ca alloy grids working at a regime of constant recharge is below the capacity of batteries with grids of normal alloy[73]). The basic reason for this phenomenon is considered by Burbank to be a change in the morphology of the PbO_2 crystals. Electron microscope examination of the active mass found, in the mass taken from a battery with grids of normal alloy, a large amount of prismatic crystals and in the mass taken from plates with grids of Pb-Ca alloy many lumpy crystals of indeterminate form. Consequently, it can be assumed that antinomy exercises considerable influence on the morphology of the PbO_2, which is partially adsorbed on the PbO_2 crystals. Another reason for the decrease in capacity is the deterioration of the contact between a grid of Pb-Ca alloy and the active mass. Autoradiographic research[73]) showed that this layer represents lead sulphate, which in practice does not oxidise into PbO_2 even at full battery charge. In the forming of this layer, obviously an important role is played by the calcium sulphate. As has already been mentioned, this defect can be eliminated by means of the introduction of phosphoric acid into the electrolyte.

Some laws of anodic corrosion of lead alloys

On the analogy with alloys with an iron base a study was made of the possibility of evolving more stable lead alloys in relation to corrosion, containing 4-7 components (from a number of those which were investigated in two-component systems and showed good results). The following were selected as alloying additives: Ag, Sb, As, Ca, Hg, Te, Tl, Co, Sn, Cd, Nb.

A study of all possible multi-component alloys containing the elements mentioned at several concentrations of each of them, naturally, was not possible. Therefore, several well-studied ternary alloys were taken as a base, to which other elements were added. The results of corrosion tests of a number of experimental alloys are given in table 4.10. Corrosion of four-component alloys in comparison with corrosion of lead-antimony alloy (6% Sb), relatively taken as 100%, amounts to 18 to 38%. The relatively small difference in the value of the corrosion of all the experimental alloys can be explained by the presence in them of such a strong anti-corrosion additive as silver. With a replacement of the three-component basis (with silver) by ordinary lead-antimony alloys (2-6% Sb) corrosion of experimental alloys containing 0.1-0.3% Te reached 60-80%.

Table 4.10: Relative anodic corrosion (in %) of multi-component lead alloys

Additive to lead %		Content of fourth component %											
		Cd		Hg		Te		Sn		Nb		Co	
Sb	Ag	0.1	0.3	0.3	1.0	0.1	0.3	0.1	0.3	0.1	0.3	0.05	0.1
1.5	0.5	29	26	31	30	-	-	31	26	23	23	20	18
4.5	0.5	25	25	27	36	21	18	25	26	19	19	18	20
6.0	0.5	27	26	33	38	22	20	31	33	23	21	-	20

Thus, in order to increase the corrosion resistance of lead-antimony alloys containing 2-6% Sb, it is sufficient to introduce up to 0.5% arsenic, 0.5% silver or 0.1-0.3% arsenic. With the presence of the additions mentioned, the introduction of other components into the alloy has little influence on the rate of corrosion of lead alloys.

Alloys compounded with cobalt form a known exception. They possess the highest corrosion resistance. What has been said refers also to antimony-free alloys of composition:

$$Pb + Ag\ (3\text{-}5\%) + Co\ (0.05\text{-}0.1\%) + Sn\ (0.05\text{-}1.0\%)$$

This alloy was studied directly in a battery and showed excellent conservation of the grids. It must, however, be borne in mind that cobalt in practice does not dissolve in lead, even at high temperatures. The introduction of cobalt requires preliminary preparation of a tin-cobalt or antimony-cobalt foundry alloy, which is connected with considerable experimental difficulties. Here solution of cobalt in the lead castings is possible[118]).

What has been said above provides a basis for concluding that, in spite of the marked anti-corrosion effect, at the present time cobalt does not provide any practical interest as a compounding component of lead alloys.

Table 4.11: Properties of some lead alloys

System	Alloying element %					Density g/cm²	Relative corrosion %	Breaking strength kg/mm²	Elongation %	Hardness kg/mm²	Specific resistance Ω·cm·10⁴
	Sb	Ag	Sn	Co	Tl						
Pb-Sb	6	-	-	-	-	10.80	100	3.8	7.5	15.4	22.24
Pb-Ag	-	-	-	-	-	11.34	28.4	2.1	14.5	12.3	19.11
	-	3	-	-	-	11.33	23.6	3.0	11.4	14.0	18.56
	-	5	-	-	-	11.26	45.3	2.1	7.4	19.1	18.20
	-	10	-	-	-	11.23	41.7	2.8	8.3	13.3	17.82
Pb-Sb-Ag	5	1	-	-	-	10.97	25.2	3.7	9.7	19.9	22.23
	5	3	-	-	-	11.00	22.1	3.2	5.4	19.2	22.60
	5	5	-	-	-	10.98	20.9	3.0	3.7	20.2	23.34
	5	10	-	-	-	10.76	22.8	3.6	5.1	19.2	26.09
Pb-Sb-Co	5	-	-	0.05	-	10.97	45	3.0	6.2	14.1	22.23
	5	-	-	0.1	-	10.98	54.3	3.1	9.0	13.6	22.05
Pb-Sb-Sn	5	-	1.5	-	-	10.86	113	3.7	3.5	17.2	22.79
	5	-	3.0	-	-	10.80	99	4.2	5.0	17.9	22.42
	5	-	5.0	-	-	10.66	101	3.3	13.5	18.3	21.87
Pb-Sb-Ti	5	-	-	-	0.5	10.98	80.0	3.1	9.0	13.6	22.05
	5	-	-	-	1.0	10.98	80.0	2.9	7.5	12.9	-
Pb-Sb--Ag-Co	5	0.5	-	0.05	-	10.98	35.0	4.3	4.8	19.3	22.42
	5	1	-	0.05	-	10.98	26.1	4.4	5.7	20.1	22.42
	5	3	-	0.05	-	10.92	24.3	3.6	8.4	18.1	23.15
	5	0.5	-	0.1	-	10.97	29.9	3.4	4.6	18.3	22.43
	5	1	-	0.1	-	10.99	29.6	3.5	4.9	19.5	22.60
Pb-Sb--Ag-Sn	5	0.5	0.5	-	-	10.91	35	3.6	9.1	22.5	22.79
	5	0.5	1.0	-	-	10.94	35.4	3.7	5.5	21.7	22.79
	5	1	0.5	-	-	10.93	32.7	3.3	4.3	21.9	22.79
	5	1	1.0	-	-	10.91	30.7	3.6	5.5	23.4	22.79
Pb-Sn--Ag-Co	-	3	0.5	0.05	-	11.30	17.3	2.8	14.1	12.7	-
	-	3	1.0	0.1	-	11.27	16.6	2.9	10.3	13.1	20.28
	-	5	0.5	0.05	-	11.28	16.6	2.9	8.8	12.0	18.56
	-	5	1.0	0.1	-	11.26	10.7	2.0	10.5	12.3	17.10
Pb-Sb-Sn--Ag-Co	2	0.5	0.5	0.05	-	11.18	31.5	2.2	7.2	16.5	22.05
	4	0.5	0.5	0.05	-	11.02	33.7	3.8	7.4	22.2	22.05
	6	0.5	0.5	0.05	-	10.86	38.6	4.0	6.7	22.2	22.15
	4	1.0	1.0	0.1	-	10.98	28.4	3.2	5.0	21.5	22.42
	4	1.0	0.5	0.05	-	11.03	30.7	3.3	5.1	20.5	22.42
	6	1.0	1.0	0.1	-	10.83	30.3	3.3	6.2	21.7	22.14
	6	1.0	0.5	0.05	-	10.84	28.4	3.2	6.0	22.2	22.23

Lead alloys compounded with tin were investigated in the work of Lander [96]). It was shown that the electro-chemical parameters of these alloys are comparable with the parameters of lead-antimony alloys. However, the alloys with tin, in contrast to the lead-antimony alloys, were not much subject to deformation in the process of utilisation in the battery. This important advantage, however, is obtained only with a content in the alloy of 5-7% Sn. Such alloys are distinguished by very high cost, therefore they cannot be recommended for widespread application in the battery industry. Low-alloy lead-tin alloys, according to our data, do not possess sufficient corrosion resistance.

A study of lead alloys compounded with thallium showed that two-component alloys of the Pb-Tl system are distinguished by sufficiently high corrosion resistance but are not suitable for manufacture of battery grids owing to a quite low mechanical strength. Alloys of the Pb-Sb-Tl system differ comparatively little in their corrosion resistance from a production lead-antimony alloy[113]. This result was subsequently confirmed in ref.[119].

The physico-mechanical and corrosion properties of a number of lead alloys investigated in the works of the authors of this book are shown in table 4.11.

A study of the kinetics of anode corrosion of a number of lead alloys of practical importance in galvano-static conditions showed[120] that the amount of oxidation products to be found on the surface of a corroding sample ΔP_2 sharply increases in the initial period of polarisation. Then the growth of the anode film is substantially slowed down, and with an increase in polarisation time the amount of anode products moves towards some sort of limit (fig. 4.51).

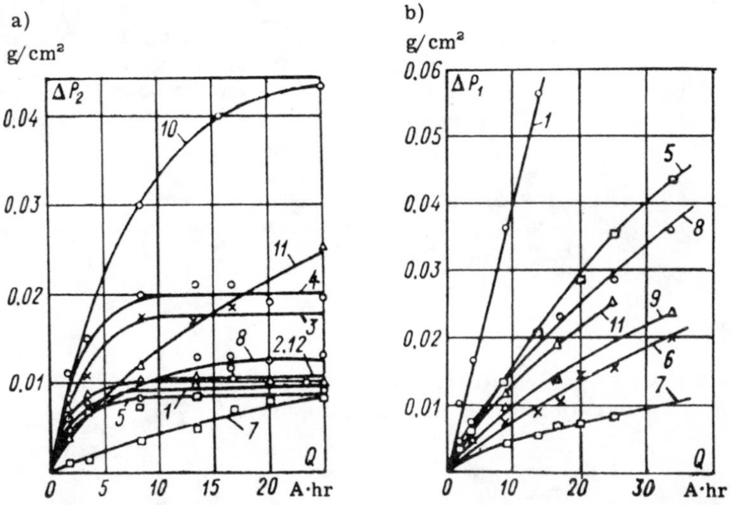

Fig.4.51 Dependence of the mass of the oxide film (a) and corrosion losses (b) on the amount of electricity in anodic corrosion of Pb and some of its alloys in H_2SO_4 solution of density 1.32 at j = 10mA/cm² and + 20°C. 1 - Pb; 2 - Pb + 5% Sb; 3 - Pb + 10% Sb; 4 - Pb + 15% Sb; 5 - Pb + 1% Ag; 6 - Pb + 3% Ag; 7 - Pb + 5% Ag; 8 - Pb + 5% Sb + 1% Ag; 9 - Pb + 5% Sb + 3% Ag; 10 - Pb + 0.3% Ca; 11 - Pb + 0.3% Ca + 1% Ag; 12 - Pb + 6% Sb + 0.2% As.

The corrosion losses of the sample ΔP_2, i.e. the total weight of the oxidised metal, increases continuously with time, in accordance with the parabolic law

$$\Delta P_1 = B_k Q^{n_k} \tag{4.100}$$

where the constant B_k changes depending on the composition of the alloy within the limits 10^{-3}-10^{-2} g(cm^2 · A·hr), and the coefficient of slope of the logarithmic graph η_k = 0.55-0.91. The value of η_k depends on the composition of the alloy and the conditions of polarisation. With an increase in anode current density $\eta_k \to 1$, and at sufficiently high currents the equation (4.100) takes on the form

$$\Delta P_1 \approx B_k Q \tag{4.101}$$

characterising the linear dependence of ΔP_1 on Q. The slowing down of the increase in the value of ΔP_2 with a continuous increasing of ΔP_1 is explained by the falling-off of the loose part of the corrosion film.

The cohesion of the dense and loose parts of the film substantially depends on the composition of the alloy. The introduction of alloying additions leads as a rule to a decrease in the falling away of the oxide film. A reduction in the rate of corrosion, as can be seen from table 4.12, was observed, however, only with the compounding of the alloy with silver.

The values of the coefficient of utilisation of current η_t and of the coefficient of adhesion β for the alloys shown in table 4.12 were calculated according to the formulae

$$\eta_t = \frac{\Delta P_1 (100 - \alpha)}{KQ} \tag{4.102}$$

where K = 1.94 - the electro-chemical equivalent of lead ($Pb \to Pb^{4+}$); α is the concentration of the alloying component %;

$$\beta = \frac{\Delta P_2 \cdot 10^4}{F \Delta P_1 (100 - \alpha)} \tag{4.103}$$

where $F = M_{PbO_2}/A_{Pb}$ is the stoichiometric factor; M_{PbO_2} = 239.2 is the molecular mass of the PbO_2; A_{Pb} = 207.2 is the atomic mass of the Pb.

With the increase in the temperature of the electrolyte, the decrease in concentration of the H_2SO_4 and in the current density (with Q = const) the amount of products of anodic corrosion ΔP_2 increases. Thus, with an increase in temperature from 20° to 60°C the mass of the anode film forming on the lead increases 1.2-1.5 times, on Pb-Sb alloys

2-3 times, on Pb-Ag 1.5-3 times, on Pb-Sb-Ag 3-4 times.

As is well known, the corrosion process can occur on the metal-oxide or on the oxide-solution interface. The zone of occurrence of the oxidising reactions will be to a considerable extent dependent on the properties of the oxide film.

The conditions causing the formation of not very porous (or non-porous) dense anode film increase its protective properties and displace the zone of occurrence of the reaction to the oxide-solution interface. Metal ions can here diffuse through the crystal lattice of the oxide. An increase in temperature, a decrease in current density and the introduction of a number of alloying additives (Sb) lead to the formation of an oxide film with sufficiently large pores. Here the corrosion process occurs, obviously, mainly in the pores of the anode film on the metal-film interface, which leads to a linear dependence of the weight losses on the amount of electricity transmitted.

It must be noted that the large-pore structure of the film, evidently causes a better adhesion of it to the base, since the considerable volume of the cavities decreases the tensions appearing in the process of the growth of the lead dioxide film. With an increase in temperature a recrystallisation of the film takes place, which considerably worsens its protective properties. An increase in temperature has a particularly marked effect on the increase in the rate of corrosion of lead-silver alloys, on the surface of which the densest oxide film forms at anodic polarisation.

Thus, the structure and physico-chemical characteristics of the oxide film to a considerable extent determine the corrosion resistance of anode-polarised lead alloy. Hence follows the importance of studying the phase composition and the properties of anode films for obtaining information about the mechanism of corrosion deterioration of battery grids. The question of the connection of the phase composition of the film with the kinetics of anode corrosion will be specially examined below.

The addition to the lead of Ca, Sb and Ag, as can be seen from table 4.12, causes a shift of the anode potential of the sample in the negative direction[120]). A particularly marked effect is observed with the introduction of silver into the alloy, which corresponds to the data examined above about the influence of this metal on the overvoltage of the liberation of oxygen. The decrease in the anode potential as a result of the addition of silver must be considered quite substantial also because this addition leads to consolidation of the oxide film, i.e. it decreases the value of the active surface of the electrode and consequently increases the true current density.

Table 4.12: **Some characteristics of anode corrosion of lead and its alloys**

Alloy	Potential (in relation to nve) established after 1 day of polarisation V	1 day		
		ΔP_1 mg/cm²	ΔP_2 mg/cm²	r[illegible]
Pb	2.195	10.0	5.8	2.[illegible]
Pb + 0.3% Ca	2.170	11.1	19.6	2.[illegible]
Pb + 0.3% Ca + 0.87% Ag	2.102	3.3	3.3	0.[illegible]
Pb + 1% Ag	2.148	3.6	4.4	0.[illegible]
Pb + 5% Sb	2.182	12.0	8.0	2.[illegible]
Pb + 6% Sb + 0.2% As	2.192	8.6	6.3	1.[illegible]
Pb + 5% Sb + 1% Ag	2.124	4.4	4.4	1.[illegible]

A decrease in the concentration of the electrolyte and an increase in the temperature lead to a decrease in the potential of the alloys under investigation as a result of the known loosening of the oxide film. The temperature coefficient (20-60°C) of the anode potential constitutes for lead 2.1-2.5mV/°C, for Pb-Sb alloys 2.5-3.5mV/°C, for Pb-Ca 3.0mV/°C and for Pb-Ag 1.5-2.3mV/°C.

In anodic polarisation of the sample under galvano-static conditions the current (I = const) may be considered as the sum of two components

$$I = I_{Pb} + I_{O_2} = \text{const} \tag{4.104}$$

where I_{Pb} and I_{O_2} are the rates of the process of oxidation of the metal and of liberation of oxygen respectively. From equation (4.104) it follows that a decrease in anode potential (oxygen overvoltage) occurs, i.e. an increase in the corrosion resistance of the alloy. In fact, a substantial decrease in the oxygen overvoltage on the introduction into the alloy of silver is an important cause of the anti-corrosion effect of this metal.

However, the introduction into the alloy of antimony, which also causes a decrease in anode potential, leads at the same time to an increase in the rate of corrosion. A symbiotic change in the oxygen overvoltage and the corrosion resistance of the alloys is observed with a change in the conditions of electrolysis (concentration of H_2SO_4, temperature and current density). All this bears witness to the fact that part of the separating oxygen is consumed in the oxidation of the metal. This part increases under the action of factors which cause a loosening of the oxide film.

an H_2SO_4 solution (d = 1.32g/cm^3, j = 10mA/cm^2 and t = 20°C)

	10 days				30 days			
β %	ΔP$_1$ mg/cm^2	ΔP$_2$ mg/cm^2	η_t %	β %	ΔP$_1$ mg/cm^2	ΔP$_2$ mg/cm^2	η_t %	β %
51.5	64.2	11.0	1.35	16.0	163.0	7.0	1.2	3.7
74.5	102.0	40.0	2.2	34.5	260.0	45.3	1.8	15.0
77.0	19.2	19.1	0.4	86.0	33.2	35.8	0.23	93.5
100.0	23.0	7.1	0.54	25.0	50.9	8.5	0.47	14.3
65.0	60.0	10.6	1.15	13.7	165.8	12.4	1.1	6.3
63.0	59.5	12.3	1.23	18.0	157.7	10.0	1.05	6.0
86.0	23.6	12.4	0.46	48.6	32.8	30.0	0.34	84.5

Thus, a shift of the anode potential in the negative direction causes an increase in corrosion resistance of lead alloys only in the event of a decrease in oxygen overvoltage not being connected with the development of the surface and a deterioration in the protective properties of the lead dioxide film.

The properties of oxide films forming in the process of anodic corrosion of lead alloys

The structure and phase composition of anode films

The phase composition, structure and properties of oxide films forming on the surface of the corroding sample show quite a substantial influence on the kinetics of the corrosion process. As was stated above, in the process of anodic polarisation of lead alloys the oxidising reactions may occur at the metal-oxide or the oxide-solution interfaces. Parallel occurrence of the processes in both zones is possible.

It is fully understandable that the relative rates of the reactions occurring in the solid phase (in the thickness of the oxide layer) and on the surface of the electrode, to a large extent, should depend on the structure of the oxide film. A knowledge of the composition and structure of anode products on the surface of the electrode can serve as an important criterion for establishing the mechanism of the process of anodic corrosion of lead alloys. In the literature there is very little information about physico-chemical properties of oxide films. This, obviously, is connected with the considerable experimental difficulties encountered in the study of this subject.

a) **Porosity of anode films**: One of the important characteristics of anode films is porosity. According to the data of ref.[121]) the porosity of films forming on the surface of lead and of a number of lead alloys (Pb + 1% Ag; Pb + 1% Ag + 0.25% Sn + 0.05% Co; Pb + 1% Ag + 1% Sn; Pb + 0.2% Sb; Pb + 1% Ag + 0.4% Sb + 0.05% Co) in the process of seven-day polarisation at a current density $0.04 A/cm^2$ in $2N{\cdot}H_2SO_4$ reaches 10-14% and does not depend much on the composition of the alloy. However, the methods used in this work (saturation of the film with spindle oil at 150°C), obviously, gives the possibility of finding only pores of sufficiently large dimensions.

We have made a study of the porosity of films appearing on lead and some of its alloys (Pb + 5% Sb and Pb + 5% Sb + 1% Ag) in different conditions of anodic polarisation[122]). The process of the growth of the oxide film was directly observed under a microscope fitted with an ocular micrometer. As samples for investigation, we used cylinders of the appropriate alloy with a diameter of 0.9-1.1mm. The following values were measured: original diameter of the sample d_o, diameter of the sample covered by the film d_1, and diameter of the same sample after dissolution of the oxide film d_2. From these data the thickness of the film δ and the depth of corrosion δ_c was calculated:

$$\delta = \frac{d_1 - d_2}{2}; \quad \delta_c = \frac{d_o - d_2}{2} \tag{4.105}$$

The volume of film on a cylindrical sample of length l is equal to:

$$V_f = \frac{\pi (d_1^2 - d_2^2) l}{4} \cong \pi \delta d_o l \tag{4.106}$$

since $\delta \ll d_o$.

The volume taken on lead dioxide is:

$$V_{PbO_2} = \Delta P_2 / d_{PbO_2} \tag{4.107}$$

where ΔP_2 is the mass of the oxide film, and d_{PbO_2} the density of lead dioxide. Hence, the porosity of the film

$$\gamma = \frac{V_f - V_{PbO_2}}{V_f} = 1 - \frac{\Delta P_2}{\pi d_{PbO_2} \delta d_o l} \tag{4.108}$$

According to the data obtained by us, with the transmission of a small amount of electricity $\delta < \delta_c$, this means that in the initial period of polarisation the film grows predominantly in the direction of the electrolyte. However, with longer polarisation the relationship of the values δ and δ_c changes, giving evidence of a change in direction of growth of the film in the direction of the corroding metal.

The porosity of the oxide film forming as a result of long polarisation of lead amounts to 50-55%. On the alloys investigated the porosity of the film varies within the limits of 75-85%. Changes of conditions of polarisation shows no marked influence on the value of γ. It is characteristic that the porosity of films forming on alloys that are essentially different in their corrosion resistance (Pb + 5% Sb and Pb + 5% Sb + 1% Ag) is practically the same.

If in the first approximation we assume that in the film there are cylindrical pores with a mean diameter d_p, then the volume of the pores $\bar{V}_p$ to be found on $1 cm^2$ of surface of the film will be equal to:

$$\bar{V}_p = \frac{\pi}{4} d_p^2 \delta N_p \tag{4.109}$$

where N_p is the average number of pores in $1 cm^2$. The porosity of the film, according to (4.108) and (4.109)

$$\gamma = \frac{\bar{V}_p}{\delta} = \frac{\pi}{4} d_p^2 N_p \tag{4.110}$$

With $\gamma \approx$ const, according to the formula (4.110).

$$d_p \sqrt{N_p} \approx \text{const} \tag{4.111}$$

i.e. a change in the diameter of the pores should in this case be compensated by a substantial opposite change in their quantity. With the presence of pores of different diameters the equation (4.111') can be written down in the form

$$\sum_k d_k N_k^{1/2} \approx \text{const} \tag{4.111'}$$

In this all subsequent conclusions remain unchanged.

It can be assumed that the protective properties of anode films depend mainly on the dimensions of the pores. With anodic oxidation of alloys characterised by high corrosion resistance, on the surface of the alloy, obviously, there is formed a film with quite fine pores. The amount of pores per unit of surface of the electrode should be fairly large here. Anodic corrosion of alloys which are distinguished by relatively low corrosion resistance, from the point of view of the ideas set forth, should be accompanied by the formation of a film with a comparatively small number of large pores. Such a film does not possess high protective properties as a result of its considerable permeability for oxidising agents.

b) Phase composition of anode films: In order to understand the mechanism of anodic corrosion of lead alloys a knowledge of the phase composition of the oxide films has great importance. Analysis of the data in literature regarding this question showed that the products of anode oxidation are quite diverse. Some of the components of oxide films described in literature may arise as a result of secondary reactions not directly connected with the electrode process.

Polarisation of lead in H_2SO_4 solutions at potentials lower than the equilibrium potential of $PbO_2 \rightleftarrows PbSO_4$ leads to the formation on the surface of the electrode of a film containing $PbSO_4$, $PbO_{tetr.}$, $Pb(OH)_2$ and also α-PbO_2 [97][99][101]. In the composition of film forming at low potentials on lead and lead-calcium alloy (<0.1% Ca) there are also found the following basic sulphates: $3PbO \cdot PbSO_4 \cdot H_2O$ and $PbO \cdot PbSO_4$. At higher potentials $> \varphi_{PbO_2/PbSO_4}$ anode films on lead consist basically of a mixture of α and β-PbO_2, while the outer layer facing the electrolyte represents the tetragonal modification of PbO_2 [100][102].

In neutral and alkaline media the oxide films forming on a lead anode contain Pb_3O_4, PbO and some oxides of intermediate composition $PbO_{1.55-1.57}$ [123]. At sufficiently high potentials the outer layers of the film contain both crystal modifications of PbO_2. The formation of β-PbO_2 in an alkaline medium is explained by a decrease in the pH value in the layer next to the anode. It is observed that intermediate compounds, the composition of which in the usual form is reflected by the formula $PbO \cdot xPbO_2$, possibly prove to be products of the chemical interaction of PbO_2 and PbO. Some contradiction is observed in data in literature regarding the presence in films formed at high anode potentials of lead oxide and other low-oxide products. A study of the influence of the conditions of electrolysis on the phase composition of anode films forming on lead showed that an increase in the concentration of the H_2SO_4 and a decrease in temperature lead to a decrease in the relative content in the film of β-PbO_2.

A thorough investigation of the nature of the products of anodic oxidation of lead in $1N \cdot H_2SO_4$ was made in the work of Pavlov and his colleagues[124]). The electrode was polarised in potentio-static conditions. The authors distinguish three fields of potentials φ:

1) The field when the anode layer represents lead sulphate is observed in the interval of change of φ from -0.956 to -0.3V (in relation to $Hg/HgSO_4$ electrode);
2) The field where the basic product of anodic oxidation of PbO (φ = -0.3 - +0.9V). At these potentials small quantities of $PbO \cdot PbSO_4$, $3PbO \cdot PbSO_4 \cdot H_2O$, $5PbO \cdot 2H_2O$ and α-PbO_2 are also formed.
3) The field of formation of lead dioxide occurs at $\varphi > 0.9V$ (in relation to $Hg/HgSO_4$). The basic component of the anode layer in this field is α-PbO_2. At $\varphi > 1.2V$ β-PbO_2 begins to form.

In ref.[102]) it is noted that an increase in the concentrations of antimony in the alloy causes an increase in the β-PbO_2 content in the anode film. In the work examined above[115]) it was shown by us that an increase in the silver content in alloys of the systems Pb-Ag and Pb-Sb-Ag leads to a similar result.

It must be noted that a deciphering of the results of radiographic or electronographic investigations of the products of anode corrosion of lead and lead alloys has presented a number of difficulties. The base lines of the oxides and sulphates of lead lie in one and the same interval of the 2θ angles and, as can be seen from fig. 4.52, are often superimposed on one another. Therefore, in many cases, with the presence in the composition of the film of several compounds, the phase analysis can be carried out only approximately. The accuracy of the deciphering of the spectrogram depends on the sensitivity of the scanning apparatus, the methods of carrying out the scan, and also on the preliminary preparation of the samples. The texture of the crystals, observed in the thin oxide layers on the lead, can have a definite influence on the results obtained. Finally, the processes of recrystallisation, connected with a deformation of the structure of the film, and also the interaction of the products of anodic corrosion with the base and with the electrolyte in the period of preparation and the carrying out of the X-ray scan - all this considerably hampers the obtaining of unambiguous and reliable results.

A systematic study of the dependency of the phase composition of the alloy and the conditions of polarisation was the subject of a paper by the authors of ref.[125]). A study was made of the phase composition of anode films forming on lead, and also on alloys of the following composition: Pb + 5-15% Sb, Pb + 1-5% Ag and Pb + 5% Sb + 1-3% Ag. Separate experiments were carried out with alloys containing Ca and As. The current density of anodic polarisation varied within the limits $1\text{-}10mA/cm^2$, the temperature from 20 to 60°C, the density of the

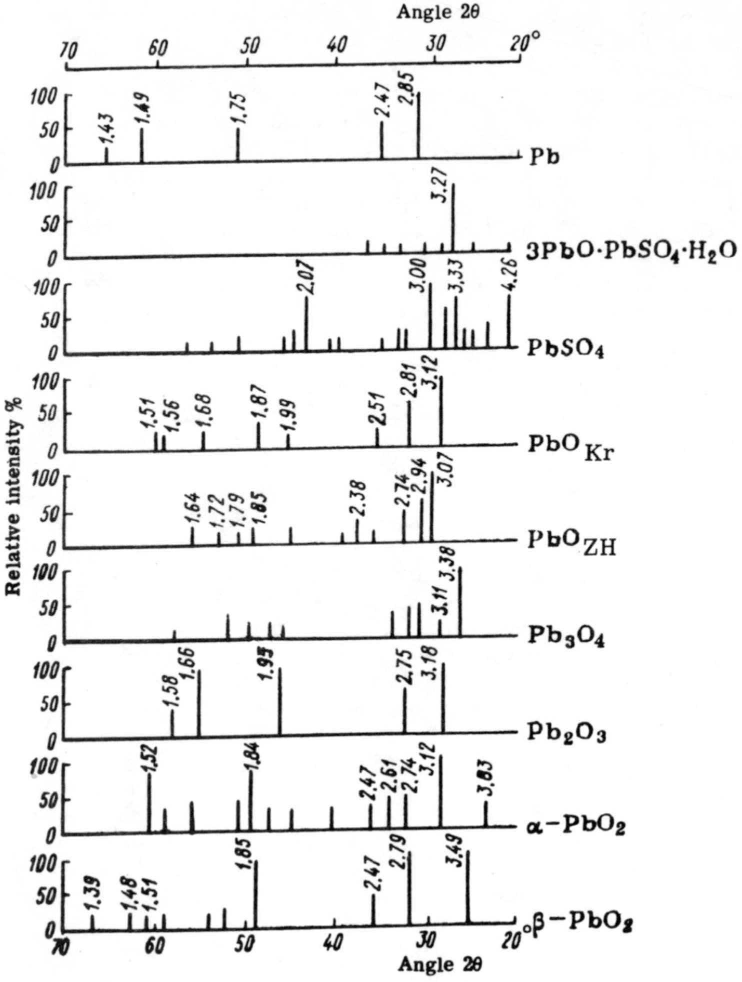

Fig.4.52 Diagrams of radiographs of lead and some of its compounds. In the figure are shown inter-plane distances corresponding to the base lines.

electrolyte 1.18-1.40g/cm^3, the time of polarisation from 6 hrs to 30 days. There were used as objects of radiographic study anode polarisation samples and oxide films taken from the surface of the electrodes. For working out a system of preparation of samples a number of X-ray photographs were taken without switching off the polarising current. In this it was established that the radiographs of samples which were quickly washed with cold water after withdrawal from the electrolyte and were dried with compressed air were completely identical to the radiographs obtained in the process of anodic polarisation (when the sample was under current). Therefore X-ray photography "under current" was not used any more. In a number of cases X-ray diffraction analysis of anode films was carried out.

According to the data obtained, the basic product of anodic corrosion of lead and all the alloys studied is the rhombic modification of lead dioxide. The content of α-PbO_2 in the anode film depending on the conditions of polarisation and the composition of the alloy varies within the limits of approximately 60 to 95%. The tetragonal modification of PbO_2 is found basically in the outer layer of the oxide film. In conformity with the data quoted above, it was shown in the works under consideration that the introduction of antimony into the alloy and, especially, of silver, causes an increase in the relative content of β-PbO_2 in the anode film. The greatest concentration of β-PbO_2 (~40%) was found in the products of anodic corrosion of lead-antimony-silver alloys. It was established that the addition of calcium (up to 0.7%) to lead and of arsenic (0.2%) to lead-antimony alloy does not cause any change in the phase composition of anode films.

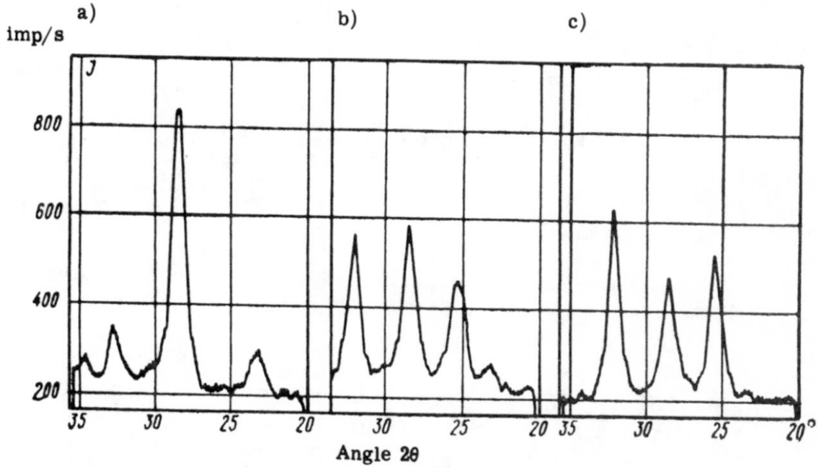

Fig.4.53 Radiographs of anode films formed on the alloy Pb + 5% Sb + 1% Ag at j = 1mA/cm² and +20°C. Density of the H_2SO_4 solution (g/cm³): a - 1.40; b - 1.32; b - 1.18.

With a decrease in concentration of H_2SO_4 the relative content of β-PbO_2 in the anode film increases. The influence of the concentration of the solution on the phase composition of the products of anodic corrosion of antimonial alloys (fig. 4.53) is particularly sharply felt. The composition of the anode products of antimony-free alloys depends on the concentration of the acid to a lesser degree.

With an increase in temperature the content of β-PbO_2 in the oxide film also increases (fig. 4.54). At high temperatures some decrease in the width of the maxima is observed on the radiographs which is evidence of the enlarging of the dimensions of the PbO_2 crystals with the increase in temperature.

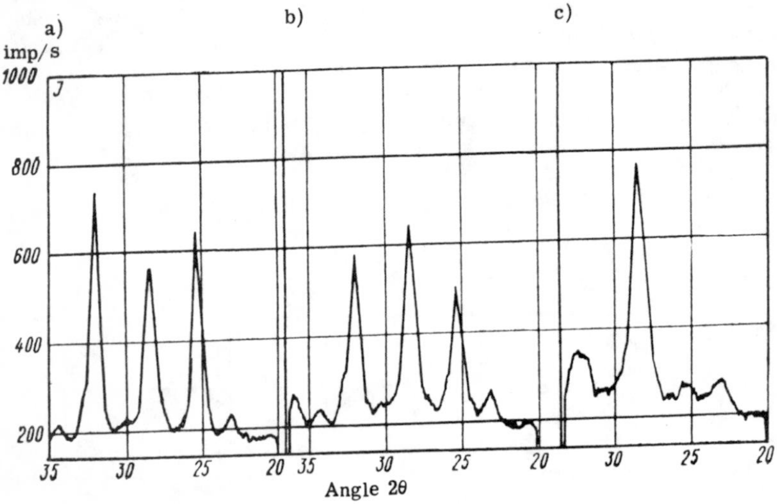

Fig.4.54 Radiographs of anode films forming on the anode Pb + 5% Sb in electrolyte with density 1.18g/cm³ at j = 5mA/cm². Temperature (°C): a - +60; b - +40; c - +20.

With increase of current density in the anode film the concentration of α-PbO_2 increases. The influence of current density on the phase composition of the products of anodic corrosion has a marked effect in dilute solutions of H_2SO_4. In proportion to the increase in concentration of the electrolyte the influence of the current density decreases.

The phase composition of oxide films suffers marked changes in the process of long anodic polarisation. As a rule the lines of α-PbO_2 are visible on the radiograph after only 30 min. polarisation. The lines of the substratum (lead) disappear in approximately 1 day. In subsequent polarisation the lines of the substratum appeared at times, which is evidence of the recrystallisation and cracking of the film. The lines of β-PbO_2 on the radiograph appear only after fairly long polarisation of the sample.

It must be noted that the radiographs of thin films which are formed, in particular, at anodic corrosion of alloys compounded with silver are distinguished by several peculiarities. In these radiographs it is possible to observe (in spite of the intense lines of Pb) comparatively strong lines with d = 3.12 and d = 2.78-2.81Å. Lines with d = 3.83Å (β-PbO_2) as a rule are absent. With long polarisation the lines of lead disappear or are weakened considerably, and the radiographs take on a normal form. Detailed analysis of this phenomenon showed that it was caused by the presence in the depth of the anode film on the film-metal interface of the tetragonal (red) modification of PbO. It should be noted that the anomalies of the form of the radiographs which have been described can be observed on all the alloys. However, in the case of the alloys which possess comparatively little corrosion resistance, the presence of $PbO_{(tetr)}$ can be registered only after quite short polarisation.

It should also be noted that in the field of current densities investigated, when the potential of the electrode exceeded the equilibrium potential of $PbO_2 \rightleftarrows PbSO_4$, at no time was any presence of lead sulphate found in the composition of the anode films. The presence of traces of $PbSO_4$ was observed only in the case when the sample even for a short time was in the electrolyte without current. Therefore, it is natural to consider that the presence of $PbSO_4$ in the composition of the oxide films formed at high anode potentials can only be the result of secondary reactions not connected directly with the process of anodic corrosion.

For a theoretical interpretation of the results obtained it is necessary, above all, to take into account the circumstance that, according to numerous experimental data, the tetragonal modification of PbO_2 is formed predominantly in acid, and the rhombic modification in alkaline and neutral media. In the process of anodic corrosion of lead alloys β-PbO_2 can appear as a result of oxidising reactions occurring on the oxide film-electrolyte interface, where the acidity of the medium is high. This process can occur by way of diffusion of lead ions through the film in the direction of the electrolyte. Obviously, such a mechanism is possible with the presence on the electrode of a quite dense microporous film. If we allow the possibility of formation of β-PbO_2 in the thickness of the film, near the film-metal interface, then this should mean that the film possesses large pores, permitting fairly fast diffusion of the acid from the solution to the corroding metal.

Taking into account the results obtained in the study of the porosity and phase composition of anode films forming on different lead alloys, it is possible to calculate that both the mechanisms of formation of β-PbO_2 described above are realised in practice. Evidence of this is provided by the presence of a considerable quantity of β-PbO_2 in the composition of the anode products obtained in the corrosion of alloys which are distinguished by comparatively low corrosion resistance (Pb-Sb) and of corrosion-resistant alloys (Pb-Ag, Pb-Sb-Ag). It can be assumed that in the first instance, thanks to the anodic dissolution of antimony and the relatively macro-crystalline structure of lead-antimony alloys, a macro-porous film appears in anodic polarisation. In the process of corrosion of lead-silver and especially of lead-antimony-silver alloys, a finely dispersed dense film is formed. Thanks to this the occurrence of the oxidation process becomes probable on the surface of the electrode which is in contact with the electrolyte. The formation of PbO and α-PbO_2 can occur by means of diffusion of oxygen through the film and the penetration of it into the crystal lattice of the metal. The presence of PbO in the depth of the oxide film, naturally, can occur only in the event of quite a dense outer layer.

Obviously a possibility is the appearance of anode films with an "intermediate" pore dimension. The diffusion of the acid through such pores is made difficult but, in the thickness of the film, molecules of water and OH' ions can diffuse, causing the well-known alkalisation of the medium in the film. Here the formation of α-PbO_2 can occur in the solution filling the pores of the film by means of oxidation of lead or of Pb^{2+} ions.

The structure of the oxide film naturally depends not only on the composition of the corroding alloy, but also on the conditions of its polarisation. A change in these conditions, obviously, leads to a change in the relative rates of oxidation reactions of different types, which shows in the phase composition of the products of anodic corrosion Thus, the above-mentioned increase in β-PbO_2 content with decrease in concentration of the electrolyte and increase in temperature, can be considered as a result of the enlargement of the crystals of the anode film and an increase in the pore dimensions.

Thus, the data obtained up to the present time are evidence of the fact that the introduction into the composition of lead alloy of one alloying component or another, as well as the change in the conditions of polarisation, can show a substantial influence on the mechanism of anode corrosion. This influence will lead to a change of relative rates of the separate stages of the oxidation process occurring in parallel in the solid and the liquid phases.

The thermodynamic theory of multi-layer oxide films

It is of interest to examine the question of the thermodynamic stability of anode film forming on the surface of lead and lead alloys[126]). As was shown above, anode films represent multi-phase systems with a definite spatial localisation of the different phases. Here it is essential to note that the degree of oxidation of the components of the anode film increases in the direction from the metal to the electrolyte. In fact, on the corrosion film-electrolyte interface there is at any rate a thin layer of the tetragonal modification of lead dioxide - the oxide characterised by the highest oxidation. At the metal-film boundary surface there is a layer of lead oxide. Finally, in the composition of anode films the rhombic modification of lead dioxide is present, which is the basic product of the corrosion of lead and its alloys.

A thermodynamic examination of the system described can be carried out by means of a generalisation of the theory of oxide electrodes with two-layer films, developed by Gëro[127]). The system representing the metal **M** (e.g. lead or any lead alloy) covered by a number of consecutively located layers of oxides MO_{n_i} $(i = 1, 2, \ldots, m_{ox})$, can be written down in the form:

$$| M \mid MO_{n_1} | \; MO_{n_2} | \; \ldots \; | \; MO_{n_m} \quad \text{and } n_{i+1} > n_i > n_{i-1}$$

We shall further assume that chemical interaction is possible only between neighbouring layers which are in direct contact. This proposition imposes definite limitations on the physico-chemical properties of the oxide layers, which must possess fairly low porosity or have considerable thickness.

Let us assume that in the system represented above, account is taken of all oxides without exception, i.e. between the layers $MO_{n_{i+1}}$ and $MO_{n_{i-1}}$ there can exist only the one oxide MO_{n_i} with an intermediate oxygen content. With the correctness of the assumptions made there can occur in the system only the reactions of disproportionation

$$(n_k - n_j)MO_{n_i} = (n_k - n_i)MO_{n_j} + (n_i - n_j)MO_{n_k} \qquad n_k > n_i > n_j \tag{4.112}$$

In the special case with $n_j = 0$ $(MO_{n_j} \equiv M)$ the equation of reaction

(4.112) takes the form

$$n_k MO_{n_i} = (n_k - n_i)M + n_i MO_{n_k} \tag{4.113}$$

and at $n_k = \infty$ ($MO_{n_k} \equiv \frac{1}{2} O_2$)

$$MO_{n_i} = MO_{n_j} + \frac{n_i - n_j}{2} O_2 \tag{4.114}$$

Finally, if at the same time $n_j = 0$ and $n_k = \infty$, then the equation (4.112) describes the dissociation of the oxide MO_{n_i}

$$MO_{n_i} = M + \frac{n_i}{2} O_2 \tag{4.115}$$

If we designate the change of free energy at constant pressure corresponding to reaction (4.112) $\Delta_i G$, then the condition of thermodynamic stability of multi-layer oxide film can be written down in the form

$$\Delta_i G = (n_k - n_i)\Delta G_j + (n_i - n_j)\Delta G_k + (n_j - n_k)\Delta G_i > 0 \tag{4.116}$$

where ΔG_i, ΔG_j and ΔG_k are the free energy of formation of the corresponding oxides.

In relation to the special cases considered above (4.113)-(4.115) we shall have at $n_j = 0$ ($\Delta G_j = 0$)

$$n_k \Delta G_i < n_i \Delta G_k \tag{4.117}$$

at $n_k = \infty$ ($\Delta G_k = 0$)

$$\Delta G_i < \Delta_j \tag{4.118}$$

at $n_j = 0$ and $n_k = \infty$ ($\Delta G_j = \Delta G_k = 0$)

$$\Delta G_i < 0 \tag{4.119}$$

The inequality (4.119) expresses the condition of stable existence of the different oxides forming the film.

For each i-th oxide in a system containing m_{ox} oxide layers there are i compounds with lower oxidation (counting also the metal M) and ($m_{ox} + 1 - i$) compounds with higher oxidation (including oxygen). Thus, the total number of reactions of the type (4.112) for an i-th oxide consists of $(m_{ox} + 1 - i)\, i$, and the number of similar reactions for all systems N_p is equal to

$$N_p = \sum_{i=1}^{m_{ox}} (m_{ox}+1-i)\, i = (m_{ox}+1) \sum_{i=1}^{m_{ox}} i - \sum_{i=1}^{m_{ox}} i^2 = \frac{(m_{ox}+2)!}{6(m_{ox}-1)!} \qquad (4.120)$$

The number N_p also defines the amount of inequalities of type (4.116) which must be investigated for determination of the thermodynamic stability of the system.

If all the oxides in the system are stable, i.e. at any i $(1 \leqslant i \leqslant m_{ox})$ at all there is observed the condition (4.119), then the number of inequalities sufficient for thermodynamic description of the system under consideration (N'_p) is equal to

$$N'_p = N_p - m_{ox} = \frac{(m_{ox}+2)! - 6m_{ox}!}{6(m_{ox}-1)!} \qquad (4.121)$$

A multi-layer oxide film is thermodynamically stable if N_p (or, in the special case, N'_p) of the inequalities of type (4.118) is satisfied. If some part of the inequalities is not correct, then the system attempts to go over into a state with a smaller number of oxide layers. It must be noted that with strict observation of the assumptions made (absence of oxides with a degree of oxidation less than n_1 and impossibility of interaction of oxide layers which are not in direct contact) the metal M is thermodynamically stable. Naturally the second condition which needs, in particular, absolute impenetrability of the film to oxygen, which is considered as the outer oxide layer with infinitely high oxidation, can be observed only approximately. Therefore, the degree of perfection of the oxide layers determines the real stability of the metal.

Passing on to a direct consideration of oxide films forming on anode corrosion of lead alloys, it is possible to write down this system in the form

$$\mathbf{Pb} \,|\, \mathbf{PbO} \,|\, \alpha\text{-}\mathbf{PbO}_{n_\alpha} \,|\, \beta\text{-}\mathbf{PbO}_{n_\beta}$$

The free energies of formation of oxides coming into this system are negative values (see table 2.1). Therefore, for calculation of the number of inequalities which determine the thermodynamic stability of the film under consideration it is possible to use formula (4.121), from which it follows that $m_{ox} = 3$ $N'_p = 7$. The results of the calculation of the values of $\Delta_i G$ are given in table 4.13.

Table 4.13: Free energies of disproportionation of lead oxides

No. of reaction	Initial oxide	Products of disproportionation	$\Delta_i G$ kcal/mol
1	PbO	Pb; β-PbO_{n_β}	+44.94
2	PbO	Pb; α-PbO_{n_α}	+45.08
3	α-PbO_{n_α}	Pb; β-PbO_{n_β}	- 0.54
4	α-PbO_{n_α}	PbO; β-PbO_{n_β}	- 0.41
5	α-PbO_{n_α}	PbO; O_2	+ 4.47
6	β-PbO_{n_β}	PbO; O_2	+ 4.87
7	β-PbO_{n_β}	α-PbO_{n_α}; O_2	+ 0.40

As can be seen from these data, the disproportionation reactions 3 and 4 can occur spontaneously, i.e. the α-modification of lead dioxide is thermodynamically unstable and must be disproportionated with the formation of the β-modification. It must be noted, however, that α-PbO_2 does not disproportionate according to scheme 5 (table 4.13). This process can occur only in the direction of oxidation of PbO:

$$PbO + \frac{n_\alpha - 1}{2} O_2 \rightarrow \alpha\text{-}PbO_{n_\alpha} \quad (4.122)$$

which confirms the possibility of the corrosion of lead as a result of subsequent oxidation according to scheme (4.84). It is possible in principle that there should be further oxidation of α-PbO_{n_α} according to reaction (2.86), leading to the formation of the β-modification of lead dioxide.

The data quoted show that lead oxide in the system under consideration is thermodynamically stable. The presence of a layer of PbO separating the metal and the lead dioxide protects the metal from oxidation, causing stabilisation of the whole system. In this connection interest is aroused by the fact that, as was shown above, the formation of PbO on the film-metal interface is especially characteristic for lead alloys compounded with silver, which are distinguished by a high corrosion resistance.

Among the oxides of lead there exist fairly stable compounds with a degree of oxidation less than unity. Therefore, the possibility of oxidation of the lead as a result of the interaction with PbO is excluded. On the other hand, the process of oxidation of the lead by the dioxide according to reaction (4.90) occurs in the solid phase with marked rapidity. Naturally, the protective effect described can play a part only in the event of separate layers of anode film, and in particular the PbO layer, possessing low penetrability for oxidising agents.

In the system examined above no account was taken of oxides of lead with a degree of oxidation of $2 > n > 1$, e.g. Pb_3O_4 and Pb_2O_3. Although these compounds are not found in radiographic study of anode films, the intermediate formation of them can take place in principle.

Calculation of the value of $\Delta_i G$ for the system

$$Pb\ |PbO\ |Pb_3O_4\ |Pb_2O_3\ |\alpha\text{-}PbO_{n_\alpha}|\ \beta\text{-}PbO_{n_\beta}$$

shows that in this case the role of the intermediate layer separating the corroding metal and the tetragonal modification of lead dioxide is fulfilled by minium. The system $Pb|\ Pb_3O_4|\ \beta\text{-}PbO_{n\beta}$ is thermodynamically stable. The absence of Pb_3O_4 in the products of anode corrosion is, obviously, evidence of the kinetic difficulties connected with the formation of this oxide.

Let us note that the presence in the composition of the film of layers with a degree of oxidation which is continuously changing according to the thickness does not alter the conclusions drawn. It is not difficult to show that within the limits of such layers and also within the limits of a layer of constant composition $\Delta_i G = 0$. In fact, if we divide the layer with changing oxidation into a number of infinitely thin layers, within the limits of each of which the oxidation can be reckoned as constant, then, using the designations introduced earlier, we can write

$$n_k = n_i + dn_i, \quad n_j = n_i - dn_i \tag{4.123}$$

and

$$\Delta G_k = \Delta G_i + \frac{\partial \Delta G_i}{\partial n_i} dn_i, \quad \Delta G_j = \Delta G_i - \frac{\partial \Delta G_i}{\partial n_i} dn_i \tag{4.124}$$

The kinetics of forming and of cathodic reduction of anodic films on lead and its alloys

The data quoted above about the phase composition of oxide films referred basically to the end products of anodic corrosion of lead and its alloys. The results of radiographic analysis are not sufficient, however, for the evaluation of the nature of the intermediate products which can appear in the process of forming and of cathodic reduction of films. This is due to the instability of the intermediate compounds and the low sensitivity of X-ray analysis.

The most acceptable method of studying the nature of the compounds appearing in the period of anodic oxidation of the metal and cathodic reduction of the oxide film is by potentiometric and impedance measurements. Potentiometric data also make it possible to determine the value of the overvoltage of the oxidation-reduction processes occurring in the anode film. These last results are needed, as will be shown below, for calculation of the values of the potentials realised on the surface of the anodic oxidation sample in partial damage to the solidity of the film which can occur as a result of deformation of the sample.

As a rule $PbSO_4$ is formed in the initial stage of anodic polarisation of lead and its alloys. An increase in current density as a result of screening of the electrode surface by sulphate film leads to a sharp increase in potential. As a result the formation of PbO_2 becomes possible. In the graph of change of potential in time (φ, τ) a number of checks in the process are observed, corresponding to the formation of various intermediate products. In the work of Eckler[128]) a check in the process is observed which the author links with the Pb/PbO or $Pb/Pb(OH)_2$ systems, and Ose[129]) explains this plateau by the formation of $PbO \cdot PbSO_4$. In a number of papers the intermediate formation of PbO is noted.

In a study of the cathodic reduction of lead dioxide films on a lead electrode, what was principally found was pauses in potentials which corresponded to the systems $PbO_2/PbSO_4$ and $PbSO_4/Pb$.

E V Krivolapova observed a pause in potential at $\varphi \approx -0.7V$ (in relation to Hg/Hg_2SO_4) and explained it by the formation of compounds corresponding to the calculation of PbO_2 and $PbSO_4$ or by the appearance of oxides of the Pb_3O_4 or Pb_2O_3 type, Ruestchi and Cahan[130]) observed separate reduction of α and β-PbO_2. Burbank[131]) found several pauses, which were connected with the formation of $PbSO_4 \cdot PbO$ and $Pb(OH)_2$. They connect the check in potential between -0.1 and -0.2V (in relation to Hg/Hg_2SO_4) with the appearance of PbO, $Pb(OH)_2$ or basic sulphates.

The charge and discharge processes of an electrode of lead-antimony alloys have been examined by a number of authors. E V Krivolapova noted that, besides $PbSO_4$ and PbO_2, a plateau was observed in the graph of change in potential under anodic polarisation of an alloy containing 8% Sb at $\varphi \approx -0.3V$ (against a Hg/Hg_2SO_4 electrode). The author considers that this is connected with the formation of antimony sulphate or an antimonous compound of another composition. Similar data are quoted in ref.[111]). In the work [132]) a plateau was found at a potential close to the potential of the equilibrium $Sb + H_2O \rightleftarrows SbO^+ + 2H^+ + 3e$. In the work[130]) reference is made to the presence of clear-cut plateaus corresponding to α and β-PbO_2 formation on the discharge of an anode film formed on lead-antimony alloys with a content of 1 to 12% Sb.

The short survey of literature given above shows that the data obtained in potentiometric study of the anode and cathode processes occurring on lead and lead-antimony alloy are in many respects contradictory. This may partly be explained by a difference in the method of preparation of the samples and carrying out the experiments. The results published in early papers cannot be considered fully correct owing to the imperfection of the methods of chronopotentiometric measurements and also through the absence or unreliability of thermodynamic data. It must be noted that the authors of the works quoted were limited by the determination of the phase composition of the anode products by means of approximate comparison of the potentials corresponding to the pauses in the graphs (φ, τ) with potentials of the corresponding equilibria. In connection with this, the results described in literature give no possibility of determining the overvoltage of the corresponding processes.

A study was made by us of the dependence of the overvoltage of the anodic oxidation of lead and a number of lead alloys, on the current of the cathodic reduction of substances formed in the process of anodic corrosion in $10N \cdot H_2SO_4$. In the calculation of the equilibrium values of the potentials the most reliable thermodynamic data, quoted in table 2.3, were used. For additional characterisation of the properties of oxide films, impedance measurements were also used in the work, along with potentiometric ones.

The samples under investigation were subjected to anodic polarisation during 15 minutes at a current density $j = 10mA/cm^2$. After this the current was switched off and the electrode was held until the establishment of stationary potential. Cathodic reduction of the electrode under investigation was carried out in the interval from $j = 3 \cdot 10^{-5}$ to $j = 3 \cdot 10^{-3} A/cm^2$. In separate experiments at $j = 10^{-4} A/cm^2$ impedance was measured in the process of cathode reduction at ν = 100Hz. Anodic oxidation was studied in the same interval of measurement of j.

For determination of the potential corresponding to one plane or another in the graph (φ, τ) a tangent to that section of the graph was constructed, and also to the sections of sharp change in potential directly adjacent to the plane. The potential at a point dividing into two equal parts the section of the tangent to the plane intersected by two other tangents was taken. The length of the corresponding plane was determined by the length of the straight section parallel to the axis of the abscissae τ and proceeding through the above-mentioned central point between the tangents constructed to the section of sharp change of potential.

In the period of anodic polarisation a gradual shift of the potential of the electrode in a negative direction is observed. Here the value of the impedance decreases. This phenomenon is obviously caused by the increase in the active surface of the electrode owing to the formation and growth of a lead dioxide film with a relatively coarse surface. The rate of change of the potential and of the impedance decreases in time and gradually approaches the constant value.

The graphs (φ, τ) obtained with anodic oxidation of lead-antimony alloys, along with the plateau corresponding to the formation of the sulphate $Pb \rightarrow PbSO_4$, show a check in potential rise corresponding to the oxidation $Sb \rightarrow SbO^+$. The introduction of Sb causes a sharper drop in potential and a more positive value. The graph (Z, τ) for Pb-Sb alloy also takes a course somewhat higher than the graph for pure lead (especially in the initial period of anodic polarisation). These data are evidence of the fact that the introduction of antimony into the alloy causes the formation during anodic polarisation of an oxide film with a lower value of active surface. Note must also be taken of the fact that antimony, as is well known, lowers the oxygen overvoltage on lead (see fig. 4.49). Therefore, the changes in anode potential shown under conditions where the basic process is the process of the liberation of oxygen, can be explained only by the considerable change in the true current density, or in other words, in the active surface of the electrode.

It is characteristic that in the graphs (φ, τ) taken during anodic oxidation of lead and its alloys a plateau is absent near the equilibrium potential of $PbO_2 \rightleftarrows PbSO_4$. It can be assumed that the phase conversion $PbSO_4 \rightarrow PbO_2$ occurs by means of gradual oxidation of the sulphate in the thickness of the anode layer through a number of intermediate oxides according to the scheme (4.58).

In experiments with a lead electrode, in the initial moment after switching off the current, a sharp jump in potential is noticed (~30mV) in a negative direction, and then a more gentle increase to a value of $\varphi = 1.165V$ (Hg/Hg_2SO_4 electrode) and a subsequent slow decrease to a stationary value close to the equilibrium potential of $PbO_2 \rightleftarrows PbSO_4$ ($\varphi = 1.161V$). Here, together with an increase in potential, the impedance also increased and the value of the latter also stabilised later. The time necessary for the establishment of stationary values of potential and impedance was ~20 min.

In the case of lead-antimony alloys, the character of the change in potential and impedance in the first period after the switching off of the current did not differ from that described above. However, after the attainment of the maximum, the drop in potential continued for a long time and a stationary value was not established. With long-term maintenance of anodic polarisation of lead-antimony alloy electrode, its potential took on values more negative than the potential corresponding to the equilibrium $PbO_2 \rightleftarrows PbSO_4$. The equilibrium value of the potential is established after 10 minutes' holding. Therefore, in our experiments, the cathodic reduction of the oxide film on lead-antimony alloy began in 10 min. after cessation of the anodic polarisation.

The character of the change in time of φ and Z at $j = 0$ can be explained in the following manner. Immediately after switching off the current desorption of oxygen occurs from the outer layers of the lead dioxide film, which causes a shift in potential in a negative direction and also a decrease in impedance. Subsequent measurements of φ and Z are obviously connected with the formation of lead sulphate in the pores of the oxide film. This process occurs as a result of the reaction (2.34), in which the lead to be found in the depth of the pores participates. Therefore, in a given period, a compromise potential of equilibria $Pb \rightleftarrows PbSO_4$ and $PbO_2 \rightleftarrows PbSO_4$ is realised on the electrode.

In principle the formation of $PbSO_4$ can also occur as a result of the reaction of sulphation of lead dioxide according to the scheme (4.74). However, this process obviously does not play an important role owing to the quite low speed of its occurrence. In addition, the fact that in the the initial period after the switching off of the current the potential falls below the value corresponding to the equilibrium $PbO_2 \rightleftarrows PbSO_4$ is evidence of the direct participation of the lead in this process.

After all the pores are basically filled up with lead sulphate a potential is established on the electrode close to the potential of the equilibrium $PbO_2 \rightleftarrows PbSO_4$ and the impedance takes on a stable value. The lead dioxide film formed on lead-antimony alloy is characterised by much greater permeability to acid than a similar film on lead. Therefore the process of self-discharge occurring according to scheme (2.34) causes much longer and more substantial decrease in potential. These data are also evidence of the fact that lead sulphate formed by self-discharge on lead-antimony alloy does not possess any marked protective properties in contrast to sulphate formed by self-discharge of an anodically polarised lead electrode, which is possibly due to the process of dissolution of the antimony in the pores of the oxide film.

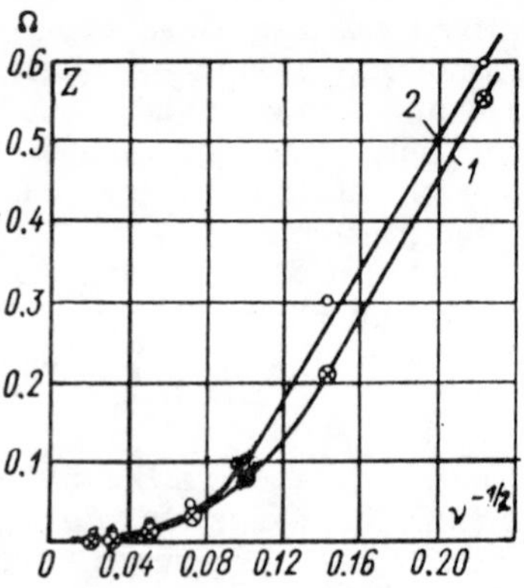

Fig.4.55 Frequency dependence of the impedance of a lead dioxide film formed on lead (1) and lead-antimony alloy (2).

As can be seen from fig. 4.55 a decrease occurred in the impedance of the electrical double layer of the oxide film formed both on a lead electrode and on a lead-antimony one, with increase in the frequency of alternating current over the range 20-1000Hz. Further increase of ν did not cause any change of impedance. It may be reckoned that at $\nu < 1000$Hz the measured value of Z represents basically the ohmic resistance of the electrolyte to be found in the pores of the oxide film and directly on the surface of the electrode R_p.

Taking the assumption made in relation to the character of the value R_p as correct,

$$l/S = R_p \varkappa \quad (4.125)$$

where $\varkappa$ is the specific electrical conductivity of the electrolyte, l the averaged value of the depth of the pores (including the layer of electrolyte directly adjacent to the surface of the electrode), S the effective value of the area of the electrode falling to the pores. For evaluation of the values of l and S it is possible to use, together with formula (4.125), the equation for the calculation of the volumetric porosity of the oxide film

$$\gamma = \frac{V_p}{V_p + (\Delta P/d)} \qquad (4.126)$$

where $V_p = lS$ - volume of pores, ΔP is the mass of the lead dioxide film, $d = 9.7 g/cm^3$ - the density of lead dioxide (α-PbO_2).

Solving simultaneously (4.125) and (4.126), we shall have

$$l = \sqrt{\frac{\Delta P \gamma R_p \varkappa}{d(1-\gamma)}} \qquad (4.127)$$

$$S = \sqrt{\frac{\Delta P \gamma}{d(1-\gamma) R_p \varkappa}} \qquad (4.128)$$

Calculation according to formulae (4.127) and (4.128) leads to the following results: for a lead electrode $l \approx 2.7 \cdot 10^{-3}$ cm; $S \approx 0.018 cm^2$ (per cm^2 of visible surface); for a lead-antimony electrode $l \approx 4.1 \cdot 10^{-3}$ cm; $S \approx 0.026 cm^2$. Thus, the results of the calculation are evidence of the increased thickness and surface porosity of the lead dioxide film formed on lead-antimony alloy. Calculation of the capacity of the double layer gives the following values: for lead $C_d \approx 3\,600 \mu F/cm^2$, for lead-antimony alloy $C_d \approx 3\,400 \mu F/cm^2$ (per visible surface of the electrode). The difference of the C_d characteristic is the increased roughness of the lead dioxide film on lead (in comparison with the lead-antimony alloy).

Graphs are shown in fig. 4.56 of the change in potential on cathodic reduction of PbO_2 on lead. On the graphs (φ, τ) there are three distinct plateaus. The potentials corresponding to the mid-points of the plateaus change depending on the current of cathodic polarisation within the following limits (in relation to Hg/Hg_2SO_4): +1.092 - +1.146V; -0.629 - -0.666V; -0.972 - -1.018V. At $j < 10^{-4} A/cm^2$ additionally one further short-duration pause in the potential at φ = +1.043 - +1.048V was observed.

In conformity with the data given in table 2.3, the first plane in the graph (φ, τ) corresponds to the process

$$PbO_2 + HSO_4^- + 3H^+ + 2e \rightleftarrows PbSO_4 + 2H_2O, \quad \varphi_p = +1.161B \qquad (4.129)$$

At potential φ = -0.619- -0.666V, reduction of monobasic sulphate into lead, probably takes place. The potential corresponding to

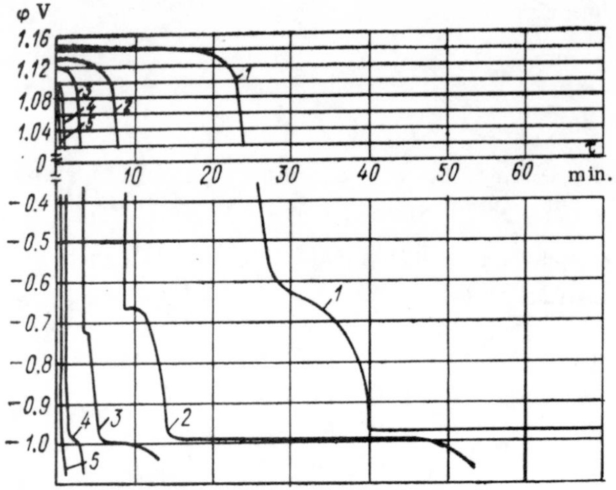

Fig.4.56 Change in potential (Hg/Hg_2SO_4) with cathodic reduction of lead dioxide film on lead at different current densities (A/cm^2): 1 - $3 \cdot 10^{-5}$; 2 - 10^{-4}; 3 - $3 \cdot 10^{-4}$; 4 - 10^{-3}; 5 - $3 \cdot 10^{-3}$.

the equilibrium

$$PbO \cdot PbSO_4 + 3H^+ + 4e \rightleftarrows 2Pb + HSO_4^- + H_2O, \quad \varphi_p = -0.669B \qquad (4.130)$$

The third plateau corresponds to the process of reduction of $PbSO_4$

$$PbSO_4 + 2e + H^+ \rightleftarrows Pb + HSO_4^-, \quad \varphi_p = -0.971B \qquad (4.131)$$

The subsequent shift of the potential in a negative direction is caused by the process of separation of hydrogen. At $j = 3 \cdot 10^{-5}\ A/cm^2$ this shift was not observed. The pause in potential that takes place at low densities of reduction current obviously reflects the process of reduction of minium into tribasic lead sulphate

$$4Pb_3O_4 + 3HSO_4^- + 11H^+ + 8e \rightleftarrows 3[3PbO \cdot PbSO_4 \cdot H_2O] + 4H_2O, \quad \varphi_p = +1.063B \qquad (4.132)$$

The graphs of change of potential in the cathodic reduction of the lead dioxide film on lead-antimony alloys (5-6% Sb) are basically similar to the graphs (φ, τ) obtained on a lead electrode examined above (fig. 4.57). In the graphs there are plateaus corresponding to the process (4.129), (4.130) and (4.131), and also a small plateau which corresponds to reaction (4.132). The values of the potentials which

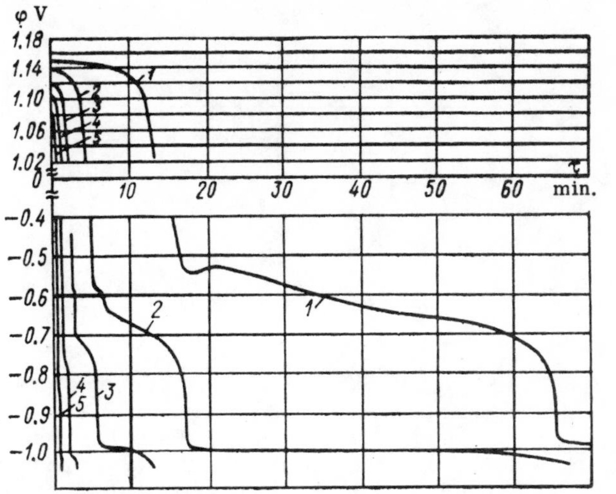

Fig.4.57 Change of potential (Hg/Hg_2SO_4 electrode) in cathodic reduction of the lead dioxide film on lead-antimony alloy at different current densities (see fig. 4.56).

correspond to the mid-points of the plateaus shown lie within the following limits (depending on the current): +1.076 - +1.150V; -0.635 - -0.822V; -0.989 - -1.001V; +1.048 - +1.054V.

Careful comparison of the potentials, corresponding to the kinks in the graphs (φ, τ) for Pb-Sb alloys with the equilibrium potentials of different oxidation-reduction reactions occurring with the participation of Sb compounds, showed that these checks cannot be ascribed to the processes in which any known antimony compounds participate. In contrast to the graphs (φ, τ) shown in fig. 4.56, in the case of Pb-Sb alloy (fig. 4.57) there occurs one other clearly-defined plane lying within the limits of the potentials φ = -0.541 - -0.626V and obviously corresponding to the process of reduction of tribasic lead sulphate to lead

$$3PbO \cdot PbSO_4 \cdot H_2O + 7H^+ + 8e \rightleftarrows 4Pb + HSO_4^- + 4H_2O, \quad \varphi_p = -0.543B \qquad (4.133)$$

It must be noted that in cathodic polarisation of an anodically oxidised electrode of lead-antimony alloy at high current densities ($j \geqslant 10^{-3}$ A/cm^2), in contrast to a Pb electrode, separate reduction of the rhombic and tetragonal modifications of lead dioxide was observed. This is evidenced by

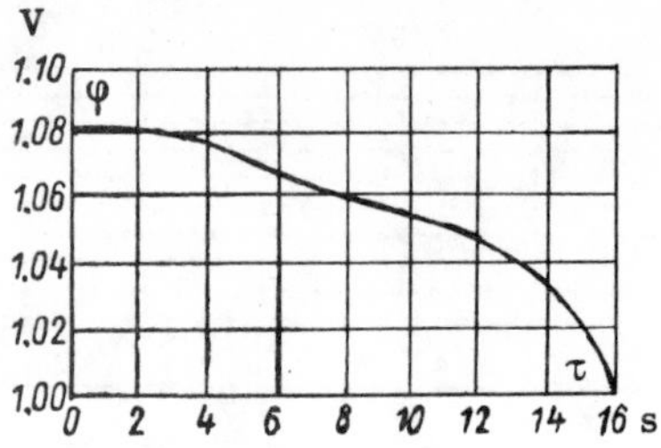

Fig.4.58 The initial section of the graph of cathodic reduction of the lead dioxide film on Pb-Sb alloy at $j = 3 \cdot 10^{-3}\,A/cm^2$.

the presence of two steps in the first stage of reduction (fig. 4.58), the distance between which amounts to approximately 15mV. This phenomenon can be explained by the increased content of β-PbO_2 in the composition of the anode films forming on lead-antimony alloy (in comparison with lead). The fact that an additional step is observed only at high current densities is probably connected with the uneven distribution of the polarisation and the preferential localisation of β-PbO_2 in the outer layers of the anode film.

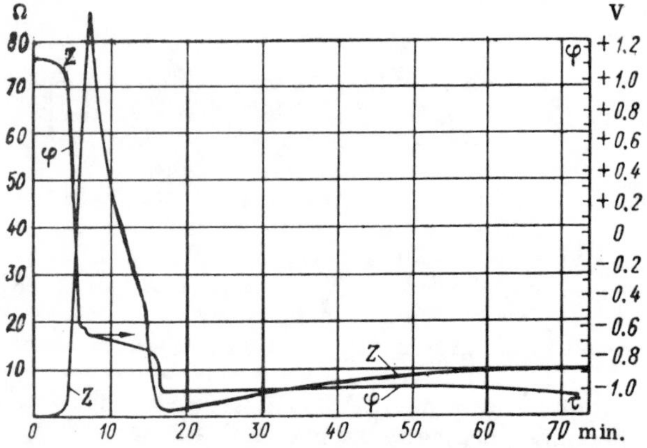

Fig.4.59 Change in potential at cathodic reduction of lead dioxide film on Pb-Sb alloy.

The character of the change of impedance in the process of reduction of the lead dioxide film on lead and lead-antimony alloy is shown in fig. 4.59. From this figure it can be seen that the reduction of PbO_2 is accompanied by a sharp increase in impedance, which is naturally connected with the formation of an insulating film consisting of sulphates of differing basicity. The progress towards the third plateau in the graph (φ, τ) is accompanied by a fall in impedance. This phenomenon can be explained by the increase in the electrical conductivity of the sulphate film as a result of the phase conversions connected with volume changes and with film as a result of the phase conversions connected with volume changes and with the appearance of through cracks. A slow increase in impedance corresponds to the process of reduction of $PbSO_4$ to lead. Obviously, this is explained by the fact that bubbles of hydrogen forming on the free surface of the metal screen this surface. The complex character of the changes in the reactive and active components of the impedance at a change in phase composition of the anode films makes a more detailed treatment of the dependencies (Z, τ) observed difficult.

Going over to an examination of the dependence of the amount of electricity q, corresponding to the separate stages of cathodic reduction of the lead dioxide film, on the current density j, it must be noted above all, that in a number of cases Peukert's equation is shown to be correct. The amount of PbO_2 reduced to sulphate increases and the amount of sulphate reduced to lead decreases with an increase in current density. The amount of basic sulphate converted to lead in the intermediate stage of reduction does not depend on the current in practice.

In the case of an electrode of lead-antimony alloy Peukert's equation is shown to be correct only for the process of reduction $PbSO_4 \rightarrow Pb$. In the remaining cases ($PbO_2 \rightarrow PbSO_4$; $PbO \cdot PbSO_4 \rightarrow Pb$) the dependence of q on j bears a more complex character. The amount of electricity expended in the reduction of tribasic sulphate does not in practice depend on the current. An essential distinction in the (φ, τ) graphs obtained on electrodes of Pb-Sb alloy is also the fact that in the process of reduction of the oxide film a considerable amount of monobasic sulphate is formed, with the amounts of electricity corresponding to the process $PbO \cdot PbSO_4 \rightarrow Pb$ not being very dependent on the current.

It is interesting to compare the amount of electricity expended on the oxidation of the electrode, i.e. on the formation of the lead dioxide film ($q_{Pb \rightarrow PbO_2}$) with the amount of electricity which corresponds to the reduction of PbO_2 calculated according to the graph φ, τ ($q_{PbO_2 \rightarrow PbSO_4}$).

It was established that in the first stage of discharge of the oxide film a comparatively small part of the lead dioxide formed in the process of anodic polarisation is reduced. This phenomenon is connected with the marked reduction $PbO_2 \rightarrow PbSO_4$ in the period of holding the sample without current. As the iodometer results show, not more than 10% of the original PbO_2 remains in the anode film when equilibrium is attained in the equation $PbO_2 \rightleftarrows PbSO_4$.

The formation of basic sulphates in the process of cathodic reduction of lead dioxide film occurs, obviously, as a result of hydrolysis of $PbSO_4$ according to the scheme $2PbSO_4 + H_2O \rightarrow PbO \cdot PbSO_4 + H_2SO_4$ which occurs in the thickness of the oxide film where the acidity of the medium is low[101]). The appearance of intermediate oxides (Pb_3O_4) is evidence of the fact that the reduction of PbO_2 partly occurs in the solid phase by means of a gradual decrease in the degree of oxidation. The final result of this process is lead oxide, whose interaction with $PbSO_4$ and with the molecules of water can also cause the appearance of sulphates of different basicity to a known extent. It can be assumed that the process of decreasing the degree of oxidation occurs basically in the period corresponding to the progression from the first plane in the graph (φ, τ) to the second. Further on, a sharp change in potential can be linked with the conversion of the basic sulphates to neutral owing to the chemical interaction with the sulphuric acid.

In conclusion let us consider the dependence of the overvoltage of the oxidation and reduction processes on the current density[143]). These dependencies are described by Tafel's equations, the coefficients of which are given in table 4.14.

Table 14: Coefficients in Tafel's equation (V)

Scheme of process	Pb		Pb + 6% Pb		Pb+5% Sb+ +0.3%As		Pb+5% Sb+ +0.5%Ag	
	a	b	a	b	a	b	a	b
$PbO_2 \rightarrow PbSO_4$	0.137	0.027	0.165	0.034	0.130	0.026	0.155	0.032
$PbO \cdot PbSO_4 \rightarrow Pb$	0.431	0.106	0.407	0.099	0.392	0.095	0.365	0.091
$3PbO \cdot PbSO_4 \cdot H_2O \rightarrow Pb$	-	-	0.180	0.036	0.194	0.037	0.149	0.027
$PbSO_4 \rightarrow Pb$	0.081	0.015	0.026	0.003	0.038	0.005	0.031	0.004
$Pb \rightarrow PbSO_4$	0.142	0.028	0.155	0.030	0.148	0.030	0.146	0.027
$Sb \rightarrow SbO^+$	-	-	0.225	0.044	0.275	0.054	0.181	0.034

What is of special interest is above all the fact that the majority of semi-logarithmic graphs of the dependence of the overvoltage on the current are characterised by low coefficients of slope. An exception is the process of cathodic reduction of monobasic sulphate. For this case Tafel's equation is characterised by a value of the pre-logarithmic coefficient close to the value which is characteristic of single electron processes.

As has already been mentioned, low values of the pre-logarithmic coefficient are characteristic for the case when the rate of the process is limited by the stage of dissociation for the disproportionation of oxides or hydroxides[56]). This circumstance is evidence of the important role of the solid phase reactions in the kinetics of the processes under consideration.

Corrosion deformation of the grids of the positive electrode

Basic ideas about corrosion deformation

The electro-chemical properties of lead alloys are insufficient for the characterisation of the corrosion behaviour of the grids of the positive electrode of a lead acid battery which are made of these alloys. In the process of the operation of the battery, along with anodic corrosion, the grids are subject to deformation. Deformation leads to an increase of the linear dimensions of the frame ("growth of grids"), buckling and fracture of the separate ribs of the grids. All these phenomena cause destruction of the positive grids and unserviceability of the battery.

Naturally, the deformation of the grids is closely connected with the character of the corrosion of the anode alloy, which depends in its turn on the structure of the alloy. The more evenly the anodic oxidation occurs, the greater (at one and the same rate of corrosion) is the service life of the grids. In the case when intercrystalline corrosion is prevalent, deterioration of the grids occurs quite intensively, even with a moderate rate of anodic oxidation of the alloy.

An essential role in the phenomena under consideration is played by the mechanical properties of the anode alloy. The factors causing an increase in the mechanical strength of the alloy should (all other things being equal) decrease the deformability of the grids in the work of the battery. Low temperatures of melting and of recrystallisation of lead alloys substantially limit the possibilities of strengthening of these alloys. A considerable increase in the mechanical strength is achieved only by alloying. The strengthening effect of alloy addition elements is reinforced by a decrease in the atomic volume of the lattice[133]).

The important significance of the mechanical properties of lead alloys is shown, in particular, in a comparison of the behaviour in a battery of positive grids made of antimony-free lead-silver alloys and of alloys of the system Pb-Sb-Ag[84]). It follows from the data quoted in fig. 4.46, that with a content in the alloy of ~3% Ag, the introduction of antimony does not have much influence on the rate of anode corrosion. Testing in a battery, however, showed that grids cast from an alloy of Pb + 3% Ag deteriorate quickly, while grids of the alloy Pb + 5% Sb + 3% Ag show good preservation after long testing by the method of continuous charge and by the method of cycling. It must be noted that with the presence of silver in the alloy the additional introduction of antimony shows no marked influence on the character of the corrosion of the alloy.

At the same time alloys containing antimony are distinguished by much better mechanical properties than antimony-free lead-silver alloys. This fact obviously determines the increased strength of grids made of alloys of the system Pb-Sb-Ag in comparison with grids made of Pb-Ag alloys. As has already been mentioned, the insufficient mechanical strength of lead-thallium alloys makes them unsuitable for use in a battery.

The anti-corrosion effect of the addition of arsenic, which at present is widely used in the battery industry, is also closely linked with the influence of this element on the process of deformation of battery grids. In fact, as has been shown in the preceding chapters, the introduction of 0.2% As into lead-antimony alloy does not cause any marked changes in the rate of corrosion of the alloy, nor in the anode potential and the phase composition of the oxide film. On the other hand, small additions of arsenic cause a change in the micro-structure of the lead-antimony alloy, which leads to amore even corrosion. In addition, as has been shown above, the introduction of arsenic causes a substantial increase in the hardness and tensile strength of a lead-antimony alloy. All these factors should cause an increased strength of grids made of lead-antimony-arsenic alloys against deformation appearing in the process of utilisation of the battery.

One of the possible reasons for the deformation of the grids may be the volume changes in the positive active mass. In fact, in the process of discharge a considerable increase in volume occurs as a result of the conversion of PbO_2 into $PbSO_4$. This increase amounts to 24.1cm^3/g-M. However, this reason does not play the main role, since the mass is not sufficiently strongly connected with the grid. Elongation of the elements of the grid is accompanied by the appearance of cavities between the grid and the active mass[68]). In addition, as is shown by the appropriate calculation, the rise in volume of the active mass in the phase conversion $PbO_2 \rightarrow PbSO_4$ occurs basically on account of a decrease in the porosity with the maintenance of the dimensions of the electrode. It must also be mentioned that at the discharge of the negative electrode of the battery there is observed a more marked increase in the active mass volume (30.5cm^3/g-M). Nevertheless, as is known, the negative plates are not deformed even with quite long usage of the battery.

It may be reckoned that the phenomenon under consideration is basically caused by the appearance of the oxide film on the surface of the metal in the process of anodic corrosion of it[134]. The molecular volume of the lead dioxide, which is the end product of anodic corrosion of the lead and its alloys, is approximately 1.4 times in excess of the atomic volume of the lead at high positive potentials. The difference in the volumes of PbO_2 and Pb increases owing to the considerable porosity of the lead dioxide film.

As was shown, the growth of the film in the process of corrosion, excluding the initial period of polarisation, is in the direction of the corroding metal. In connection with this the film exerts a definite pressure on the surface of the metal, which may cause deformation of the metal. This mechanism of corrosion deformation is possible only in the case when the oxide film possesses sufficient strength, since otherwise under the influence of the pressure it will crack and peel off from the metal. It is therefore natural that deformation is caused only by that part of the anode film which is strongly connected with the surface of the metal. Let us also note that the low creep-resistance of lead alloys at normal temperature causes the possibility of deformation at comparatively low tensions.

Corrosion deformation of a freely suspended bar

Experimental study of the deformation of freely suspended thin strips of lead and of a number of lead alloys under the influence of anodic corrosion was carried out by Lander[134]. The author showed that the relative elongation of the corroding sample is increased with an increase in the thickness of the oxide film, following the linear law.

A similar dependence was obtained by the authors by means of an elementary theoretical examination of the process of deformation under the influence of the pressure of the oxide film[84]. If we allow that the deformation is proportional to the difference of volumes of the anode film forming on the side surface of the bar up to a definite moment in time and of the oxidising metal, then, as is shown by calculation[84], the relative elongation of a bar ($\Delta l/l$) representing a regular prism with a number of side faces n_f and a long side of base a is equal to

$$\frac{\Delta l}{l} = \frac{K \tan\frac{\pi}{n_f}\left(a + \delta \tan\frac{\pi}{n_f}\right)\delta}{a^2}\left[1 - \frac{A_M d_{fi}}{M_{fi} d_M}(1 - \gamma)\right] \quad (4.134)$$

where K is a coefficient depending on the mechanical properties of the corroding metal and of the oxide film, δ is the thickness of the film, γ

the porosity of the film, A_M the atomic mass of the metal, M_{fi} the molecular mass of the film (corrosion product), d_M the density of the metal, d_{fi} the density of the production of corrosion.

If the thickness of the film is small in comparison with the thickness of the corroding base which is equal to: $a \cot \frac{\pi}{n_f}$, then the equation (4.134) can be written down, substituting known numerical values, in the form

$$\frac{\Delta l}{l} = \frac{K_1 \delta \sqrt{n_f \tan(\pi/n_f)}}{\sqrt{S_c}} (0.28 + 0.72\gamma) \qquad (4.135)$$

where S_c is the area of cross-section of the bar, and $K_1 = K/2$.

The data obtained by Lander[134]) point to the existence of a certain minimum value of the thickness of the oxide film δ_0 necessary for the beginning of deformation of lead and lead alloys. This fact can be formally taken into account by replacement of the value δ in formulae (4.134) and (4.135) by the value $\delta - \delta_0$. Equation (4.135) in this case takes the form

$$\frac{\Delta l}{l} = \frac{K_1 \sqrt{n_f \tan(\pi/n_f)}}{\sqrt{S_c}} (0.28 + 0.72\gamma)(\delta - \delta_0) \qquad (4.136)$$

The presence of a limiting value of the thickness of the oxide film ($\delta_0 \neq 0$) is obviously connected with the characteristics of the growth of the film in the initial period of anodic polarisation considered above.

From equation (4.136) it follows that the relative loss of elongation of a freely suspended bar caused by film corrosion in a linear function of the thickness of the oxide film, which is in conformity with the experimental data[134]). The values of K_1 and δ_0 in (4.136), depending on the composition of the alloy and the conditions of polarisation, can be determined from the slope of the graph ($\Delta l/l$, δ) and the extrapolated value of δ at $\Delta l/l = 0$. According to (4.136) the value of relative elongation decreases with an increase in the area of cross-section of the bar under consideration and a decrease in porosity of the anode film. With a given area of cross-section the elongation of a freely suspended bar decreases with an increase in the number of its faces (n_f). In fact $d\sqrt{n_f \tan(\pi/n_f)}/dn_f < 0$.

The value $\Delta l/l$ will have its maximum magnitude at $n_f = 3 \left(\sqrt{3 \tan\frac{\pi}{3}}\right) = 2.279$ and its minimum at $n_f = \infty \left(\lim_{n_f \to \infty} \sqrt{n_f \tan\frac{\pi}{n_f}}\right) = 1.772$, In the usual case the transition from a prismatic bar with a number of faces n_f to a cylindrical one with one and the same area of cross-section should lead to a decrease in deformation proportional to the value $\sqrt{\frac{\pi}{n_f}\cot\frac{\pi}{n_f}}$. Therefore it is possible to ascertain the reduction in the cross-section area of the corroding bar, owing to its transition to a cylindrical form, and this leads to a marked decrease in consumption of the metal. The ideas developed here were used for the creation of new, economical designs of grids of the positive electrode of a lead acid battery, the practical realisation of which led to a considerable saving of lead.

It is not difficult to show that an increase in the number of faces n_f for a given area of cross-section leads to a decrease in the side surface of the bar. A cylindrical bar has the minimum value of side surface. A decrease in the area of side surface of the ribs of a battery grid causes a reduction in the rate of transfer to the solution of the alloying components of the anode alloy, which is quite desirable from the point of view of the conditions of work of the negative electrode of a battery. Thus the analysis carried out points to the advisability of using positive grids with a cylindrical configuration of the ribs in batteries.

The theory of corrosion deformation of a rigidly fixed cylindrical bar

The elongation of a freely suspended bar does not sufficiently fully reflect the conditions occurring in corrosion of a battery grid. The grid represents a collection of bars rigidly attached at both ends. A model of the oxide film forming in the process of anodic corrosion can be represented as an envelope, also attached at the ends and exerting pressure on the metal. Examination of such a model was carried out in refs. [135],[136] for the case of a cylindrical bar. Here use was made of the theory of deformation of cylindrical envelopes under the influence of uniform internal pressure[137].

The flexure ω of a cylindrical envelope with radius r and length l which is under pressure p is given[137] in the usual case by the equation

$$\omega = -\frac{pr^2}{E_S\delta} + C_1 \sinh \zeta x + C_2 \cos \zeta x \cosh \zeta x \qquad (4.137)$$

where δ is the thickness of the envelope, E_S is the Young's modulus of the envelope material, x the co-ordinate of a given point (the x axis coincides with the axis of the envelope)

$$\zeta = \frac{\sqrt[4]{3(1-\nu^2{}_P)}}{\sqrt{r\delta}} \qquad (4.138)$$

ν_p is the Poisson's coefficient of the material of the envelope.

If the origin of the co-ordinates (x = 0) is located in the middle of the envelope being examined, then the conditions of rigid attachment of the ends of the envelope can be written down in the form $\omega_{x=l/2} = 0$ and $(d\omega/dx)_{x=l/2} = 0$. Carrying out the substitution $x = l/2$ in the equation (4.137) and in the derivative $d\omega/dx$ and equating the expressions obtained with zero, we have a system of two equations, the solution of which makes it possible to determine the constants C_1 and C_2. After substitution of the constants C_1 and C_2 calculated in this way in (4.137) this equation takes on the form

$$\omega = \frac{pr^2}{E_S\delta}\left[\frac{2(\sin\zeta_1\cosh\zeta_1 - \cos\zeta_1\sinh\zeta_1)\sin\zeta x\sinh\zeta x}{\sin 2\zeta_1 + \sinh\zeta_1} + \frac{2(\sin\zeta_1\cosh\zeta_1 + \cos\zeta_1\sinh\zeta_1)\cos\zeta x\cosh\zeta x}{\sin 2\zeta_1 + \sinh 2\zeta_1} - 1\right] \tag{4.139}$$

where

$$\zeta_1 = \frac{\zeta l}{2} = \frac{l\sqrt[4]{3(1-\nu_p^2)}}{2\sqrt{r\delta}} \tag{4.140}$$

The maximum value of flexure, according to (4.139), is equal to

$$W = \frac{pr^2}{E_S\delta}\chi(\zeta_1) \tag{4.141}$$

where

$$\chi(\zeta_1) = 1 - \frac{2(\sin\zeta_1\cosh\zeta_1 + \cos\zeta_1\sinh\zeta_1}{\sin 2\zeta_1 + \sinh 2\zeta_1} \tag{4.142}$$

In formula (4.142) account is taken of the fact that in the case of corrosion deformation the pressure is directed towards the metal. For evaluation of the value $\chi(\zeta_1)$ it can be reckoned that $l \approx 10r$, $\delta = 0.1r$ and $\nu \approx 0.3$. Substituting these values in the formula (4.140) we obtain $\zeta_1 = 20$ and, according to (4.142), $\chi(\zeta_1) \approx 1$. Thus equation (4.141) is simplified

$$W \cong \frac{pr^2}{E_S\delta} \tag{4.143}$$

The value p can be expressed by the volume V and the compressibility C_M of the corroding metal

$$p = -\int_{(2)}^{(1)} \frac{dV}{C_M V} \tag{4.144}$$

If we assume that in the interval of change of volume from V_1 to V_2 C_M is constant then

$$p = \frac{1}{C_M} \ln \frac{V_1}{V_2} \tag{4.145}$$

where V_1 and V_2 are respectively the volume of the corroding bar in the absence and in the presence of pressure of the oxide film. For more accurate calculation of p it is possible to use empirical formulae expressing the link between the relative change of volume of the metal ($\Delta V/V$) and the pressure. Experimental results obtained by Bridgeman[138]) in the study of the compressibility of lead can be expressed by the formula

$$p = A(\Delta V/V)^{\mu} \tag{4.146}$$

where $A = 7.92 \cdot 10^{11}$ dynes/cm^2 and $\mu = 1.16$. Formula (4.146) is correct in the interval of change of pressure from 0 to 40tonf/cm^2. For the case of deformation under consideration here (under the influence of the pressure of the corrosion film) it is possible to rewrite formula (4.146) in the form

$$p = A\left(\frac{V_1 - V_2}{V_1}\right)^{\mu} \tag{4.147}$$

The value of V_2 is determined by the obvious relationship

$$V_2 = \pi l(r - \delta)^2 \tag{4.148}$$

For calculation of V_1 we introduce the following symbols: m_M is the mass of the corroded metal, r_0 the original radius of the bar (before the start of corrosion), V_S the volume occupied by the production of corrosion and V_{fi} the volume of the corrosion film. Obviously

$$V_S = V_{fi}(1 - \gamma) \tag{4.149}$$

where γ is the volumetric porosity of the film.

It is possible to write further that

$$V_1 = \pi l r_0^2 - \frac{m_M}{d_M} = \pi l r_0^2 - \frac{A_M d_{fi}}{M_{fi}\, d_M} V_S \qquad (4.150)$$

Substituting (4.149) in (4.150) we obtain

$$V_1 = \pi r_0^2 l - \frac{A_M d_{fi}}{M_{fi}\, d_M} (1 - \gamma) V_{fi} \qquad (4.151)$$

The volume of the film is equal to

$$V_{fi} = \pi l \left[r^2 - (r - \delta)^2 \right] = \pi l \delta (2r - \delta) \qquad (4.152)$$

Substituting this expression (4.152) in formula (4.151) we shall finally have

$$V_1 = \pi l \left[r_0^2 - \frac{A_M d_{fi}}{M_{fi}\, d_M} (1 - \gamma) \delta\, (2r - \delta) \right] \qquad (4.153)$$

The equations for calculation of the maximum flexure of a corroding bar under the pressure of the oxide film are obtained by calculation of formulae (4.143) and (4.146)

$$W = \frac{Ar^2}{E_S \delta} \left(\frac{V_1 - V_2}{V_1} \right)^{\mu} \qquad (4.154)$$

Substituting in formula (4.154) the expressions for V_1 and V_2 (4.153) and (4.148), we obtain

$$W = \frac{Ar^2}{E_S \delta} \left[\frac{r_0^2 - \frac{A_M d_{fi}}{M_{fi}\, d_M} (1 - \gamma) \delta\, (2r - \delta) - (r - \delta)^2}{r_0^2 - \frac{A_M d_{fi}}{M_{fi}\, d_M} (1 - \gamma)\, \delta\, (2r - \delta)} \right]^{\mu} \qquad (4.155)$$

Since the value of δ is small in comparison with r, in equation (4.155) it is possible to ignore the members containing δ^2. In addition, as shown by experimental data, $r_0 \approx r$. Therefore equation (4.155) takes the form

$$W \approx \frac{Ar^2}{E_S \delta} \left(\frac{2\delta \left[1 - \frac{A_M d_{fi}}{M_{fi}\, d_M} (1 - \gamma) \right]}{r - \frac{A_M d_{fi}}{M_{fi}\, d_M} 2\delta\, (1 - \gamma)} \right)^{\mu} \qquad (4.156)$$

If we characterise the depth of corrosion and the degree of deformation with dimensionless parameters: $\Delta = \delta/r$ and $\omega = W/r$ the link between the corrosion and the deformation, according to (4.156), is given by the formula

$$\omega \approx \frac{A}{E_S \Delta} \left\{ \frac{2\Delta \left[1 - \frac{A_M d_{fi}}{M_{fi} d_M} (1 - \gamma) \right]}{1 - \frac{A_M d_{fi}}{M_{fi} d_M} 2 (1 - \gamma)} \right\}^{\mu} \tag{4.157}$$

If we use as an initial equation formula (4.145), then

$$\omega \approx \frac{2.3}{E_S C_M \Delta} \lg \frac{1 - \frac{A_M d_{fi}}{M_{fi} d_M} 2 (1 - \gamma) \Delta}{1 - 2\Delta} \tag{4.158}$$

The approximate character of the assumption about the constancy of values C_M, situated at the base of the conclusion of formula (4.158) makes this formula unusable in the case of low-thickness films. In fact, according to (4.158)

$$\lim_{\Delta \to 0} \omega = 2 \left[1 - \frac{A_M d_{fi}}{M_{fi} d_M} (1 - \gamma) \right] / (E_S C_M)$$

whence it follows that $\lim\limits_{\Delta \to 0} \omega \neq 0$ at any value of γ $(0 \leqslant \gamma \leqslant 1)$, while in conformity with the physical sense of the value of ω its limit value in the condition shown should be equal to zero. The equations (4.156) and (4.157) are shown to be suitable in any range of change of δ (or Δ), since, according to (4.157), $\lim\limits_{\Delta \to 0} \omega = 0$.

If we introduce into equations (4.156) and (4.157) a correction as in (4.136), and substitute numerical values, then they take the form

$$W \approx \frac{Ar^2}{E_S(\delta - \delta_0)} \left[\frac{2(\delta - \delta_0)(0.28 + 0.72\gamma)}{r - 1.44(\delta - \delta_0)(1 - \gamma)} \right]^{\mu} \tag{4.159}$$

$$\omega \approx \frac{A}{E_S(\Delta - \Delta_o)} \left[\frac{2(\Delta - \Delta_o)(0.28 + 0.72\gamma)}{1 - 1.44(\Delta - \Delta_o)(1 - \gamma)} \right]^{\mu} \tag{4.160}$$

Here $\Delta_o = \delta_0/r$. According to (4.160), $\lim\limits_{\Delta \to \Delta_0} \omega = 0$.

Analysis of the equations obtained shows that deformation of the corroding sample increases with the growth in thickness of the corroding film ($\partial\omega/\partial\Delta > 0$). However, in contrast to the case of the freely suspended bar examined earlier, the slope of the graph (ω, Δ) changes with the growth in thickness of the film. This difference is explained by the fact that, in proportion to the deepening of the corrosion of a rigidly attached bar, along with an increase in the pressure of the film on the metal causing an increase in flexure, there is also an increase in resistance to deformation shown by the growing corrosion film.

From equation (4.159) it follows that the flexure of a corroding bar, calculated per unit of cross-section $[W/\pi r^2]$, decreases with an increase in the thickness of the bar. It must also be noted that, according to equations (4.159)-(4.160), the deformation of a rigidly attached bar under the influence of the oxide film does not depend on its length. It can be assumed that the dimensions of the cells should not influence the deformation of battery grids. This fact points to the possibility in principle of some reduction in the consumption of metal owing to a decrease in the number of longitudinal and transverse ties in the grid.

Naturally, in the constructional redesign of battery grids, account must be taken of the necessity of maintaining sufficiently high electrical conductivity and mechanical strength of the plates. For calculation of the dependence of deformation on the thickness of the oxide film it is necessary to know the Young's modulus of the film E_S. Since such data are non-existent in literature, experimental determination of E_S was carried out by us[135]) by observation of the flexure of thin cylindrical bars of lead in the process of anode corrosion in a solution of H_2SO_4 (density 1.32) at a current density of $j = 10mA/cm^2$. For the measurements special grids were made in the form of a rectangular frame (50 x 35mm) of circular section with a diameter of 3.5mm and having five cylindrical vertical ribs 0.6mm in diameter and 30mm long. The frame was given a preliminary insulation with acid-resistant mastic. Continuous polarisation was carried out over a period of 10 days.

Statistical processing of the results obtained showed that with a thickness of the oxide film $\delta \approx 0.005cm$, the maximum flexure of the ribs amounts to $W \approx 0.1cm$ on average. According to the results considered above, $\gamma = 0.52$. Substituting these values of A and μ in the formula (4.159) we obtain*) $E_S \approx 2.8 \cdot 10^{11}$ dynes/cm^2. The calculated value of Young's modulus of a lead dioxide film forming in the process of anode corrosion of the lead exceeds the Young's modulus of lead ($E_{Pb} = 1.6 \cdot 10^{11}$

*) In calculation of E_S and also of graphs (ω, Δ) it was assumed that $\delta_o = 0$.

dynes/cm^2) and approximates to the value of this constant for bismuth and magnesium. The value of E_S obtained is far lower than the Young's modulus of dense electrolytic deposits of lead dioxide. Consequently, the lead dioxide forming as a result of anodic oxidation of lead possesses considerably less rigidity than dioxide obtained by deposition on an inert anode at optimum conditions of electrolysis.

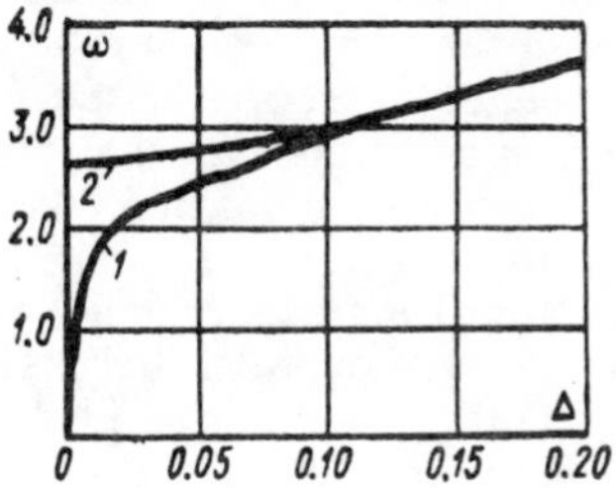

Fig.4.60 Dependence of the deformation ω of a lead bar on the thickness Δ of the oxide film. 1 - graph calculated according to (4.160); 2 - according to (4.158).

In fig. 4.60 the graphical calculation of the dependence of deformation of a rigidly attached lead bar on the relative thickness of the oxide film is shown. In the field of low film thicknesses the values of ω, calculated according to equations (4.158) and (4.160), differ markedly. With an increase of Δ these values come closer to each other, and at $\Delta > 0.1$ calculation according to both formulae gives practically one and the same result. As can be seen from fig. 4.60, the graph of the dependence of ω on Δ (graph 1) shows a sharp increase of ω in the field of very small relative thicknesses of the film and a slow increase in ω at $\Delta > 0.02$. It can be assumed that the initial section of the graph (ω, Δ) reflects the deformation in the absence of marked resistance of the oxide film, i.e. a process similar to the deformation of a freely suspended corroding bar. The film shows increasing resistance to deformation in proportion to the thickening which causes a decrease in the slope of the graph (ω, Δ).

An experimental study of the kinetics of corrosion deformation of lead and its alloys in the process of anodic polarisation is connected with great difficulties. In the survey[139]) there was enunciated by us a proposition about the possibility of the use for this purpose of methods of strain measurement. Experiments on the study of corrosion deformation of lead and lead-antimony alloy (6% Sb) by the tensometric method were carried out simultaneously with N K Mikhailova. The samples investigated represented cylinders with a diameter of 3mm and length 100mm.

The samples were attached on both sides in a clamp of organic glass and submerged to approximately half their length in electrolyte (10N · H_2SO_4). Four strain gauges were stuck to the top part of the sample, which is above the electrolyte, and joined in polarity on a paper base with a resistance of 100 ohms to which was soldered a conductor for the supply of current. The strain gauges were stuck with the aid of nitrocellulose lacquer and were insulated on the outside from acid vapours. Cylindrical bars of rigid PVC of the same dimensions to which strain gauges were stuck in the same manner. were also place in the acid for checking. The absence of change in the resistance of these last strain gauges was evidence of the fact that strain gauges glued to corroding samples really fix the deformation of the samples. The strain gauges were joined to a tensometric amplifier. Measurement of the current leaving the amplifier was carried out by means of periodic measuring of the voltage drop on the resistance boxes included in the amplifier circuit. Polarisation of the samples was carried out by means of periodic measuring of the voltage drop on the magnesium elements of the resistances included in the amplifier circuit. Polarisation of the samples was carried out at a current density of 10mA/cm^2 over a period of 3-5 days.

The data obtained do not possess sufficient reproducibility for a quantitative characterisation of the process of corrosion deformation. This is connected principally with the fact that the direction of flexure of the corroding bar is arbitrary where the deformation is quite small. Nevertheless, the results of the measurements qualitatively confirm the scheme of the process set out above.

No deformation of the sample is observed in the initial period of polarisation. Then there is fairly rapid increase in flexure, after which no further change in the condition of the rod occurs. The absence of any marked deformations at the beginning of the polarisation is explained by the fact that a certain minimum thickness of the oxide film δ_0* is necessary for the appearance of deformation. The rapid increase in flexure obviously corresponds to the period of the process when the film does not yet show resistance to deformation. Finally, the constant mechanical condition of the sample is probably due to the growing resistance to deformation shown by the oxide film. In addition, it is necessary to bear in mind also the fact that, as shown earlier, the rate of growth of the anode film in the polarisation process slows down considerably and stops almost

* This initial period was, as a rule, longer in the testing of the alloy Pb + 5% Sb than in the testing of lead.

completely when the experiment is long enough. Of course, the constancy of the thickness of the oxide film also gives rise to the invariability of the time at which flexure of the corroding sample occurs.

A theoretical examination of corrosion deformation of rigidly attached prismatic samples leads to the conclusion that an increase in the number of faces with a constant cross-sectional area leads to a decrease in the deformability of the sample. This conclusion qualitatively corresponds to the results described in subsection 2 of the present section. However, a reduction in the moment of inertia of the cross-section in proportion to the increase in the number of its sides, causes some decrease in the effect mentioned (compared with the results described above, which were obtained in an examination of the deformation of freely suspended prismatic rods).

The influence of the mechanical load on anode corrosion of lead alloys

Owing to the absence of data in literature on the influence of mechanical loads on the corrosion behaviour of lead alloys used in the manufacture of batteries, this question has been the subject of a special study by us[140]. The objects of the study were, besides lead and the usual lead-antimony alloy, production alloys containing silver (~0.5%) and arsenic (~0.2%). The corrosion tests were carried out in a 10N solution of H_2SO_4 at $j = 10mA/cm^2$. The value of the mechanical load amounted to 70% of the breaking strength measured at minimum rate of displacement of the movable clamp.

The results of corrosion tests are shown in fig. 4.61. According to the data obtained, the mechanical load leads to an increase in the rate of anodic corrosion of lead and of lead-antimony alloy. This result is in conformity with data in literature. However, it must be noted that the influence of the mechanical load shows up only after a period of anodic polarisation. It can be assumed that the thin oxide layers forming in the initial period of electrolysis possess a high elasticity. Therefore, the application of the load does not lead in this period to any noticeable change in the protective properties of the anode films.

The increase in the rate of corrosion of lead and of lead-antimony alloy with relatively high amounts of electricity transmitted in the process of anodic polarisation is obviously connected with the decrease of the protective properties of the film, owing to the breaking of its solidity as a result of the deformation of the sample.

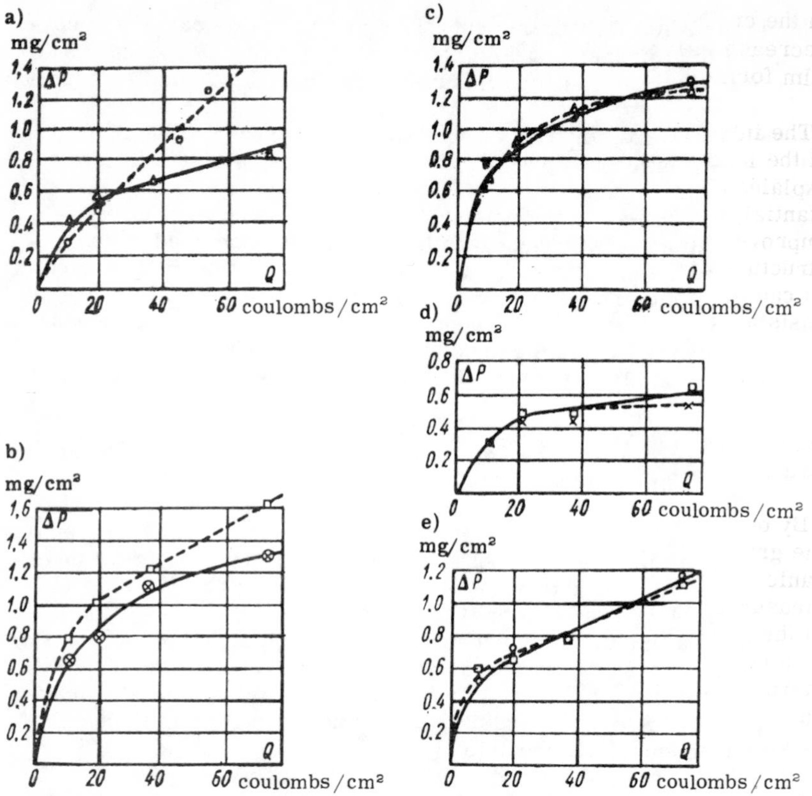

Fig.4.61 Dependence of the weight of products of anodic corrosion ΔP on the amount of electricity Q: a - Pb; b - Pb + 6.6% Sb; c - Pb + 5.0% Sb + 0.17% As; d - Pb + 4.9% Sb + 0.45% Ag; e - Pb + 5.3% Sb + 0.17% As + 0.48% Ag. (—— corrosion without load; ---- corrosion under mechanical load).

The introduction of anti-corrosion additives (Ag and As) into a production alloy leads to the mechanical load having practically no influence on the rate of anode oxidation. From these data it follows, in particular, that the anti-corrosion effect of the arsenic alloying addition is directly connected with the influence of this element on the process of deformation of battery grids. In fact, as follows from a comparison of fig. 4.61, b and c, the addition of 0.2% As to lead-antimony alloy in the absence of a mechanical load does not cause any change in the rate of anodic oxidation of the alloy. With the application of a load the addition of arsenic considerably decreases the rate of corrosion, which can be explained principally by an increase in the creep-resistance of the alloy, as a result of which there is a decrease in the deformability (creep) of the sample and of the oxide film forming on it.

The introduction of silver into the alloy also removes the influence of the load on the rate of anodic corrosion. This phenomenon can be explained by the fact that the addition of silver, along with a substantial increase in the corrosion resistance of the alloy, markedly improves the mechanical properties due to the dispersal of the structure of the alloy. A quaternary alloy of the composition studied, as can be seen from fig. 4.61, is a little inferior in its corrosion resistance to lead-antimony-silver alloy. The mechanical load has no influence on the corrosion behaviour of this alloy.

Deformation of anodic oxidation samples made of lead and its alloys

By destroying the continuity of the oxide film, the deformation of the grids leads to the formation of numerous short-circuited galvanic cells on its surface. Their action leads to a lowering of the measured potential. The oxidation-reduction processes occurring in the pores and on the surface of the oxide film are accompanied by a change in the phase composition of the film, as a result of which there is in particular a change in its conductivity and in the impedance of the electrode being investigated. Hence it follows that the potentiometric and impedance measurements can be used as methods of studying the deformation of the corrosion films. Such investigations were carried out by use in the study of the deformation of anodic oxidation samples made of lead and its alloys compounded with antimony (5-6%), silver (0.5%), and arsenic (0.2%).

Let us begin by examining the results obtained with deformation of a lead electrode (fig. 4.62). At the first moment of loading the sample a jump in potential of approximately 20mV in the negative direction is observed in the graph of change of potential in time (φ, τ), which can be explained by a breaking of the solidity of the corrosion film as a result of the stretching of the sample. On the bared sections of a lead electrode the process of oxidation of lead into sulphate occurs. As a result of this reaction the places where defects of the film occur are covered with a layer of sulphate which, as can be seen from fig. 4.62, leads to an increase in potential. In practice the equilibrium deformation corresponds to the moment of stabilisation of the potential. After this period of creep has set in, the rate of elongation gradually increases and rupture of the sample being tested ensues.

The potential drop observed in this is linked with a considerable increase in the surface of the anode sections in connected with the rupture of the oxide film.

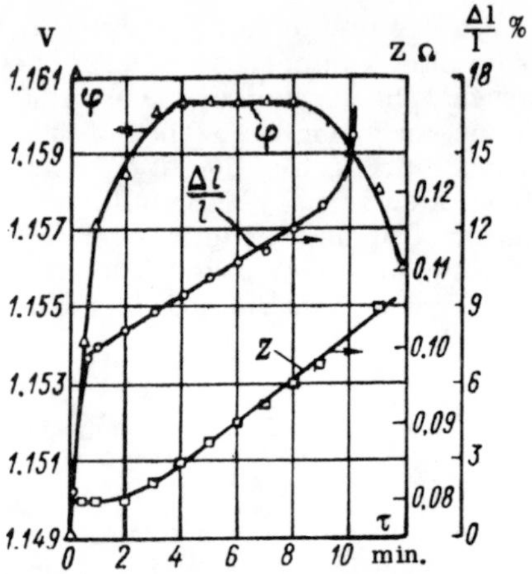

Fig.4.62 Change in potential φ, impedance Z and relative elongation Δl/l of anodically oxidised lead under the influence of a mechanical load.

The creep that has set in can be described[141]) by the equation

$$\frac{\Delta l}{l} = \left(\frac{\Delta l}{l}\right)_0 + \beta\tau^m + k\tau \qquad (4.161)$$

where $(\Delta l/l)_0$ is the deformation of the sample directly after the application of the load, and β, m and k are constants not depending on the time. According to the data obtained, for lead $(\Delta l/l)_0 = 7.0$, $\beta = -0.143$, $m = -0.13$ and $k = 0.643$.

From fig. 4.62 it follows that the impedance of the double layer in the course of the basic period of the experiment increases with time. The increase in impedance can be explained by the gradual reduction $PbO_2 \rightarrow PbSO_4$. In fig. 4.63 the change in elongation of lead alloys with time depending on the load is shown. The process of deformation of lead and of the alloys investigated is characterised by a stage of initial elongation, after which a state of creep sets in. The coefficients of equation (4.161), describing the creep which has set in (k) and the deformation of the sample after the application of the load $(\Delta l/l)_0$, are shown in table 4.15.

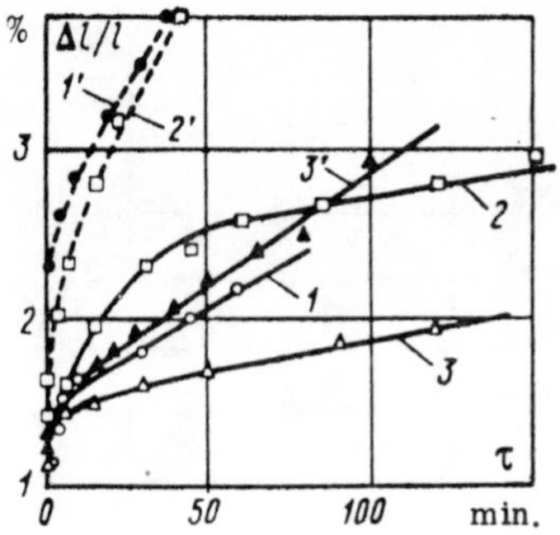

Fig.4.63 Dependence of relative deformation $\Delta l/l$ of a number of lead alloys on time τ: 1 - Pb-Sb($0.7\sigma_B$); 2 - Pb-Sb-As($0.7\sigma_B$); 3 - Pb-Sb-Ag($0.7\sigma_B$); 1' - Pb-Sb ($0.8\sigma_B$); 2' - Pb-Sb-As($0.8\sigma_B$); 3' - Pb-Ab-Ag($0.8\sigma_B$).

Table 4.15: Parameters characterising the deformation of lead alloys

Composition of the alloy	$p = 0.7\ p_{rupt.}$		$p = 0.8\ p_{rupt.}$	
	k	$(\Delta l/l_o)$	k	$(\Delta l/l_o)$
Pb + 6.6% Sb	0.011	1.50	0.040	2.54
Pb + 5.0% Sb + 0.17% As	0.004	2.38	0.033	2.30
Pb + 4.9% Sb + 0.45% Ag	0.004	1.50	0.014	1.54

According to the results obtained the rate of creep of lead-antimony alloy is higher than for alloys compounded with arsenic or silver. With an increase in the load, differences in the creep resistance of the alloys become less marked. The data obtained are evidence of the fact that arsenic and silver substantially increase the creep-resistance of a lead-antimony alloy, particularly at relatively low loads. It must be noted that in the work with grids of positive plates of a lead acid battery the deforming loads, obviously, are not large.

Fig. 4.64 shows the graphs of change of potential and impedance with time for the processes of spontaneous reduction of lead dioxide films formed on the lead alloys investigated. In contrast to lead, on the anodic-polarisation samples made of lead-antimony alloys, when not subjected to mechanical load, a substantial decrease in potential is observed, which bears witness to the presence of straight-through pores in the oxide film.

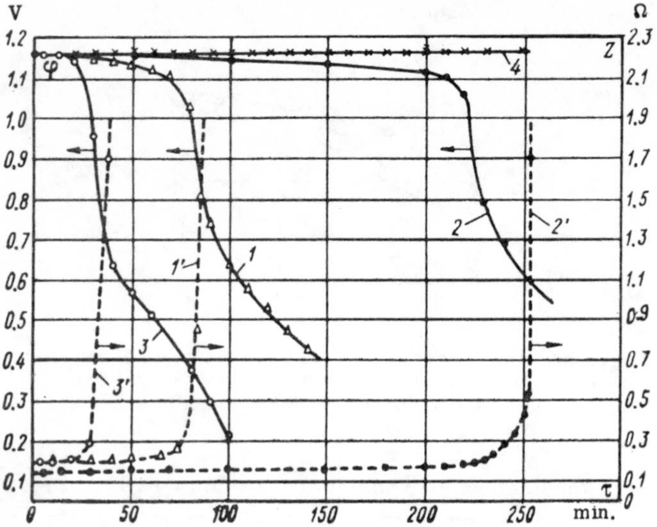

Fig.4.64 Change in potential (solid lines) and impedance(dotted lines) in the process of spontaneous reduction of the anode film on lead alloys. 1 - Pb-Sb; 2 - Pb-Sb-A 3 - Pb-Sb-Ag; 4 - Pb.

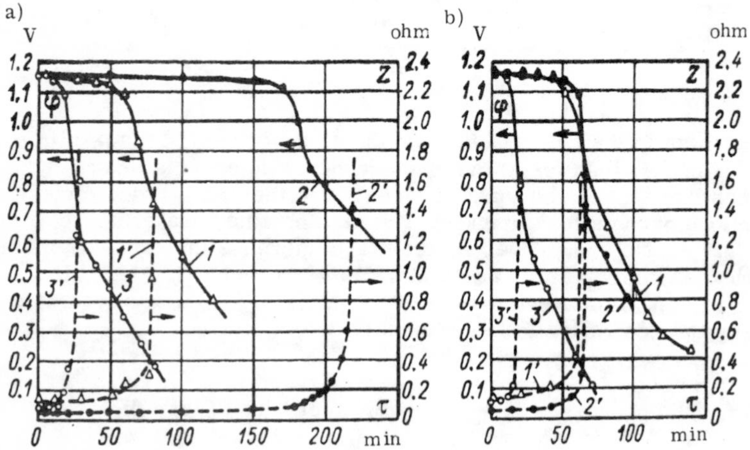

Fig. 4.65 Change of potential and impedance of anodically oxidised alloys under the influence of a load equal to $0.7\sigma_B$ (a) and $0.8\sigma_B$ (b). Symbols - see fig. 4.64.

In fig. 4.65 it can be seen that the films that are reduced most easily of all are those obtained on samples of Pb-Sb-Ag alloy. Silver, as is well known, substantially increases the corrosion resistance of lead-antimony alloy. In this connection, for the same time of anodic polarisation, considerably less lead dioxide is formed on Pb-Sb-Ag alloys than on lead-antimony alloy. This fact determines the relatively rapid fall in potential and increase in impedance observed in the process of spontaneous reduction of the anode film on Pb-Sb-Ag alloys.

The presence of the As addition, as can be seen from fig. 4.64, inhibits the occurrence of the oxidation-reduction reactions which cause the observed fall in potential and rise in impedance. Since the addition of arsenic does not change the rate of anodic oxidation of Pb-Sb alloy, this result is evidence of the fact that the introduction of As into the alloy leads to a decrease in the porosity of the anode film.

The results of potentiometric and impedance measurements characterising the influence of the load on the process of reduction of anode films are shown in fig. 4.65. As can be seen from this figure, with an increase in the load the oxidation-reduction processes in the anode film speed up considerably, under the influence of a load equal to $0.8p_{rupt.}$ showing up most substantially in the testing of Pb-Sb-As alloys. The mechanism of the action of the load is basically similar to that described above for lead. It is only necessary to emphasise this essential difference, that the mechanical deformation of the lead is the direct cause of the appearance of straight-through porosity, and consequently of the possibility of the occurrence of the oxidation reactions in the pores of the film. In the case of Pb-Sb alloys the straight-through porosity occurs in the originally formed anode film. Therefore, the role of mechanical deformation leads to an increase in the dimensions of the pores in which the oxidation reactions occur, which leads to a speeding up of these reactions.

If we assume that only two processes occur on the electrode (the oxidation one and the reduction one) and reckon its surface to be equipotential, then the potential of the electrode can be written down in the form

$$\varphi = \varphi_{+} - \eta_{+} = \varphi_{-} + \eta_{-} \tag{4.162}$$

where φ_{+} and φ_{-} are the equilibrium values of the potential corresponding to the cathode and anode reactions, and η_{+} and η_{-} are the overvoltages of these processes.

With the aid of equation (4.162) it is possible to calculate the portion of the surface of the electrode on which the anodic process occurs (S_-). If the dependence of the values η_+ and η_- on the current density j is described by Tafel's equation[142]), then according to (4.162) we have

$$S_- = (1 + 10^{A+B\phi})^{-1} \tag{4.163}$$

where

$$A = \frac{-\varphi_+ + a_+}{b_+} - \frac{\varphi_- + a_-}{b_-},$$

$$B = \frac{b_+ + b_-}{b_+ b_-},$$

a_+, a_-, b_+ and b_- are the coefficients of Tafel's equations ($\eta_+ = a_+ + b_+ \lg j$, $\eta_- = a_- + b_- \lg j$). An orientational calculation of the values of S_- according to equation (4.163) shows that the most probable oxidation processes occurring in the pores of a lead dioxide film are the formation of basic sulphates of lead and the oxidation of antimony ($Sb \rightarrow Sb^+$). The decreased degree of ease of oxidation of the medium in the pores of the film increases the thermodynamic stability of the basic sulphates.

Chapter 5: The negative electrode of a lead acid battery

The mechanism of the charge-discharge process

The basic rules of anodic passivation of lead and of reduction of sulphate

In the process of discharge of the negative electrode of a lead acid battery lead sulphate is formed on its surface in conformity with the equation of reaction (2.20). This salt practically possesses no electrical conductivity; the specific resistance of $PbSO_4$ is characterised by a value of 10^{10} ohm·cm [1]). Therefore, the appearance of a sulphate film leads to the passivation of the surface of the electrode.

The basic laws of anodic passivation of lead in a sulphuric acid electrolyte were studied in the classic investigations of B N Kabanov [2]). In fig. 5.1 a typical graph is shown of the dependence of the potential (overvoltage) on the amount of electricity transmitted in the process of galvano-static anodic polarisation of lead in a solution of H_2SO_4. The graph (η, Q) is similar to the discharge graphs of the negative electrode of a lead acid battery at long discharge regimes, when it is possible with complete justification to neglect the ohmic potential drop and the change of the concentration of the electrolyte in the pores of the active mass.

The initial shift of potential is connected with the overvoltage of the process of formation of a new phase ($PbSO_4$) on the surface of the lead. An important reason causing the appearance of this overvoltage is the 2-10 fold oversaturation of the solution with Pb^{2+} ions which precedes the appearance of centres of crystallisation of $PbSO_4$ [2]). The value of the initial displacement of the potential in practice does not depend on the current density, while the interval of time from the beginning of polarisation (discharge) to the maximum potential decreases with an increase in current [3]). After the beginning of crystallisation of sulphate the potential of the electrode decreases a little, as can be seen from fig. 5.1, but it still remains at a more positive figure than the equilibrium value, which is explained by the slowness of growth of the centres of crystallisation of $PbSO_4$. The process of formation of a sulphate film on the surface of the electrode needs, according to data [2]), a definite over-

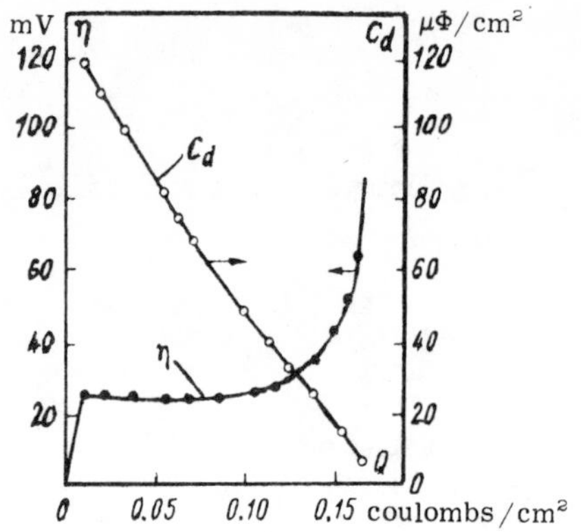

Fig.5.1 Dependency of overvoltage η and capacity of the double layer C_d on the amount of electricity transmitted in the process of anodic polarisation of lead in a solution of H_2SO_4.

saturation of the layer of solution next to the electrode.

In the interval of current densities $j = 10^{-5}-10^{-3}$ A/cm², between the overvoltage η and the current density j the following relation exists:

$$\eta = \eta_0 + \frac{RT}{2F} \ln j^p \quad (5.1)$$

where p = 0.55-0.65. At higher levels of current a linear link between η and j is observed.

As was shown by the results of the impedance measurements [2)4)], the considerable shift of potential $Q \gtrsim 0.15$ coulombs / cm² (fig. 5.1) is not connected with the ohmic potential drop in the sulphate film, the maximum resistance of which does not exceed 20 ohms. In the process of anodic polarisation of lead its surface is uniformly covered in time with an insulating sulphate film, which leads to a linear fall in capacity of the double electrical layer. The collection of data contained in the works of B N Kabanov made it possible to establish that the basic reason for the shift of potential at a constant strength of polarising current (at any rate, in the initial stages of passivation) is the increase in overvoltage of ionisation of lead as a result of a sharp increase of true current density on the surface of the lead not covered by the sulphate film.

The thickness of the passivating layer, the presence of which causes the shift of anode potential of the lead electrode by 0.1-0.2V, increases with an increase in temperature and decreases with an increase in the concentration of the H_2SO_4. A symbiotic change in the thickness of the sulphate layer and in the solubility of the $PbSO_4$ is observed. The dependence between the time of passivation τ and the current density j is satisfactorily described by Peukert's equation

$$\tau j^n = K \tag{5.2}$$

where the constant n changes within the limits from 1.1 to 1.4, increasing with an increase in concentration of the acid, which causes a sharper dependence of the time of passivation (discharge) on the current in strong solutions of H_2SO_4.

Equation (5.2) was introduced by B N Kabanov[2]), starting from the proposition about the diffusion mechanism of the growth of sulphate crystals and from formula (5.1). This equation provided confirmation in the work of Hillebrandt and Lome[5]). According to the data of these authors, in the range of concentrations of H_2SO_4: 1.19-10.2g·m/l, of temperatures -22 - +50°C and of current densities $j = 3.1 \cdot 10^{-5}$ - $1.76 \cdot 10^{-1}$ A/cm^2 the coefficient n = 1.4, and the coefficient K varies within the limits $1.4 \cdot 10^{-3}$ - $1.4 \cdot 10^{-2}$, increasing with an increase in temperature and with a decrease in concentration of the acid.

From the data quoted, it follows that the formation of lead sulphate at the discharge of the negative electrode of a battery is preceded by the transference to the solution of ions of Pb^{2+}, i.e. discharge proceeds according to the scheme

$$Pb \xrightarrow{-2e} Pb^{2+} \xrightarrow{+HSO_4^-} PbSO_4 \tag{5.3}$$

The process of cathodic reduction of $PbSO_4$, which takes place during the charging of the electrode under consideration, obviously occurs basically according to a similar scheme (from right to left), i.e. also with participation of Pb^{2+} ions. The results reported in[6]) bear witness to the intermediate formation of Pb^{2+} ions and their participation in the reduction process, in which a study was made of the dependence of the limit current of discharge of these ions on lead, on the concentration of H_2SO_4 and on temperature.

The energy of activation of the process of reduction $PbSO_4 \rightarrow Pb$ amounts to 8-22kcal/mol and decreases with an increase in current density[7]). These values are evidence of the fact that polarisation of the process occurring at charge of the negative electrode has basically a chemical (activation) character. At high current densities the diffusion limitations appear, which cause the slowness of transfer of the reacting matter to the surface of the electrode. Together with Pb^{2+}

ions, judging by some data, ions of $Pb(SO_4)_2^{2-}$, and also the ions pairs $Pb\text{-}SO_4$ [6]) may be present in the solution. Of course, the possibility is not excluded of participation of these formations in the charge-discharge process.

Electron microscope study of the sulphate film forming under anodic polarisation of lead showed that a decrease in the concentration of H_2SO_4 leads to an increase in the dimensions of the crystals of $PbSO_4$ [9]). Thus, a decrease in the density of the electrolyte from 1.28 to 1.12g/cm^3 leads approximately to a 3-fold increase in the dimensions of the $PbSO_4$ crystals forming on the surface of the lead electrode at $j = 175 mA/cm^2$. This causes an increase in the effective thickness of the passivating film in proportion to the decrease in concentration of the H_2SO_4, i.e. an increase in the discharge capacity of the electrode, which amounts to 2.3-3.3 coulombs/cm^2 in a solution of density 1.12g/cm^3 and 0.4-0.6 coulombs/cm^2 in a solution of density 1.28g/cm^3. The result obtained is explained in the work [9]) by an increase in the solubility of $PbSO_4$ with a decrease in the concentration of the electrolyte. The increase in the solubility of the $PbSO_4$ causes an increase in the rate of growth of the crystals of this salt (in comparison with the rate of formation of new centres of crystallisation).

Microscopic study of the phase conversions in the active mass of the negative electrode showed that the formation of lead in the reduction of sulphate generally begins on the grid-active mass interface. In some cases reduction is observed to begin on the surface of the electrode [10]). Here the lead crystals forming on the surface of the sulphate retain the form of the $PbSO_4$ crystals. The metasomic conversion $PbSO_4 \rightarrow Pb$ is evidence of the possibility of the partial occurrence of the reduction process in the solid phase. However, the basic mass of the lead crystals forming in the charge process is characterised by a needle-like structure, which is completely different from the structure of the sulphate [10]). It can therefore be assumed that the charge-discharge process on the negative electrode of a battery proceeds basically through the solution, i.e. with the participation of lead ions. In the literature the presence is noted of a small quantity of lead sulphate (of the order of a few per cent) in the fully charged active mass of a negative electrode [11]). The concentration of $PbSO_4$ in the active mass increases with the service life. It is assumed that the $PbSO_4$ particles may serve as centres of crystallisation of the sulphate in the initial period of discharge.

The mechanism of anodic passivation of lead in a sulphuric acid electrolyte has been subjected to further study in recent investigations. Pavlov and Popova [12]) carried out measurements of potential, capacitance of the double layer and resistance of the lead electrode, under conditions of galvanostatic anodic polarisation and with open circuit. Using also electron microscope and X-ray structural data, these authors showed that the phenomenon of passivation is caused by the processes occurring in the spaces between the $PbSO_4$ crystals which form a polycrystalline layer on the surface of the electrode. Pavlov and Popova differentiate stable and unstable passivity of lead. The character of the passivation is determined by the dimensions of the interlayers between the $PbSO_4$ crystals where the basic sulphates or oxides of lead are localised. If the dimensions of the intercrystalline interlayers are very small (of the order of the diameter of the ions), then the sulphate film behaves similarly to a selectively penetrated membrane. Ions characterised by small dimensions (H_3O^+, OH^- and Pb^{2+}) may reach the surface of the metal, while the access to it of the larger sulphate ions is to a large extent hampered. In this case the electrolyte at the surface of the lead becomes more alkaline, which causes deposition of basic sulphates of lead, which produce stable passivation of the electrode.

If the distances between the $PbSO_4$ crystals exceed those shown above, then passivation takes place only with anodic polarisation. When polarisation stops, the basic sulphates which are to be found in the intercrystalline spaces dissolve and the electrode is spontaneously depassivated. As a rule, there are intercrystalline spaces of both types in the sulphate layer. The authors also observed spontaneous passivation of lead which, however, generally occurs very slowly[12].

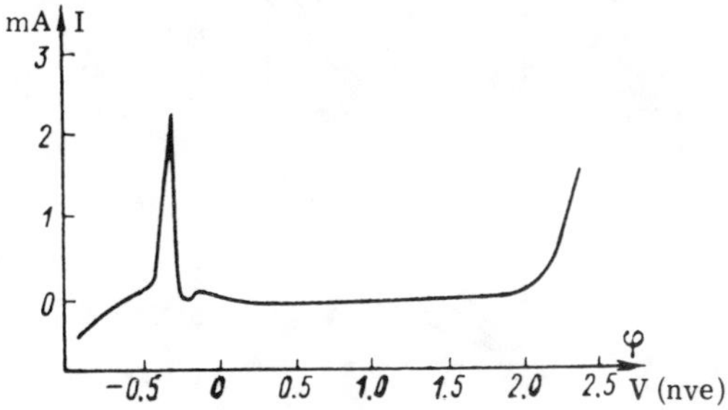

Fig.5.2 Potentiometric graph taken on lead in a solution of H_2SO_4 (3.03M) at +23°C. Rate of scanning of the potential 58.3mV/s, surface of electrode $3.3 \cdot 10^{-2} cm^2$.

In the paper of Carr, Hempson and Taylor[13], use was made of the linear change of voltage with current for study of the mechanism of mass transfer through a passivating sulphate film, and this method is often called the potentio-dynamic method in Russian literature. The electrode is anodically polarised with the aid of a potentiostat, which generates a rapid linear change of potential over a wide range. Here the graph of dependence of the current I on the potential φ is recorded (fig. 5.2). The limits of change of potential were determined from the following condition: at the outermost points there was observed a separation of hydrogen ($\varphi \approx 1.0$V nve) and oxygen ($\varphi \approx 2.3$V nve).

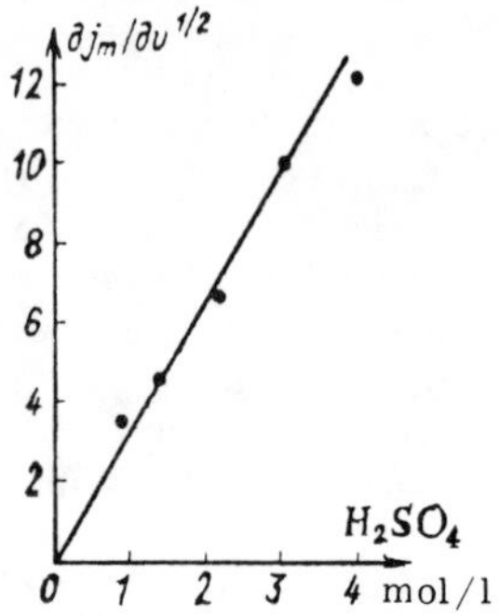

Fig.5.3 Influence of the concentration of H_2SO_4 on the coefficient of slope $\partial j_m/\partial\nu^{1/2}$ for the process of anodic polarisation of $PbSO_4$.

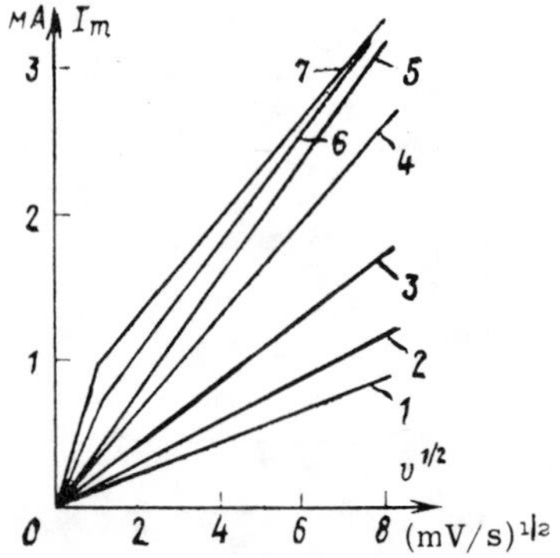

Fig.5.4 Dependence of the maximum current value in the potentiometric graph I_m on the rate of scanning of the potential at different concentrations of H_2SO_4 (mol/l): 1 - 0.91; 2 - 1.41; 3 - 2.09; 4 - 3.03; 5 - 3.88; 6 - 5.11; 7 - 8.88.

The sharp maximum in the graph (I, φ) corresponds to the oxidation of Pb → $PbSO_4$ (fig. 5.2). In ref.[13]) it is shown that the value of the current at the maximum I_m is directly proportional to the concentration of sulphuric acid (fig. 5.3) and to the square root of the rate ν of the scanning potential (fig. 5.4). The latter dependency, as can be seen from fig. 5.4, is strictly observed for all concentrations of the solution in the range of relatively low rates of scanning. At high values of ν the straight lines (I_m, $\nu^{-1/2}$) go through the origin of the co-ordinates in the case when the concentration of H_2SO_4 does not exceed ~4.5mol/l.

For the case under consideration here, that of the formation of an insoluble deposit, the growth of which is ensured by stationary diffusion, the theory of linear change of voltage with curent leads to the following equation for current density at the maximum (at 25°C)

$$j_m = 3.67 \cdot 10^5 \cdot z^{3/2} D^{1/2} c \nu^{1/2} \qquad (5.4)$$

where z is the charge of the ions reacting on the surface of the electrode, D is the coefficient of diffusion and c the concentration of these ions in the thickness of the solution.

The experimental data quoted above correspond basically to equation (5.4), which points to the essential role of diffusion in the kinetics of the forming on lead of a passivating sulphate layer. From the slope of the straight line shown in fig. 5.3 it is possible with the aid of equation (5.4) to determine the coefficient of diffusion, which turns out to be equal to $D = 1.03 \cdot 10^{-5}\ cm^2/s$. The authors ascribe this value to the ion SO_4^{2-}, reckoning that the diffusion of sulphate ions in the solution controls the rate of the process under consideration at relatively low rates of change of potential and concentration of H_2SO_4 [13]).

The sharp change of slope of the graphs (I_m, $\nu^{-1/2}$) at $c > 4.5$mol/l in the range of high rates of scanning of the potential (fig. 5.4) is explained in ref.[12]) by the change in the mechanism of diffusion. Under conditions of rapid increase in the thickness of the sulphate layer by a process limiting the rate, the diffusion of ions of Pb^{2+} and SO_4^{2-} through the $PbSO_4$ layer comes to a halt. This leads to a substantial change in the concentration and in the coefficient of diffusion of the reacting substances and, according to equation (5.4) leads to a change in the coefficient of slope $\partial j_m / \partial \sqrt{\nu}$.

The authors of ref.[14]) also used the potentio-dynamic method (ν = 0.01-0.1V/s) for a study of anodic passivation of lead. The samples studied were executed in the form of rotating disc electrodes with different quality of surface finish. Data obtained in the experiments with lead which had been previously subjected to electropolishing bear witness to the intermediate formation of Pb^{2+} ions, the appearance of particles of $PbSO_4$ in the solution and the subsequent deposition of them on the electrode. The results of the experiments carried out with electrodes subjected only to mechanical treatment enable us to assume the formation of lead sulphate by means of direct interaction of the sulphate ions with the surface of the electrode. These data are in conformity with the observations described above[10]), pointing, in principle, to the possibility of the partial occurrence of the charge-discharge process [equation (2.20)] in the solid phase. The formation of $PbSO_4$ due to the solid-phase reaction is characteristic at high values of electrode potential[15]).

Adsorption of organic compounds on a lead electrode

At the present time different organic additives are used in the manufacture of the active mass of the negative electrode of a lead acid battery. For an explanation of the mechanism of the influence of these substances on the charge-discharge characteristics of an electrode, it is of interest to consider some general laws of adsorption of organic substances on lead.

As is well-known, the adsorption of surface-active compounds shows a quite substantial influence on the kinetics of the electrode processes. The laws of adsorption of organic substances on electrodes have been intensively studied in recent years. The basic results of this study are set out in ref.[16]). The greater part of the investigations in this field relates to a mercury electrode.

The adsorption of many types of organic molecules, as a rule, is maximal on an uncharged surface of mercury and decreases with an increase in the electrode charge. Aromatic and heterocyclic compounds form an exception, as the desorption of these is hampered with a positively charged surface of the electrode as a result of the π-electron interaction. Adsorption of organic substances increases with an increase in their volumetric concentration, and also with an increase in the concentration of the electrolyte (background). The dependence of the degree of filling of the surface of the electrode with organic molecules Θ on their concentration in the solution c is described by the adsorption isotherm. Among many isotherm equations postulated by different authors, the best for describing the adsorption of aliphatic compounds on the electrode turned out to be Frumkin's isotherm equation

$$Bc = \frac{\Theta}{1 - \Theta} e^{-2a\Theta} \qquad (5.5)$$

where B is the constant of adsorption equilibrium and a the attraction constant taking into account the interaction of the adsorbed molecules. At a = 0 equation (5.5) changes into the well-known Langmuir's isotherm equation.

In addition to equation (5.5), the assumption that the electrical double layer can be represented in the form of two parallel condensers, filled respectively with water molecules and those of the organic compound, lies at the basis of current theory of adsorption of organic substances on electrodes. The charge of the liquid cover of the double layer ϵ is expressed in this case by the formula

$$\epsilon = \epsilon_0 (1 - \Theta) + \epsilon_1 \Theta \qquad (5.6)$$

where ϵ_0 and ϵ_1 are the values of ϵ at $\Theta = 0$ and $\Theta = 1$.

As detailed analysis showed, the real systems diverge somewhat from the model described by equation (5.6). The reasons for these deviations include the discrete character of the liquid plane of the double layer, the change in the perpendicular component of the dipole moment of the adsorbed molecules with the degree of coverage, and the dependence of the surface area per adsorbed molecule on the degree of coverage[16]).

The divergences of the system from the model of two parallel condensers may be formally reckoned to be due to the dependence of the attraction constant in the isotherm equation (5.5) on the potential. In particular, in this condition the theory leads to the following equation for differential capacity of the double layer (C_d)

$$C_d = C_0 (1 - \Theta) + C_1 \Theta - A_m \frac{d^2 a}{d\varphi^2} \Theta (1 - \Theta) +$$

$$+ \frac{1}{A_m} \left[\epsilon_0 + C_1 (\varphi_N - \varphi) + A_m \frac{da}{d\varphi} (1 - 2\Theta) \right]^2 \frac{\Theta(1 - \Theta)}{1 - 2a\Theta(1 - \Theta)} \qquad (5.7)$$

where C_0 and C_1 are the values of C_d respectively at $\Theta = 0$ and $\Theta = 1$, φ_N is the shift of the point of zero charge in transition from $\Theta = 0$ to $\Theta = 1$, $A_m = RT\,\Gamma_m$, Γ_m is the limit value of adsorption Γ at $\Theta = 1$.

The equation (5.7) well describes the graph of differential capacity (C_d, φ) in adsorption of aliphatic compounds on mercury. Here the constant a shows a small linear dependence on the potential φ. The more complicated organic compounds (aromatic and heterocyclic ones) are capable of being adsorbed in two different positions of the molecules on the surface of the electrode: flat and vertical. For a description of such systems a model was proposed of three parallel condensers, respectively filled with water, with molecules of organic matter in a vertical position, and with the same molecules but in a flat position[17]). A similar model is also suitable for quantitative interpretation of the adsorption of two different substances. In the special case when molecules of different type differ only in the value of the adsorption jump of the potential φ_N the behaviour of the system may be described with the aid of equations (5.4) and (5.6), but taking into account the fairly strong dependence of a on φ.

The adsorption of organic compounds on to solid metals with high hydrogen overvoltage, and particularly on lead, is in many respects similar to that of adsorption on mercury. The graph (C_d, φ) taken on a lead electrode in dilute solutions quantitatively coincides with a similar graph for mercury, if the potential φ is related to the point of zero charge of the metal[18]). The capacity of the double layer of a smooth lead electrode in 1M · HCl and H_2SO_4 amounts to 12.5-16μF/cm² and does not depend much on the potential[19]). The authors of ref.[18]) observe that at low negative surface charges the structure of the double layer on lead differs little from that on mercury.

In recent years a comparative study has been undertaken by N B Grigoryev and D N Machavariani of the adsorption on Pb and Hg of a number of aliphatic compounds from solutions of Na_2SO_4 and of thiourea from solutions of NaF[20])[21]). It was established that the adsorption characteristics of aliphatic compounds: ethylene glycol, ethylene diamine and glycerine (a, φ_N, B) on Pb and Hg almost show a quantitative coincidence. The constants of adsorption equilibrium of these aliphatics on lead are somewhat lower than on mercury, which is explained by the difference in the energy of adsorption of water molecules on these metals The adsorption of glycerine on Pb is greater than its adsorption on Hg. The authors link this with the specific interaction of lead with OH groups. Thiourea is adsorbed on lead less than on mercury, which confirms the presence of a correlation between the tendency to complex formation and adsorbability[21]).

In the presence of the aliphatic substances being investigated on lead desorption peaks were observed in the cathode region. It is noticeable that the desorption peaks on solid metals were more spread out along the potential and are distinguished by a lower height than on mercury. This is probably connected with the heterogeneity of energy of the surface and with the slowing down of the processes of adsorption and desorption of organic substances. In ref.[22]), where a study was made of the adsorption of diphenylamine, α and β-naphthol on lead in solutions of KCl and $NaClO_4$, no desorption peaks were observed in the graph (C_d, φ).

In addition, some peculiarities of the adsorption of organic substances on solid electrodes[16]) should be noted. On the dissolution of the metal, the molecules adsorbed partially transfer to the solution, and with deposition of the metal a part of the matter penetrates the electrolytic deposit. With sufficiently rapid renewal of the surface, the concentration of the adsorbed matter becomes lower than the equilibrium concentration, if the rate of adsorption is less than the rate of formation of the new surface. In the absence of external polarisation, low adsorbability is observed on metals in which the exchange current or rate of self-dissolution is greater than the rate of adsorption.

The kinetics of the adsorption of organic substances on solid surfaces can be described by the Roginsky-Zeldovich equation

$$\frac{d\Theta}{d\tau} = ke^{b_a\Theta} \tag{5.8}$$

where k and b_a are constants. With a sufficiently long time of adsorption ($T \gg b_a/k$) the degree of adsorption Θ is a logarithmic function of the time

$$\Theta = \frac{1}{2} \ln \frac{k}{b_a} \tau \tag{5.9}$$

The rate of adsorption can also be limited by the diffusion of the adsorbate towards the surface of the electrode.

The dependence of the adsorption on a heterogeneous surface on the concentration of the matter being adsorbed in the solution is described by Temkin's isotherm equation

$$\Theta = \frac{1}{f_a} \ln \frac{1 + B_{max}\, c}{1 + B_{min}\, c} \tag{5.10}$$

where B_{max} and B_{min} are constants of adsorption equilibrium corresponding to the highest and lowest values of free energy of adsorption ΔG_a, f_a is the factor of heterogeneity of the surface. The value of ΔG is connected with the constant of adsorption equilibrium by the formula $B = \exp(-\Delta G_a/RT)$. Adsorption on solid metal electrodes is often subject to Langmuir's equation. This is explained by mutual compensation of the two factors reflected by the exponential members of equations (5.5) and (5.10).

The free energy of adsorption may be written down in the form

$$\Delta G_a = \Delta G_1'' - n\Delta G_1' - RT \ln \frac{p_{org}}{p^n_{H_2O}} + RT \ln \frac{c_s}{c} \tag{5.11}$$

where $\Delta G_1'$ is the change of free energy in adsorption of the water from its vapours (at 1 atm) on the surface of the metal, $\Delta G_1''$ is the same for organic matter, p_{H_2O} and p_{org} the pressure of the saturated water vapours and of the organic compound at temperature T, c_s the concentration of the saturated solution of organic matter in the water. The first two members in the right-hand part of (5.11) characterise the energy of interaction of the organic matter and the water with the surface of the metal, and the third and fourth members the properties of the adsorbate itself. From equation (5.11) it follows that ΔG_a decreases (adsorption increases) with a decrease in the solubility of the matter being adsorbed (c_s). In fact, with an increase in the length of the hydrocarbon chain, the solubility of organic compounds in water decreases and the adsorbability increases.

A quite complicated and comparatively little studied matter is the question of the influence of the structure of the organic compounds on their adsorbability from aqueous solutions. An analysis of the numerous experimental data carried out by A K Lorenz led to the conclusion that there was no single indication according to which it would be possible to make any judgement about the tendency of one substance or another to adsorption on the electrode.

As has already been shown, the adsorption of organic compounds generally increases with an increase in the length of the hydrocarbon chain. In other words, within the limits of one homologous series an increase in molecular weight leads to an increase in adsorbability. Aliphatic compounds are placed in the following sequence according to the degree of adsorbability of them: acids > amines > alcohols > ethers[16]). The asymmetry of the molecules causes their adsorption on the electrode. Therefore, the factors characterising the degree of asymmetry (dipole moment, molecular refraction etc.) also to a known extent indicate the tendency of the organic substance to adsorption.

Molecules of compounds containing active groups which are electron donors (-CN, -CNS, -CHO, =CO, -CHO, $-NH_2$) are chemisorbed on the surface of metals which have unfilled electron orbits. Among such metals (with unfilled d-orbit) is lead. A condition of the formation of a chemisorption link is a high value of the work of the release of the electron from the metal and a low potential of ionisation of the compound being adsorbed or the reverse (low work of release and high potential of ionisation).

An important role in the determination of the adsorbability of organic substances, particularly ionogenic surface-active compounds, is played by the sign of the charge of the electrode surface, i.e. the position of the potential realised on the surface of the electrode in relation to the potential of the point of zero charge.

In the conditions of utilisation of a lead acid battery the potential of the negative electrode changes approximately within the limits of -0.23 to -0.60V (in relation to hydrogen zero). The potential of zero charge of lead in sulphuric acid, according to the capacity change data, is -0.62 - -0.65V[23]. Consequently the surface of the lead in the region of potentials indicated is positively charged. This should cause adsorption on lead of anionic surface active substances, and also of negatively charged colloidal particles. In the adsorption of dipole molecules on a lead electrode, these should predominantly orientate themselves towards the surface of the metal with their negative end.

In the process of the operation of a battery, metals are deposited on the surface of the negative electrode which are alloying components of the anode alloy. Among these metals there is, above all, antimony and also (with the use of lead-antimony-silver alloys) silver. With the use in the battery of leaded copper negative plate grids the deposition of copper on to the surface of the electrode under consideration is also possible.

The electro-chemical properties of all these metals, which are to be found on the surface of a lead electrode in the form of phase mixtures, differ essentially from the electro-chemical characteristics of lead. Thus the potential of the point of zero charge of antimony is -0.20V (in relation to nve)[24]. This means that the surface of the antimony, at potentials changing within the above-mentioned limits, carries a negative charge. The point of zero charge of silver lies at a potential of -0.70 (nve)[24], and consequently the sections of the electrode surface occupied by silver do not differ in their charge sign from the surface of the lead. Finally, the potential of zero charge of copper is 0.0V[24], i.e. in the conditions of operation of the electrode under consideration the surface of the copper carries a considerable negative charge.

Thus, simultaneous adsorption of organic substances on a lead electrode containing phase mixtures of the above-mentioned metals can be expected only in the event of the adsorption not being very dependent on the surface charge of the electrode. This may be the case with the adsorption of some molecular-active substances.

The current state of the theory of adsorption of organic substances on electrodes is insufficient for an a priori judgement on the surface activity of one compound or another. In experimental selection and study this renders necessary surface-active additives which ensure the necessary utilisation characteristics of the negative electrode of a lead acid battery. Important results in this field were obtained by means of measurement of the capacity of the electrical double layer of a spongy lead electrode in the presence of different organic additives[25][26].

For measurement of the differential capacity of the double layer of porous electrodes, a method which is acceptable is one based on the determination of the slope of the graphs of change of potential in time at the switching off or momentary change (switchover) of current. The bases of this method with reference to a spongy lead electrode were worked out by B N Kabanov and P Yudkievich[27]. For calculation of the value of C_d we use in the references quoted[25][26] the formulae

$$C_d = I/\frac{d\varphi}{d\tau}, \quad C_d = (I - I')/\frac{d\varphi}{d\tau} \tag{5.12}$$

where I is the current of cathodic polarisation (charge), I' the final value of the current at the switchover of it, $d\varphi/d\tau$ the change of potential of the electrode in a unit of time equal to the tangent of the angle of slope of the tangent drawn to the switch-off graph (φ, τ) at its initial point or to the switchover graph at its mid-point.

In calculation of the angle α formed by the tangent and the axis τ it is possible to use the formula[28]

$$\tan\alpha = \frac{L\sqrt{4R^2 - L^2}}{2R^2 - L^2} \tag{5.13}$$

where R is the radius of the arc drawn between the axis τ and the tangent to the graph (φ, τ) from the point of their intersection, and L is the chord spanning this arc.

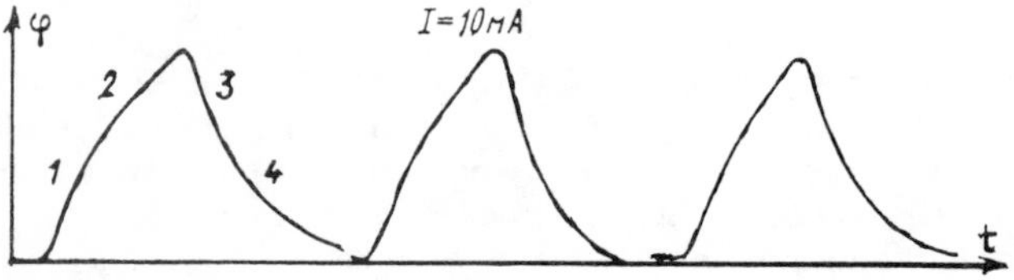

Fig.5.5 Graphs of change of potential of a porous lead electrode of type RG at switching-off and switching-on of current.

In fig.5.5 typical graphs are shown of change of potential at switch-off (sections 1 and 2) and switch-on (sections 3 and 4) of current. The initial sections of the discharge and charge branches (1 and 3) are characterised by practically uniform angles of inclination to the axis of the abscissae. The shift of potential in these sections is caused by the discharge and charge of the double layer. The bend in the graphs (φ, τ) and the change of angle of their slope are connected with the electro-mechanical processes of the formation of lead sulphate (section 2) or its reduction (section 4). For calculation of C_d we used section 1 of graph (φ, τ), which characterises the process of discharge of the double layer. Calculation of C_d according to the graphs of switch-over of the current (from I to I') led to results which do not differ from the results obtained by processing the switch-off graphs.

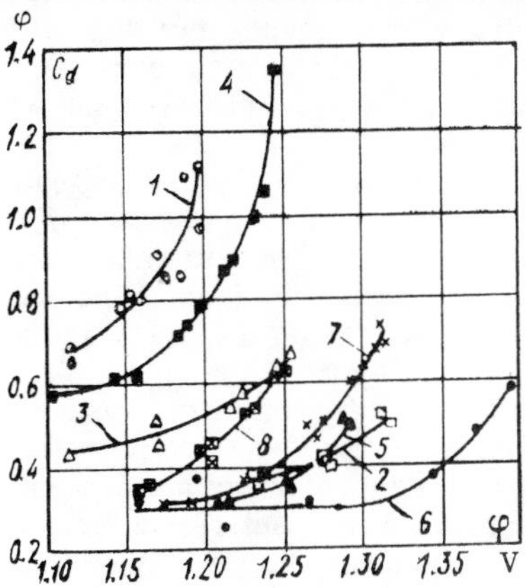

Fig. 5.6 The influence of surface-active additives on the capacitance of the double layer C_d of a porous lead electrode in a solution of H_2SO_4 with a density of 1.32g/cm^3. The potential is shown in relation to a Hg/Hg_2SO_4 electrode: 1 - electrode without organic additives; there was introduced into the active mass; 2 - 1% of humic acid; 3 - 0.6% of tanning preparation No. 4; 4 - 0.5% of disperant NG; 5 - 0.1% of α-naphthol; 6 - 0.5% of α-oxy-naphthalic acid; 7 - 0.4% of tanning preparation No. 4 and 0.2% of α-naphthol; 8 - 0.5% of disperant NF and 0.2% of β-oxy-naphthalic acid; surface of the electrode - 33cm^2.

A study was made of organic additives partially used in the production of lead acid batteries as expanders (depassivators) of the negative electrode, additives which prove to be inhibitors of self-discharge, as will be shown below, and also calculations of expanders and inhibitors. The results of the measurement are partially shown in fig. 5.6.

All the organic substances studied by us, as can be seen from fig.5.6, lower the capacity of the double layer, which is evidence of the adsorption of these substances on a lead electrode. The graphs (C_d, φ) point to a marked dependence on the potential. With an increase in cathodic polarisation the capacity of the double layer increases. A sharp increase in C_d occurs also in the case of an electrode which does not contain organic additives. Obviously, this phenomenon is linked with the partial desorption of the sulphate ions from the negatively charged surface of the electrode. The increase in capacity, with an increase in cathode potential in the presence of the additives investigated, may be the result of desorption of these substances and also of sulphate ions from the surface of the electrode. In this, it is characteristic that a rise in the values of C_d in the electrodes with additives occurs at more negative values of potential than in an electrode which does not contain organic compounds. It can be assumed that this difference is connected with the displacement of the point of zero charge of the lead in a negative direction as a result of the adsorption of the substances investigated.

It must be noted that a known influence on the character of the graphs (C_d, φ) may be shown by the specific properties of a porous electrode, which are examined in Chapter 3. In this case the specific property resides in the fact that the active surface of the electrode depends on its potential, owing to the screening of part of the surface, especially in the depth of the pores, by hydrogen bubbles. The duration of the bubbles remaining on the surface, and also their dimensions and form depend on the electrode potential. The breakaway of the bubbles is facilitated in proportion to the increase in cathode polarisation, and this is equivalent to an increase in the active surface and the capacity of the double layer, with an increase in the cathode potential of a spongy lead electrode.

The effect described is caused to a known extent by the non-uniform character of the distribution of the polarisation over the thickness of the electrode, which shows up particularly at high current densities, when the rate of the process of separation of hydrogen on the outer surface considerably exceeds the rate of this process in the depth of the pores. At low polarisation, when the formation of hydrogen occurs relatively evenly over all the surface of the electrode, a screening of part of the surface is more likely to arise in the thickness of the eléctrode.

The values of capacity which correspond to the minimum or to the horizontal sections of the graph (C_d, φ) lie within the limits $(1\text{-}3)\cdot 10^4$ $\mu F/cm^2$ of the visible surface. If we use these values for calculation of the true surface of the electrode, then the size of the latter amounts to 500-1 500cm^2 per 1cm^2 of the visible surface. This result conforms with the data obtained in its time in ref.[27]). However, it must be noted that the calculation of the true surface, according to the value of C_d, in the presence of the substances being adsorbed, bears an orientational character. Many surface-active expanders which cause an increase in the true surface of a spongy lead electrode at the same time cause a considerable decrease in the capacitance of the double layer. Obviously, this effect is linked with the decrease in the dielectric constant and the increase in space between the coatings on the double layer. The effect of the factors indicated on the value of C_d prevails over the opposite effect, caused by an increase in the surface of the electrode. Even in the absence of surface-active additives, the adsorption on the surface of the lead of sulphate ions and also the specific properties of porous electrodes examined above, do not provide any possibility of using capacitance measurements for accurate determination of the true surface of the electrode under consideration.

The influence of surface-active substances and barium sulphate on the discharge characteristics of the negative electrode

The use of surface-active additives is seen to be a necessary condition for ensuring the normal work of the negative electrode of a lead acid battery. An active mass which does not contain organic components shows a comparatively rapid fall in discharge capacity in the process of cycling. The decrease in capacity is caused principally by recrystallisation of spongy lead, which leads to a substantial decrease in the true surface. This process, caused by the system seeking to reduce the free surface energy, occurs in the case of a lead electrode with fairly great rapidity owing to the low recrystallisation temperature of the lead. In order to combat this phenomenon anti-contraction additives (expanders) are used. Widespread use has been made in current battery production of barium sulphate along with organic expanders.

The mechanism of the action of barium sulphate on the characteristics of the active mass of a negative electrode was the subject of study by E A Byelitski, A K Lorenz, B N Kabanov, Ya B Kasparov, I I Koval, Willihnganz, Zakhlin and others. In a number of papers the positive influence of this additive on the discharge characteristics of the electrode are linked with isomorphism of the crystals of $BaSO_4$ and $PbSO_4$. This point of view received subsequent development in the works of A K Lorenz.

It is suggested that $BaSO_4$ particles may serve as centres of crystallisation of lead sulphate. The appearance of mixed crystals of the type $(Pb, Ba)SO_4$ is then possible. The lead forming as a result of the reduction of such crystals should be distinguished by high dispersability. In addition the crystallisation of $PbSO_4$ on barium sulphate causes an increase in the porosity of the sulphate film, which leads to an increase in the discharge capacity of the electrode. The additive $SrSO_4$, the crystals of which are also isomorphous with $PbSO_4$, acts similarly to barium sulphate[29]).

The salts indicated are characterised by a rhombic lattice with the parameters (in Å):

Compound	a	b	c
$PbSO_4$	8.45	5.38	6.93
$BaSO_4$	8.85	5.44	7.13
$SrSO_4$	8.36	5.36	6.84

The introduction into the active mass of the negative electrode of 0.5-1% $BaSO_4$ (or $SrSO_4$) leads to a considerable decrease, or even to a complete elimination, of the initial shift of discharge potential caused by the difficulty of appearance of centres of crystallisation of $PbSO_4$. This circumstance can be considered as a direct experimental proof of the important role of the phenomenon of isomorphism in the mechanism of the effect of $BaSO_4$ on the characteristics of the electrode[30]).

Organic additives used in the manufacture of the negative electrode of a battery, cause an anti-contraction effect resulting from the adsorption of organic molecules on the lead and a corresponding reduction in free energy on the electrode-solution interphase boundary, as does barium sulphate also. However, the role of organic components of the negative active mass is not limited by the effect mentioned. These substances show quite a substantial influence on the process of anodic passivation of lead, which takes place at the discharge of the negative electrode. In the presence of additives (depassivators) there is an increase in porosity and in effective thickness of the sulphate film, which is equivalent to an increase in the discharge capacity of the electrode. The influence of organic substances on the passivation of lead shows up particularly at the discharge of the electrode at high current densities and at low temperatures.

A survey of the large number of patents for additives to the active mass of the negative electrode is given in ref.[31]). Of the 380 compounds described, the author sees particularly good prospects for the use as organic expanders (depassivators) of humic and lignosulphonic acids, and also of sulpho-acids of phenol, naphthalene and anthracene. The influence of a considerable number of organic compounds on the characteristics of porous lead at short discharge regimes was studied by A K Lorenz. In the works of this author, the high effectiveness of humic acid, of salts of lignosulphonic acid and some other substances that cause a substantial increase in discharge capacity is demonstrated.

Further investigations, carried out by E G Yampolski, G I Eidman and others, revealed a group of effective depassivators of the lead electrode, among which are numbered the tanning preparation No. 4, the BNF tanning preparation, a casting strengthener (potassium lignosulphonate) and NF disperser. BNF has obtained widespread use in the battery industry. Finally, a recently undertaken study of lignosulphonic acid, the molecules of which are enlarged by polymerisation and condensation with phenol, made it possible to suggest a modified lignosulphonic acid and its barium salt as a new, completely effective depassivator [32]).

It must be noted that there is a complete absence of theoretical ideas about the mechanism of the action of organic depassivators in the literature. In the works of B N Kabanov and his colleagues, the useful effect of depassivators is explained by the adsorption of surface-active particles on the growing faces of the lead sulphate which is formed at anodic polarisation (discharge). Thanks to this, a loose film is obtained, consisting of large $PbSO_4$ crystals. Such a film for a long time (until the attainment of considerable thicknesses) does not hinder the penetration of the sulphuric acid towards the surface of the active mass. Without organic additives the sulphate film consists of fine crystals and fairly quickly screens the basic part of the surface of the lead electrode [30]) [33]).

The authors of the references quoted consider that barium sulphate plays the part of a distinctive 'depot' for organic depassivators in the active mass of the negative electrode. The organic substances are adsorbed on $BaSO_4$ crystals and gradually progress into the zone of crystallisation of $PbSO_4$, distending the sulphate film. Evidence in favour of this proposition is provided by experimental results, according to which the introduction into the negative active mass of $BaSO_4$ (without organic additives) does not cause any noticeable increase in the discharge capacity of the electrode [30]).

In the works of A K Lorenz a decrease in the passivation of the negative electrode of a lead acid battery, in the presence of organic additives, is explained by the adsorption of surface-active particles on the lead. In the opinion of the author there is an increase in the energy of formation of centres of crystallisation of $PbSO_4$ as a result of the adsorption, which causes a growth of the separate sulphate crystals, which are loosely connected with the surface of the lead. The probability of crystallisation of $PbSO_4$ directly on the surface of the metal is decreased; crystallisation occurs basically outside the layer of adsorbed particles. The opinion was expressed by A K Lorenz that the adsorption of surface-active substances on lead sulphate leads to a strengthening of the passivation of the electrode, since with it the growth of $PbSO_4$ crystals is hampered and the process goes on principally owing to the formation of new centres of crystallisation of the sulphate on the still free sections of the surface of the metal.

The arresting of the growth of the crystals in the presence of organic molecules being adsorbed on their surface is increased with an increasing concentration of the organic substance c in conformity with the formula[34]):

$$\nu = \nu_0 \sqrt{1 - kc^h} \tag{5.14}$$

where ν is the rate of growth of the crystal in the presence of the organic additive, and ν_0 the rate of growth in a 'pure' solution (with c = 0). The coefficient k depends on the type of crystals, and h on the character of the adsorption. If the molecules are adsorbed on the steps of growth, then h = 1, but if the adsorption takes place on the plane surface of the crystals, h = 0.5.

According to the data of A I Levin, V F Lazarev and other, surface-active substances (in particular humic acid and α-oxynaphthalic acid) are suitable for adsorption on lead and lead sulphate[35]). In the works of these authors the proposition is also put forward that, at anodic polarisation of a lead electrode, organic substances can change the degree of oversaturation of the layer next to the electrode with lead ions as a result of the formation of adsorption compounds with $BaSO_4$ and $PbSO_4$. This phenomenon also impedes rapid passivation of the electrode.

A study of the adsorption of ammonium lignosulphonate undertaken in the work of Sharp[36]) showed that for this substance a characteristic feature is the multi-layer chemisorption of surface-active anions on lead. Lignosulphonate is not adsorbed in practice on crystals of lead sulphate. Studying a number of organic compounds (rhodamine B, pyrogallol, naphthalene sulphonate, gallein, ammonium lignosulphonate, cerulene), Sharp showed that the more active the product as a depassivator, the more it lowers the capacity of the double layer of a lead electrode[37]).

A potentiodynamic study of the influence of a lignin expander on a lead sulphate electrode[38]) showed that this additive arrests the regeneration of Pb^{2+} ions and facilitates the regeneration of $PbSO_4$ crystals. The authors consider that the organic molecules being adsorbed on the surface of the electrode in a continuous layer hinder the penetration of Pb^{2+} ions[38]). This leads to supersaturation of the solution in the layer next to the electrode and precipitation of the sulphate crystals in the space between the surface of the electrode and the layer of adsorbed molecules. We note that, as was established in ref. [39]), the organic molecules being adsorbed on a lead electrode can suffer considerable modifications as a result of electro-chemical oxidation-reduction reactions.

An investigation was carried out by the authors of this book into the influence of a number of organic substances on the crystallisation of $PbSO_4$, the electro-crystallisation and anodic passivation of Pb[40]. The objects of investigation were organic expanders used in the production of lead batteries: humic acid, tanning preparation No. 4, BNF tanning preparation, and sodium ligosulphonate, and also inhibitors of atmospheric and acid corrosion of lead: α-oxynaphthalic acid, α-naphthol, β-naphthol, α-nitrode, β-naphthol, β-nitroso-α-naphthol, and sulphanol.

As was mentioned above, the formation of lead sulphate in the process of discharge of a negative electrode is generally preceded by a transference to the solution of lead ions, which then interact with sulphate ions. Lead sulphate is thus formed as a result of a secondary chemical reaction. This last process can be modelled on the deposition of $PbSO_4$ from the solution with a known degree of approximation. Lead sulphate crystals in this case appear without any participation of the metal electrode. Therefore, a study of the influence of organic additives on the crystallisation of lead sulphate from the solution, may give some evidence about the adsorbability of one substance or another on $PbSO_4$ crystals.

For deposition of lead sulphate we used 1N solution of $Pb(NO_3)_2$, to which was added an equal volume of 20N solution of H_2SO_4. The acid solution contained one or more organic substances within the limits of concentration investigated. Deposition of $PbSO_4$ was studied under an optical microscope. It was established that none of the organic substances under investigation showed any marked influence on the habit of $PbSO_4$ crystallites. In all cases the formation of dendritic particles is observed, the dimensions of which vary from a few microns to a few tenths of a micron.

Several changes of structure of the $PbSO_4$ took place in the presence of the inhibitors. Thus, with the presence in the solution of α-nitroso-β-napthol the formation of large, strongly oriented crystals of $PbSO_4$ was observed. The introduction into the electrolyte of α-oxynaphthalic acid dispersed the sulphate deposit. These effects can be explained by the adsorption of inhibitors on the separate faces of the lead sulphate crystals.

Electron microscope investigation carried out recently on lead sulphate deposited from $9.6N \cdot H_2SO_4$ in the presence of tanning preparation No. 4 showed that this expander causes a marked enlargement of the sulphate crystals[41]. Thus $PbSO_4$ crystals deposited without an expander have a dimension of 0.3-0.8μm, and in the presence of the tanning preparation 1-3μm. The authors consider this result as confirmation of the mechanism of the action of the expander which postulates adsorption on $PbSO_4$ [41]).

The adsorption of expanders (depassivators) on lead causes a shift in the negative direction of the cathode potential of electro-deposition of lead from a solution of $Pb(NO_3)_2$ [40]). In addition, the expanders investigated show a definite influence on the structure of the cathodic deposit of lead, which bears witness to the prevalent adsorption of the substances mentioned on the separate faces of the lead crystals. Let us note in connection with this that, as we showed in ref. [42]), sodium lignosulphonate - which is one of the effective expanders (depassivators) of the negative electrode - can at the same time be successfully used as an additive to a hydrofluosilicic acid lead electrolyte. The use of an electrolyte containing 1.5-2.0g/l sodium lignosulphonate makes it possible to obtain quite smooth lead coverings at high current densities.

The influence of a number of surface-active additives on the structure of the passivating sulphate film and on the discharge properties of a smooth lead electrode are shown in figs. 5.7 and 5.8.

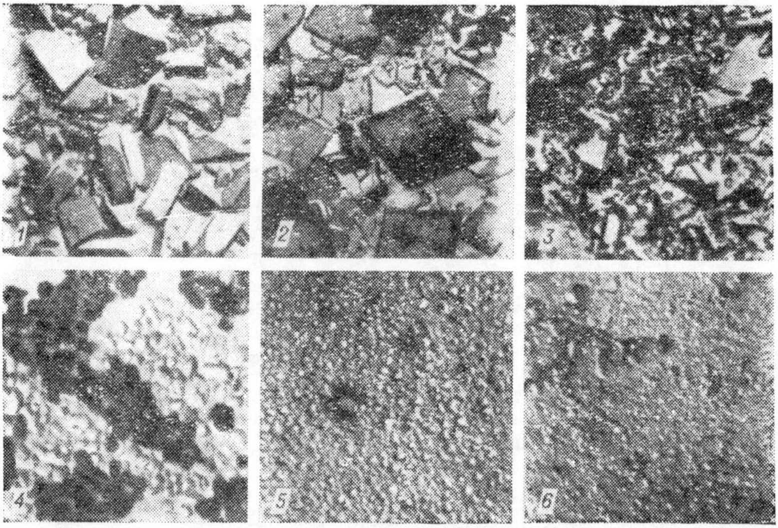

Fig. 5.7 Electron micrographs of sulphate films obtained on discharge of a lead electrode in $12N{\cdot}H_2SO_4$ with a current of $0.1mA/cm^2$. 1 - solution without additives; 2 - tanning preparation No. 4 added; 3 - α-oxy-naphthalic acid; 4 - α-naphthol; 5 - α-nitroso-β-naphthol; 6 - β-nitroso-α-naphthol).

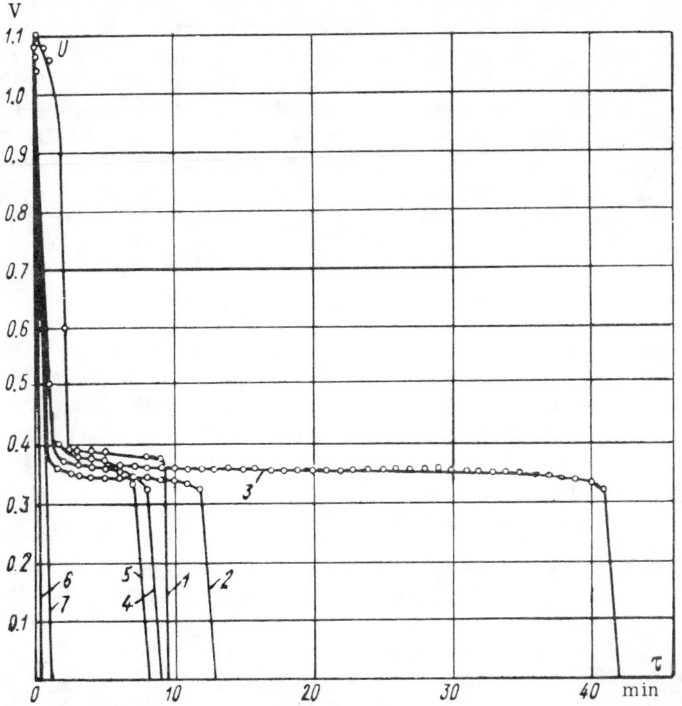

Fig. 5.8 Discharge graphs of a lead electrode in $12N \cdot H_2SO_4$, $j = 0.1 mA/cm^2$. 1 - in solution without additives; additions; 2 - humic acid; 3 - tanning preparation No. 4; 4 - α-naphthol; 5 - α-oxynaphthalic acid; 6 - α-nitroso-β-naphthol; 7 - β-nitroso-α-naphthol.

A lead electrode with a mirror-smooth surface was investigated being initially cathodically polarised to achieve a steady potential at a current density $j = 0.1 mA/cm^2$. Then anodic polarisation (discharge) was carried out with current of the same density until a sharp fall in voltage between the electrode under consideration and the auxiliary platinum electrodes.

The graphs of change of voltage in the process of discharge show a sharp voltage drop in the initial period. Then in the course of a definite period of time the voltage hardly changes, after which it falls sharply to zero. From fig. 5.8 it can be seen that the discharge capacity of a lead electrode substantially depends on the nature of the organic additives. A considerable increase in capacity is observed with the introduction into the solution of tanning preparation No. 4. The introduction of humic acid causes a noticeably smaller effect. It must, however, be noted that for this depassivator a characteristic feature is the long, gradual increase in capacity in the process of cycling, which is probably connected with definite chemical changes suffered by the humic acid. The presence in the electrolyte of inhibitors causes a lowering of the discharge capacity of a lead electrode, which is especially considerable with the introduction of α-nitroso-β-naphthol and β-nitroso-α-naphthol. This result shows in particular that the use of inhibitors in a battery is possible only with simultaneous use of effective depassivators.

From examination of the electron microphotographs of sulphate films (fig. 5.7) it can be seen that the structure of the $PbSO_4$ crystals that form the passivating film shows a substantial dependency on the nature of the organic additive. In the presence of depassivators the dimensions of the sulphate crystals increase somewhat. Thus, if in a "pure" H_2SO_4 solution, the dimensions of the $PbSO_4$ crystals amount approximately to $1\mu m$, then with the presence in the solution of tanning preparation No. 4 this size is increased to 1.5-$2\mu m$. The introduction into the solution of inhibitors leads to a sharp dispersal of the $PbSO_4$ crystals. Particularly fine crystals (0.1-$0.15\mu m$) are formed in the presence of α-nitroso-β-naphthol and β-nitroso-α-naphthol. Naturally, the decrease in dimensions of the $PbSO_4$ crystals leads to an increase in the density of the sulphate film. It is therefore not surprising that additives which disperse the structure of the sulphate cause a decrease in the discharge capacity, i.e. decrease in the thickness of the sulphate film sufficient for passivation of the electrode. Substances causing an enlargement of the $PbSO_4$ crystals cause an increase in capacity owing to the increase in the porosity of the passivating film and the increase in its thickness.

The thickness of the passivating film (δ) can be evaluated with the aid of the formula

$$\delta = \frac{Э j \tau}{F d_c} \tag{5.15}$$

where $Э = 151g$ - the equivalent mass of the $PbSO_4$, $F = 96\,500$coulombs - the Faraday number, $d_c = 6.2 g/cm^3$ - the density of the $PbSO_4$, $j = 10^{-4} A/cm^2$ - the current density, τ - the time of discharge s. The value of δ in the absence of additives is $0.14\mu m$, in the presence of humic acid $\delta = 0.16\mu m$, in the presence of tanning preparation $\delta = 0.64\mu m$, in the presence of α-oxynaphthalic acid $\delta = 0.12\mu m$, but under the influence of α-nitroso-β-naphthol this value is reduced to $0.004\mu m$.

The value of δ calculated according to formula (5.15) may not fully correspond to the real thicknesses of the sulphate layer δ' if the latter possesses marked porosity. In this case $\delta' > \delta$. The difference between δ' and δ obviously is particularly great in the case of macrocrystalline films. For fine-dispersal films, the porosity of which is negligible, $\delta \approx \delta'$. Thus, taking into account the possible porosity of the sulphate, the influence of organic additives on the effective thickness of the passivating film is shown to be even sharper.

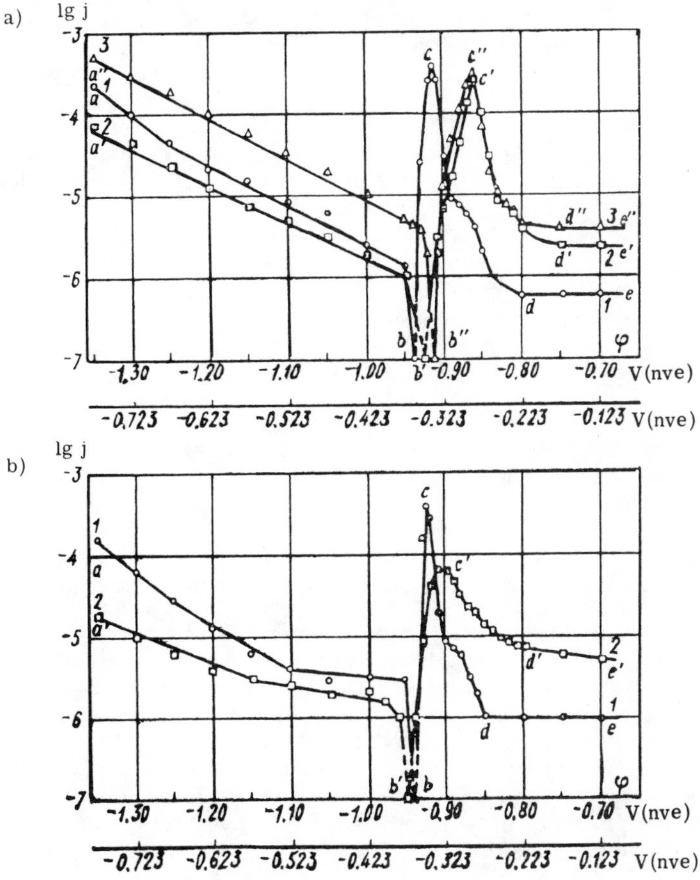

Fig. 5.9 Potentiodynamic graphs of a lead electrode in $10N \cdot H_2SO_4$. a) 1 - Pb in $10N \cdot H_2SO_4$ (initial graph); 2 and 3 - Pb in $10N \cdot H_2SO_4$ in the presence of tanning preparation No. 4 (1g/1). b) 1 - Pb in $10N \cdot H_2SO_4$ (initial graph); 2 - Pb in $10N \cdot H_2SO_4$ in the presence of α-naphthol (1g/1).

Some additional evidence about the mechanism of the influence of organic additives on the characteristics of a lead sulphate electrode can be obtained with the use of the potentiodynamic method. In fig. 5.9 potentiodynamic graphs taken at slow change of potential (250mV/hr) are shown, i.e. in conditions approximating to the stationary, in the region of potentials realised on the negative electrode of a battery[43]. The potential is shown in relation to a normal hydrogen electrode and a mercury-mercurous sulphate one.

From fig. 5.9 it can be seen that after the switching on of the sweep of potential the current density established in "pure" H_2SO_4 solution at $\varphi = -1.35V$ at a level of $j = (3\text{-}5)\cdot10^{-4}\ A/cm^2$ slowly begins to decrease (section a-b). At potential $\varphi = -0.94V$, which is close to the equilibrium value of the potential of the $Pb \rightleftarrows PbSO_4$ system, the current density becomes equal to zero. At the beginning of the anodic region of potentials there is observed a sharp increase in j (section b-c of graph 1), followed by a drop (section c-d). The value corresponding to the peak in graph 1 is $\varphi = -0.92V$ and current density $j \approx 3\cdot10^{-4}\ A/cm^2$. At $\varphi > -0.9V$ the drop in potential slows up substantially and at $\varphi > -0.8V$ right to $\varphi = -0.65V$ the current density practically does not change, remaining equal to $(4\text{-}10)\cdot 10^{-7}\ A/cm^2$ (section d-e).

The introduction into the solution of tanning preparation No. 4 (fig. 5.9a, graph 2) causes a decrease in the cathodic portion of the potentiodynamic graph, which is evidence of an increase in the hydrogen overvoltage on the lead. The introduction of the depassivator under investigation causes a considerable shift of the anode peak (an approximately similar effect is shown on the course of the potentiodynamic graph by tanning preparation BNF). This expander possesses, however, increased inhibiting properties, thanks to which there occurs in its presence a more substantial decrease in the cathodic branch of graph (φ, j).

In the presence of α-naphthol (fig. 5.9b, graph 2) the current density established at $\varphi = -1.35V$ at a level of $(2\text{-}4)\cdot10^{-5}\ A/cm^2$ was approximately an order less than in a solution of H_2SO_4 which does not contain additives. The introduction into the solution of α-naphthol causes a marked alteration in the slope of the cathodic portion of the graph (φ, j), and also a shift of the passivation potential in a positive direction by 20-30mV. The passivation section (independence of current from potentials) is shifted in the presence of α-naphthol to a positive 50mV more positive than in pure sulphuric acid.

In contrast to tanning preparation No. 4, the introduction of α-naphthol into the solution does not lead to an increase in the active surface of the lead, therefore the graphs (φ, j) taken at the second and third passages in the presence of α-naphthol coincide with each other.

The increase in current at the beginning of the anodic region of potentials is obviously caused by active dissolution of the lead ($Pb \rightarrow Pb^{2+} + 2e$). After the attainment of sufficient oversaturation of the layer next to the electrode by Pb^{2+} ions at the maximum of the graph (φ, j) crystallisation of $PbSO_4$ begins, causing a fall in current. The presence of tanning preparation No. 4 and of α-naphthol in the solution, as can be seen from fig. 5.9, leads to an arresting of both processes (ionisation of lead and formation of sulphate), which causes a reduction in the steepness of the maximum. This phenomenon may be considered as a result of the adsorption of additives on the lead, which impedes the egress of Pb^{2+} ions from the most active places of the crystal lattice of the lead and the formation on the electrode surface of centres of crystallisation of $PbSO_4$. This is evidenced by the shift in the anodic direction of the maximum in the graph (φ, j).

As can be seen from fig. 5.9, in the presence of these organic substances the forming of a passivating sulphate film (section c'-d') finishes up at a more positive value of the potential than in "pure" acid (section c-d). Thus the adsorption of α-naphthol and, in particular, of tanning preparation No. 4, hinders the formation of a passivating layer. The increase in current in section d'-e' of graph 2 (in comparison with section d-e of graph 1) in the first passage of the graph, when the surface of the electrode is not yet dispersed, is evidence of the fact that the introduction of additives causes an increase in the permeability of the sulphate film. This effect, obviously, is partly caused by the chemical heterogeneity of the passivating layer as a result of the capture of the adsorbed molecules of the surface-active substances.

The value of maximum anode current in the presence of tanning preparation No. 4 is close to the corresponding value in the electrode without additives. Therefore the shift of the maximum anode current in this case conforms well with the data regarding the increase in discharge capacity, since for the attainment of a passive condition of the electrode with the presence in the solution of tanning preparation No. 4 it is necessary to expend a greater amount of electricity. With the introduction into the solution of α-naphthol, the value of the maximum anode current is substantially reduced and the shift of the corresponding value of the potential in the positive direction is less than in the presence of tanning preparation No. 4. Therefore in this case we must not expect an increase in the discharge capacity of the electrode.

At the present time, a method based on analysis of the potentiodynamic graphs is used in laboratory practice for studying the mechanism of the influence of various organic substances on a lead electrode. This method can be used for a fairly rapid evaluation of the character of the action of various additives on the cathodic and anodic behaviour of the negative electrode of a lead acid battery.

In conclusion, it can be affirmed that the question of the mechanism of the influence of organic substances on the behaviour of the negative electrode of a lead acid battery is not yet sufficiently explained. The selection of the additives necessary for the ensuring of high utilisation characteristics of the battery, up to the present time, has been basically undertaken empirically. To a known extent this is caused by the absence of clear ideas about the character of the influence of additives on the kinetics of the processes occurring on a lead sulphate electrode. Substantial differences in the chemical structure of surface-active additives make it possible to assume the possibility of differences also in the mechanism of their action on anodic passivation of lead.

Self-discharge of the negative electrode

Basic laws of self-dissolution of lead

Spontaneous dissolution of lead in a sulphuric acid solution can be caused, in principle, by the occurrence of the following reactions:

$$Pb + H_2SO_4 \rightarrow PbSO_4 + H_2 \qquad (5.16)$$

$$Pb + \tfrac{1}{2}O_2 + H_2SO_4 \rightarrow PbSO_4 + H_2O \qquad (5.17)$$

The rate of reaction (5.17) is limited by the diffusion of the dissolved oxygen to the surface of the electrode, since the concentration of oxygen in the sulphuric acid is extremely small, and the stationary potential of self-dissolution of lead is almost 1.5V lower than the potential of the equilibrium $O_2 \rightleftarrows H_2O$. As is well known, the solubility of oxygen decreases with an increase in the concentration of H_2SO_4 and a rise in the temperature. The rate of self-discharge of the negative electrode of a battery increases with an increase in the concentration of the acid and the temperature. This fact, and also a number of other factors, and in particular the substantial dependence of the rate of self-discharge on the cathodic potential of the electrode, show that reaction (5.17) does not play a big part in the kinetics of self-dissolution of lead in sulphuric acid.

The basic laws of self-discharge of the negative electrode considered below are obtained as a result of analysis of the kinetics of process (5.16)[44]). The equation of reaction (5.18) represents a summary of two connected processes.

$$\left.\begin{array}{l} Pb + HSO_4^- \rightarrow PbSO_4 + H^+ + 2e \\ 2H^+ + 2e \rightarrow H_2 \end{array}\right\} \qquad (5.18)$$

The stationary potential of self-dissolution of lead in sulphuric acid is practically equal to the potential of the equilibrium $Pb \rightleftarrows PbSO_4$, since the exchange current of this equilibrium exceeds by a few orders the exchange current of $H^+ \rightleftarrows H_2$. Taking into account what has been said and using as an expression for the stationary potential formula (2.22), we may write that

$$\varphi^0 - \frac{RT}{2F} \ln a_{H_2SO_4} = -\eta_H \qquad (5.19)$$

where η_H is the overvoltage of separation of hydrogen on the electrode. Since

$$\eta_H = a + \frac{RT}{\alpha F} \ln j \qquad (5.20)$$

where a is a constant equal to η_H at $j = 1A/cm^2$ and α is the transfer coefficient; then substituting (5.20) in equation (5.19) and carrying out a few conversions, we obtain the expression for the specific rate of self-dissolution of lead

$$j = a_{H_2SO_4}^{\alpha/2} \exp\left[-\frac{\alpha F}{RT}(\varphi^0 + a)\right] \qquad (5.21)$$

Substituting in (5.21) the numerical values of φ^0, α, R and F, the formula can be better written as:

$$j = a_{H_2SO_4}^{1/4} e^{\frac{5815(0\ 356-a)}{T}} \qquad (5.22)$$

Equations (5.21)-(5.22) express the rate of the reaction of formation of sulphate or the rate, which is equal to it, of the process of liberation of hydrogen, calculated per unit of the electrode surface. In the process of self-discharge the active surface of the electrode S is continuously decreasing as a result of its screening by lead sulphate. In connection with this the rate of self-discharge also decreases with time.

The volume of hydrogen V ml, separating in the time τ at self-discharge of the negative electrode can be expressed by the equation[45]):

$$V = 0.164 m^{0.75} \gamma_{\pm}^{0.75} e^{\frac{5815(0.356-a)}{T}} \int_0^{\tau} S(\tau) d\tau \qquad (5.23)$$

For calculation of V according to formula (5.23) it is necessary to know the form of functional dependency of the value S on the time τ. If, in the first approximation, we assume that in the course of a definite interval of time τ the value of S does not change, then the integral in (5.23) can be replaced by the product $S\tau$. In that case the formula (5.23) is suitable for an approximation evaluation of the volume of hydrogen separating in the process of self-discharge of the negative electrode of a lead acid battery.

Let us consider how the concentration of sulphuric acid influences the rate of separation of hydrogen at self-discharge. For this we shall log the equation (5.23) and differentiate the result obtained by m with T = const:

$$\left(\frac{\partial \ln V}{\partial m}\right)_T = \frac{0.75}{m} + 0.75\left(\frac{\partial \ln \gamma_{\pm}}{\partial m}\right)_T - \frac{5815}{T}\left(\frac{\partial a}{\partial m}\right)_T + \left(\frac{\partial \ln \int_0^{\tau} S d\tau}{\partial m}\right)_T \qquad (5.24)$$

The mean coefficient of activity of H_2SO_4 in strong solutions ($m > 2$) employed as electrolyte of lead acid batteries increases with an increase in the concentration of the acid, i.e. $(\partial \ln \gamma_{\pm}/\partial m)_T > 0$.

The overvoltage of hydrogen separation on lead over a wide range of concentrations of sulphuric acid in practice does not depend on the concentration. In concentrated solutions of H_2SO_4 the hydrogen overvoltage drops somewhat with a rise in concentration of the acid, therefore $(\partial a/\partial m)_T \leqslant 0$. For determination of the sign of the last member on the right hand side of equation (5.24), let us assume that the active surface of the electrode decreases with time according to the linear law

$$S = S_0 - \nu_S \tau \qquad (5.25)$$

where S_0 is the initial value of the surface, and ν_S the rate of change of the surface. The results of the potentiometric study of lead and lead alloys which were considered in Chapter 4 show (e.g. see fig.

4.34) that, excluding the initial section, the graph of the change of current in time at potentials corresponding to the formation of $PbSO_4$ is close to a straight line, which corresponds to formula (5.25) since in those conditions the current is directly proportional to the area of the active surface of the electrode. According to (5.25)

$$\left(\frac{\partial \ln \int_0^T S d\tau}{\partial m}\right)_T = -\frac{\tau}{2S_0 - \nu_S \tau}\left(\frac{\partial \nu_S}{\partial m}\right)_T > 0$$

since $(\partial \nu_S / \partial m)_T < 0$ (with an increase in the concentration of H_2SO_4 the rate of change of the active surface of the electrode decreases). Comparison of the inequalities obtained with the equation (5.24) shows that $(\partial \ln V/\partial m)_T > 0$. i.e. the rate of self-discharge increases with an increase in the concentration of H_2SO_4, which accords with the experimental data. From equation (5.24) it also follows that the concentration dependence of the rate of self-discharge decreases in proportion to the increase in concentration of H_2SO_4.

In the range of sulphuric acid concentrations m = 3-8 *) the dependence of the mean coefficient of activity of H_2SO_4 on m may be expressed by the empirical formula

$$\ln \gamma_\pm = -2.591 + 0.205m \qquad (5.26)$$

The error in the calculation of $\gamma_\pm$ according to this formula amounts on average to $\pm 0.35\%$.

If we substitute (5.26) in equation (5.24) and ignore the concentration dependence of the constant a and of the value $\int_0^T S(\tau)d\tau$, i.e. calculate that within the defined limits of change of concentration of H_2SO_4 (from m_1 to m_2) the hydrogen overvoltage and the character of the change of the active surface of the electrode with time do not depend on m, then equation (5.24) takes the form

$$\left(\frac{\partial \log_e V}{\partial m}\right)_T \cong \frac{0.75}{m} + 0.154 \qquad (5.27)$$

---

*) This range includes practically the whole range of concentrations of battery electrolytes. A corresponding range of densities of H_2SO_4 solution is d = 1.15-1.35g/cm².

Integrating (5.27) within the limits mentioned and taking the exponential of both sides

$$V_2 \cong V_1 \left(\frac{m_2}{m_1}\right)^{0.75} e^{0.164\,(m_2 - m_1)} \tag{5.28}$$

where V_2 and V_1 are the volumes of hydrogen which have separated in the determined time in a solution of H_2SO_4 with a molar concentration equal to m_2 and m_1.

Formula (5.28) can be used for evaluation of the influence of the concentration of the electrolyte on the rate of separation of hydrogen at self-discharge. In particular, calculation according to this formula shows that an increase in the density of the battery electrolyte from 1.27 to 1.32 leads to an increase in the rate of self-discharge of the negative electrode of approximately 40%. The use in a number of types of current batteries of an electrolyte with an increased H_2SO_4 content increases the role of the self-discharge, which must be taken into account in the utilisation of these batteries.

The temperature dependence of the rate of self-dissolution of lead (or the rate of hydrogen separation which is equal to it) can be obtained by differentiating the logarithm of the temperature of equation (5.23):

$$\left(\frac{\partial \ln V}{\partial T}\right)_m = 0.75\left(\frac{\partial \ln \gamma_\pm}{\partial T}\right)_m - \frac{2070+5815\left[T\left(\frac{\partial a}{\partial T}\right)_m - a\right]}{T^2} + \left(\frac{\partial \ln \int_0^\tau S d\tau}{\partial T}\right)_m \tag{5.29}$$

The coefficient of activity of H_2SO_4 decreases somewhat with an increase in temperature, i.e. $(\partial \ln \gamma_\pm/\partial T)_m < 0$. The second member in the right-hand part of equation (5.29) is positive, since $a > 1$ and $(\partial a/\partial T)_m < 0$. The third member in the right-hand part of (5.29), according to (5.25), is a negative value:

$$\left(\frac{\partial \ln \int_0^\tau S d\tau}{\partial T}\right)_m = \frac{\tau^2}{2}\left(\frac{\partial V_S}{\partial T}\right)_m < 0$$

since $(\partial \nu_S/\partial T)_m > 0$ (the porosity of the sulphate film and the rate of change of the active surface of the electrode increase with a rise in temperature). Taking into account, however, that the temperature change of the magnitudes $\int Sd(\tau)$ and $\gamma_\pm$ is small, from equation (5.29) it is possible to draw the conclusion that the rate of self-discharge increases with a rise in temperature, whilst in proportion to the rise in temperature the product $(\partial \ln V/\partial T)_m$ decreases, i.e. the temperature dependency of the rate of the process under consideration weakens.

If we ignore in equation (5.29) the first and third members and calculate $(\partial a/\partial T)_m \approx -0.003V/\text{degr.}$, then it is possible to write the following approximate equation

$$\left(\frac{\partial \ln V}{\partial T}\right)_m \approx \frac{5815a-2070}{T^2} + \frac{17.4}{T} \qquad (5.30)$$

Integrating (5.30) in the range of temperatures from T_1 to T_2 we have:

$$\ln \frac{V_{T_2}}{V_{T_1}} \approx (5815a_{av}-2070)\left(\frac{1}{T_1} - \frac{1}{T_2}\right) + 17.4 \ln \frac{T_2}{T_1} \qquad (5.31)$$

where a_{av} is the average value of the overvoltage of separation of hydrogen (at $j = 1A/cm^2$) in the temperature range under consideration, which we consider as independent of the temperature.

According to (5.31)

$$V_{T_2} \cong V_{T_1}\left(\frac{T_2}{T_1}\right)^{17.4} \exp\left[\frac{(5815a_{av}-2070)(T_2-T_1)}{T_2T_1}\right] \qquad (5.32)$$

Let us allow that $T_2 = T + 1$, and $T_1 = T$, then according to equation (5.32)

$$\frac{V_{T+1}}{V} \cong \left(1 + \frac{1}{T}\right)^{17.4} \exp\left[\frac{5815a_{av}-2070}{T^2}\right] \qquad (5.33)$$

If $T \approx 300^oK$ and $a_{av} \approx 1.4V$, then, as is shown by calculation according to formula (5.33), $V_{T+1}/V_T \approx 1.13$. This result accords well with the experimental data of ref. [46]), according to which the rate of separation of hydrogen from a lead acid battery at self-discharge increases 12% with an increase of temperature of 1° in the temperature range 15-45°C. Let us note that more accurate calculation of the value of V_{T+1}/V_T, taking into account the temperature dependence of $\gamma_\pm$ and φ^0, leads to a very close value[45]).

The presence of admixtures of different metals on the surface of the negative electrode of a lead acid battery can exert considerable influence on the rate of self-dissolution of the lead as a result of the change in the value of the hydrogen overvoltage. Practically all metals encountered as admixtures in the battery raw material or introduced in the form of special additives have a lower value of overvoltage of separation of hydrogen than the corresponding value for pure lead. Therefore, the presence of extraneous metals on the surface of the negative electrode, sometimes even in quite small quantities, leads to an increase in the rate of self-discharge. Naturally, the lower the hydrogen overvoltage on the metal, the more deleterious its effect on the negative electrode.

For a quantitative characterisation of the influence of added metals on the rate of self-discharge it is necessary to know the value of the change of hydrogen overvoltage as a result of the appearance of the admixture in question. If the constant a in equation (5.20) under the influence of an admixture falls by Δa, and the value of the coefficient of transfer a does not change, then according to equation (5.23) the volume of hydrogen V' separating in the time τ on an electrode contaminated by an admixture will be equal to

$$V' = 0.164 m^{0.75} \gamma_\pm^{0.75} \exp\left[\frac{5815(0.356 - a + \Delta a)}{T}\right] \int_0^\tau S(\tau) d\tau =$$

$$= V e^{\frac{5815 \Delta a}{T}} \qquad (5.34)$$

where V is the volume of hydrogen separating in the same time on a pure lead electrode. Here we are assuming that the presence of the admixture has no influence on the character of the change in time of the active surface of the electrode. The value of Δa can be determined experimentally according to the change in the final charge potential of the electrode. As will be shown below, it is also possible in a number of cases to calculate this value theoretically, the magnitude of which is directly linked with the surface concentration and the electro-chemical properties of the admixture. Experimental verification of equation (5.34) showed that it describes completely satisfactorily the change of gas separation at self-discharge, caused by the influence of the admixtures antimony and silver.

Adsorption of surface-active substances can cause a change in the rate of self-discharge of the negative electrode basically owing to the following two effects: a) screening of the surface of the electrode and b) change in the structure of the electrical double layer, which amounts formally to a shift of the ψ_1 potential. Naturally, a decrease in the active surface as a result of the adsorption of organic particles leads to a decrease in the rate of self-discharge. As far as the influence of the ψ_1 effect is concerned, this question can be examined with the use of the dependence of the constant a on ψ_1 [47]):

$$a = \psi_1 + \frac{RT}{F} \ln m_{H^+} + (1 - 2\alpha') \frac{RT}{F} \ln \gamma_{H^+} + \text{const} \qquad (5.35)$$

Here m_{H^+} is the concentration, and γ_{H^+} the coefficient of activity of H^+ ions, α' the coefficient characterising the change of the energy of solution of these ions with the concentration. According to (5.23) and (5.35), a decrease in the rate of self-discharge of the negative electrode must be expected in the event of the adsorption of organic additives leading to a shift of the ψ_1 potential in a positive direction.

At the beginning of this chapter it was said that self-dissolution of lead can in principle occur with oxygen depolarisation, i.e. according to the scheme of (5.17). Although up to the present time experimental data gathered give convincing evidence of the occurrence of this process according to reaction (5.16), various attempts are encountered in the literature to describe the self-dissolution of lead in sulphuric acid as a result of the oxidation of the metal by dissolved oxygen. Therefore it is appropriate to consider in greater detail the question concerned.

The process (5.17) should occur with a maximum rate which (in electrical units) is equal to

$$j = 2F \frac{c_{O_2}}{\delta} D_{O_2} \qquad (5.36)$$

where δ is the thickness of the diffusion layer, c_{O_2} the concentration of the dissolved oxygen, and D_{O_2} the coefficient of diffusion of oxygen towards the surface of the metal. For carrying out a calculation according to formula (5.36) it is possible to use the following values: $\delta \approx 10^{-2}$ cm, $D_{O_2} \approx 10^{-3}$ cm^2/s and $c_{O_2} \approx 3.1{:}10^{-7}$ g.eq./cm^3. In this case $j \approx 6 \cdot 10^{-8}$ A/cm^2. Calculation of j's value according to formula (5.22) at a = 1.4V leads to the following result: $j = 4 \cdot 10^{-9}$ A/cm^2. The true current density, corresponding to a 20-hour discharge regime, amounts to $\sim 2 \cdot 10^{-6}$ A/cm^2.

Thus, the rate of self-discharge occurring with oxygen depolarisation is approximately 4 orders higher than the rate of this process occurring with hydrogen depolarisation. Obviously, if self-discharge in fact occurred according to scheme (5.17), the possibility of using a lead acid battery in many cases would be made extremely difficult owing to rapid loss of capacity.

Among the reasons which sharply curtail the reaction of reduction of oxygen on lead, clearly the basic role is played by the formation and growth of the sulphate film. It may be assumed that the $PbSO_4$ layer appearing already at the first moment of contact of the lead with the sulphuric acid is practically impervious to O_2 molecules, the dimensions of which (in comparison with the dimensions of the hydrated ions of H^+, Pb^{2+} and HSO_4^-) are fairly large. The presence of a sulphate layer may be interpreted as the reason for a sharp decrease in the value of δ along with a decrease of D_{O_2} and c_{O_2}. In connection with this it is interesting to note that self-dissolution of lead in a solution of perchloric acid, in all probability, occurs with oxygen depolarisation[48]. A characteristic feature distinguishing this electrolyte from a solution of H_2SO_4, is the good solubility of lead chlorate, which does not form a phase layer on the electrode.

It may therefore be reckoned that the appearance of a layer of $PbSO_4$ from self-dissolution of lead in sulphuric acid is the reason for the sharp slowing down of the rate of the process in question as a result of the substantial change in its kinetics. In addition, the porous structure of the active mass and the considerable gas filling of the pores should cause a curtailment of the diffusion of oxygen to the electrode surface and a de-aeration of the electrolyte in the layer next to the electrode.

Electrolytic transfer of components of the anode alloy to the negative electrode

A basic source of metal admixtures falling on to the surface of the negative electrode of a lead acid battery is the electrolytic transfer of alloying components of the anode alloy. This is directly linked with corrosion of the grids of the positive electrode and the different constituents of the alloy passing into solution.

The laws of electrolytic transfer of antimony have been studied in detail by many researchers. In particular, it has been established that electro-deposition of antimony takes place mainly in the surface layer of the active mass of negative plates, with 99% of the Sb settling in the layer of thickness <1mm. The quantity of antimony transferred increases with an increase in its content in the anode alloy and with an increase in the amount of electricity transmitted in the process of charging the battery. The introduction of silver into the anode alloy considerably decreases the transfer of antimony as a result of an increase in the corrosion resistance of the alloy.

As has been shown by research of recent years, in the process of corrosion of the grids of the positive electrode antimony passes into the solution basically in the form of ions of $Sb_3O_9^{3-}$[49]. The greater part of these ions is adsorbed by lead dioxide and they only partially transfer to the negative electrode. Ions of $Sb_3O_9^{3-}$ are adsorbed on lead sulphate, which occurs in the active mass of negative plates, with with consequent reverse passage into the solution or with reduction into compounds of Sb^{3+} in the charge process. The reduction $Sb^{5+} \rightarrow Sb^{3+}$ basically takes place in a period of overcharge. Compounds of trivalent antimony exist in cathodic and anodic form: SbO^+ and $SbOSO_4^-$. These compounds, in contrast to ions of $Sb_3O_9^{3-}$, are capable of being reduced to metallic antimony on settling on the negative electrode.

Dowson and others[49]) note that Sb can be deposited on negative plates of a battery also as a result of the reaction of electro-chemical substitution

$$2SbO^+ + 3Pb + 3H_2SO_4 = 2Sb + 3PbSO_4 + 2H_3O^+ \qquad (5.37)$$

Reverse migration of ions of Sb^{3+} is possible to the positive electrode, where these compounds are adsorbed on PbO_2 and are oxidised to Sb^{5+}.

The laws of electrolytic transfer of antimony are complicated by the fact that part of the antimony deposited on the cathode interacts with the hydrogen, converting into stibine. The rate of formation of SbH_3 changes with a change in the concentration of Sb on the surface of the negative electrode (see section under "The kinetics of separation of stibine in the charging of a lead acid battery").

The influence of added arsenic on the electrolytic transfer of Sb has not yet been much studied. Arsenic itself is not generally found in the composition of the negative active mass, which is evidently the result of it being carried away in the form of arsine in the battery charge process.

With the addition of 0.05-0.15% silver to the anode alloy, this metal is in practice not transferred to the negative electrode. Research into alloys containing 0.3, 0.5 and 1% Ag has showed that transfer of silver to the cathode decreases with an increase in its content in the alloy owing to an increase in the corrosion resistance of the latter[50]).

Considerable prospects for the use of ternary lead-antimony-silver alloys were the reason for the diversified study of electrolytic transfer of silver and antimony carried out by us in refs.[28][51][52]. It was established that an increase in the silver content of the alloy from 1 to 10% leads to an increase in the amount of silver transferred to the cathode (fig. 5.10). Here, the amount of electrolytically transferred silver increases particularly noticeably on going over to anode alloys containing more than 3% Ag, which is connected with a decrease in the anti-corrosion effect of high concentration of silver. With an increase in the amount of electricity transmitted in the process of continuous electrolysis, the amount of silver transferred to the cathode increases proportionally.

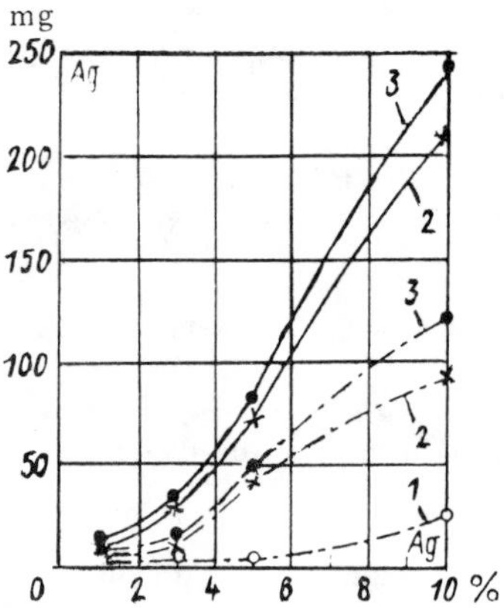

Fig. 5.10 Dependence of electrolytic transfer of silver on the content of it in the anode alloy Pb + 5% Sb + Ag. 1 - Ag content on the surface of the cathode; 2 - Ag content in cathode deposit; 3 - total amount of anode dissolved silver. (——) over 145A·hr, (- - - -) over 63A·hr.

The data described above, obtained in experiments with smooth electrodes, found confirmation in the testing of grids of lead-antimony-silver alloys in a battery. It was established that the silver content in the surface layer of negative plates (P_{Ag} %) increases in direct proportion to the increase in concentration of the Ag in the composition of the positive grids (q_{Ag} %) in accordance with the formula (4.52)

$$P_{Ag} \approx 2q_{Ag} \qquad (5.38)$$

in which the value of P_{Ag} is determined after continuous long-duration charge of starter batteries (20 000 A·hrs transmitted at an overall current density of $1A/dm^2$). The antimony content in the surface layer of negative plates after the transmission of 20 000 A·hrs of electricity in continuous polarisation amounts on average to 0.2% and in practice does not depend on the composition of the anode alloy [Pb + 5% Sb + (0.5-5)% Ag].

The transfer of silver in the process of cycling of the battery also increases with an increase in the content of Ag in the anode alloy. However, in continuous polarisation, the amount of silver deposited on the cathode exceeds by approximately three times the corresponding value obtained in the process of cycling (at one and the same amount of electricity transmitted through the battery in the course of continuous long-duration polarisation and in the period of charges). This phenomenon may be explained by the fact that periodic passivation of the positive plates, which takes place in cycling, hinders the passing of silver ions into solution.

To study the kinetics of electrolytic transfer of silver and antimony periodic measurements were carried out by us of the potential and the capacity of the electrical double layer of a coated lead electrode (RG type) in the process of continuous polarisation with positive electrodes, the grids of which were made of lead-silver and lead-antimony-silver alloys. It was established that the capacity of the double layer does not suffer any marked changes in the process of the experiment. In other words, electrolytic transfer of Ag and Sb shows no influence on the value of the true surface of a porous lead electrode. This result accords with the data obtained in the testing of batteries, according to which the discharge capacity does not depend on the composition of the anode alloy [Pb + 5% Sb + (0.5)% Ag].

The results of potentiometric measurements are partially shown in fig. 5.11. The graphs (φ, Q) are characterised by three sections. In the initial period of polarisation a considerable reduction of the cathode potential occurs, obviously corresponding to the transfer of alloying components of the anode alloy from the surface layer of the grids of the positive plates. After that, the potential of the negative electrode changes comparatively little in time, which bears witness to the decrease in the rate of transfer. It may be assumed that the oxide film forming on the positive grids curtails the passing into the solution of the ions of the alloying metals. The slight rise in potential on the section of the graphs under consideration (fig. 5.11c), obviously, is explained by a certain decrease in the surface concentration of antimony as a result of the formation of stibine.

In the last period of electrolysis the cathode potential again falls noticeably, which points to an increase in the rate of electrolytic transfer. In this period the grids of positive electrodes have already deteriorated to a considerable extent. Therefore, the porosity increases

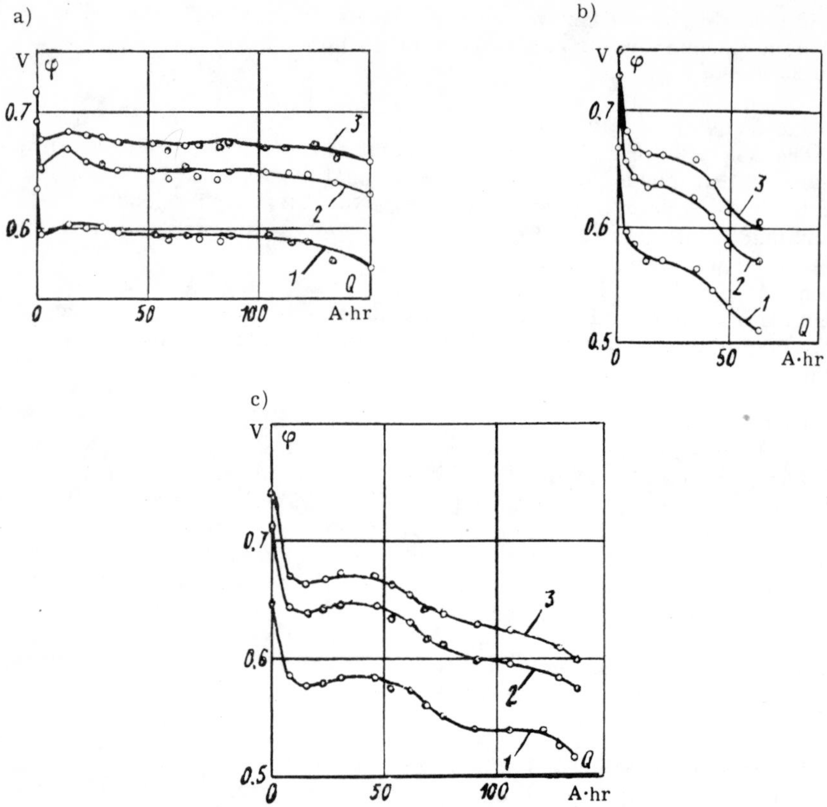

Fig. 5.11 Dependence of the potential φ of the negative electrode (in relation to Hg/H_2SO_4) on the amount of electricity transmitted Q. The grids of the positive plates are made of alloys of the following composition: (a) Pb + 1% Ag; (b) Pb + 5% Sb; (c) Pb + 5% Sb + 1% Ag. The geometric surface of the electrode is $33 cm^2$: 1 - 20mA; 2 - 60mA; 3 - 100mA.

markedly and the protective properties of the anode film deteriorate, which naturally leads to an increase in the concentration of ions of the alloying metals in the solution and in the rate of transfer of them in the solution and in the rate of transfer of them to the cathode under investigation.

The influence of the composition of the anode alloy on the kinetics of the transfer may be characterised by the change in time of the shift in potential of the negative electrode Δφ from its original value (fig.

5.12). As can be seen from fig. 5.12, in the initial period of polarisation the values of $\Delta\varphi$ decrease with an increase in the silver content in the anode alloy. In this period the influence on the corrosion resistance of the composition of the alloy from which the positive grids are made, and the rate of transfer of the alloying metals, is fully similar. Towards the end of the experiment the location of the graphs ($\Delta\varphi$, Q) changes substantially: with an increase in the concentration of silver in the anode alloy $\Delta\varphi$ increases. In this region the rate of transfer is directly determined by the composition of the anode, which is probably due to the deterioration of the screening properties of the lead dioxide film with considerable deterioration of the positive electrodes.

The $\Delta\varphi$ values are practically independent of the polarisation current (in the investigated range of currents), and this is determined by the parallel forms of the (φ, Q) curves (fig. 5.11) recorded for various currents I. Thus, the electrolytic transfer of Ag and Sb, which lowers the value of the cathode potential of a spongy lead electrode, has no influence on the coefficient of slope of the graphs of the dependence of potential on current. Naturally, the pre-logarithmic coefficient of graphs (φ, lg I) also does not change in the process of electrolysis, remaining equal to 0.11V.

The stationary potential of self-dissolution of lead in the process of electro-deposition of Ag and Sb on a lead electrode does not change. The value of this potential, as has already been shown, in practice coincides with the potential of the $Pb \rightleftarrows PbSO_4$ equilibrium, calculated according to equation (2.22).

The decrease in the cathode potential of lead observed in the process of transfer of silver and antimony to the negative electrode thus is exclusively the result of the appearance on the surface of the electrode of phase admixtures characterised by a lower value of hydrogen overvoltage. The constancy of the true surface of the electrode, of the coefficient of slope of the semi-logarithmic graph of hydrogen overvoltage (coefficient of transfer) and of the stationary (equilibrium) potential, gives a basis for the use of equation (5.34), which describes completely satisfactorily the influence of electrolytic transfer on the rate of self-discharge of the negative electrode of a lead acid battery.

The possibilities of sufficiently effective decreasing of the rate of electrolytic transfer in a battery are quite limited. In ref.[53]) it is shown that the rate of transfer of antimony may be decreased with lead plating of the grids of the positive electrode. This result was obtained, however, in comparatively short-duration testing. The subsequent verification carried out by us showed that, for a marked

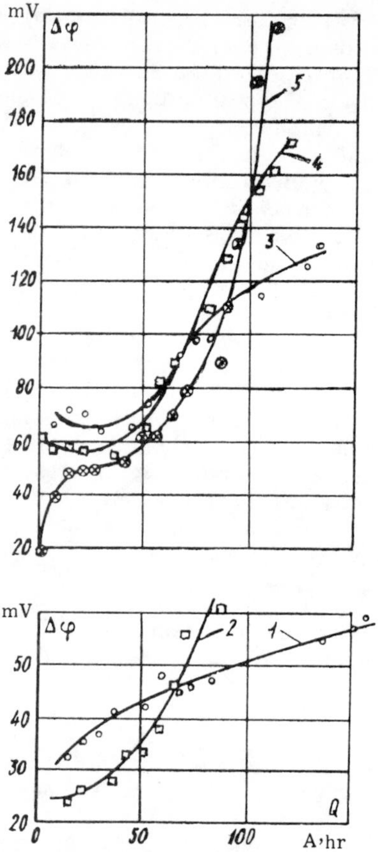

Fig. 5.12 Dependence of the shift in potential of the negative electrode on the amount of electricity transmitted. The grids of the positive electrodes are made of the alloys: 1 - Pb + 1% Ag; 2 - Pb + 3% Ag; 3 - Pb + 5% Sb + 1% Ag; 4 - Pb + 5% Sb + 2% Ag; 5 - Pb + 5% Sb + 3% Ag.

decrease in the rate of transfer of antimony and silver in the course of a large number of charge-discharge cycles, it was necessary to use thick lead coverings (≥30 μm). However, as was shown in Chapter 4, the use of thick lead coverings leads to a speeding up of the deterioration of the active mass of the positive electrode as a result of the deterioration in adhesion of the mass to the grid. In the case of coverings of low thickness, which do not lower the service life of the positive electrode, a decrease in the rate of transfer of the alloying metals is observed only in the initial period of testing the battery.

The known decrease in the rate of electrolytic transfer of antimony and silver was achieved by us as a result of a change in the construction of the grids of the positive electrode[52]. A decrease in the total surface of the grids, and also the use of grids with "sunken" ribs, leads to a lowering of the rate of self-discharge of the negative electrode and a decrease in the concentration of alloying components of the anode alloy in the composition of the negative active mass. This effect is caused by a decrease in the current density on the surface of the positive grids, and also by the screening influence of the active mass.

Finally, it must be mentioned that the use of microporous separators can also markedly curtail electrolytic transfer, particularly if the separators are made in the form of jackets pulled over the positive plates, and thus dividing off the electrode spaces[51][54]. In ref.[54] it is proposed to characterise the quality of the separator by the product of its electrical resistance and the coefficient of diffusion of the ions of antimony through this separator. This value for synthetic separators lies within the limits of $(2\text{-}90) \cdot 10^{-4}$ ohm$\cdot$ cm^3/min and depends both on the chemical nature of the material and also (to a greater extent) on the structure of the pores.

The separator that may be considered to be the best is the one characterised by the minimum value of the magnitudes mentioned. Such a separator possesses a high electrical conductivity (basically caused in the H_2SO_4 solution by the movement of the hydrogen ions) and at the same time considerably retards the electrolytic transfer of the components of the anode alloy. At the present time, however, separator jackets have not been widely used owing to the technological difficulties involved in the assembly of the batteries.

The overvoltage of hydrogen evolution on the negative electrode

The overvoltage of hydrogen evolution is quite an important characteristic of the negative electrode of a lead acid battery. The value of the hydrogen overvoltage determines not only the rate of self-discharge of the electrode, but also the efficiency of use of the current in the charging process. The overvoltage of hydrogen evolution on lead alloys to some extent characterises the corresponding effect of alloying additions on the negative electrode. In the literature there is also mention of the relationship between the hydrogen overvoltage and the corrosion resistance of the alloy when anodically polarised. A large number of investigations have been devoted to the process of separation of hydrogen on a lead cathode from sulphuric acid solutions. The basic results[55] which are described in the literature, are examined by us in ref.[55]. The collection of experimental data on hydrogen overvoltage on lead finds a satisfactory explanation from the point of view of the theory of delayed discharge. In concentrated acid aolutions the dependence of the hydrogen overvoltage η_H on current density j and concentration of the hydrogen ions can be written in the form[47]

$$\eta_H = \text{const} + \left(1 - \frac{1}{\alpha}\right) \nu \lg \; H^+ + \left(1 - \frac{\alpha'}{\alpha}\right) \nu \lg f_{H^+} + \left(\frac{1}{\alpha} - 1\right) \psi_1 + \frac{\nu}{\alpha} \lg j \qquad (5.39)$$

Formula (5.39) taking account of the dependence of the ψ_1 potential on the concentration of the acid makes it possible to explain the decrease in hydrogen overvoltage on lead with an increase in concentration in strong solutions of H_2SO_4 (>8N).

The influence of the state of the surface of the electrode on the overvoltage of separation of hydrogen on a number of metals (Pb, Cd, Tl) is investigated in detail in the works of Ya M Kolotyrkin and his colleagues[56][57]. The existence of two regions of linear dependence of η_H on lg j were established. The deflection in the graph (η_H, lg j), taken at a wide range of cathode polarisation currents, occurs in the interval of potentials close to the potential of the point of zero charge of the metal (fig. 5.13). The effect mentioned is connected with reverse adsorption of sulphate ions on the positively charged surface of the metal and the shift in the negative direction of the ψ_1 on lg j in a wide field of polarisation of lead may be expressed according to Ya M Kolotyrkin by the equation

$$\eta_H = a + \Delta\varphi_0 + b \lg j \qquad (5.40)$$

where: $\Delta\varphi_0$ is the displacement of the point of zero charge of lead as a result of the adsorption of anions. In the region of the deflection of the graph (η_H, lg j) $\Delta\varphi_0$ changes from 0 (on the negatively charged surface of the metal) to a constant value (at potentials lying at a more positive value than the point of zero charge). In a 1N solution of H_2SO_4 b = 0.12V, a = 1.56V and the maximum value of $(\Delta\varphi_0)_{max}$ = -0.16V[56]. Similar values of the coefficients a and b are obtained in refs.[19][58]. In the literature, however, several other values of the coefficients in the Tafel's equation for hydrogen overvoltage on lead in 2N H_2SO_4 (a = 1.33V, b = 0.1V) are quoted[59]).

The hydrogen overvoltage on a porous lead electrode in 11.2N H_2SO_4 in the range of overall current densities of $6 \cdot 10^{-4}$ $3 \cdot 10^{-3}$ A/cm^2 is expressed by the equation

$$\eta_H = 1.31 + 0.11 \lg j \tag{5.41}$$

The current density j in equation (5.41) is calculated for the true surface of the electrode, determined with the aid of measurement of the capacity of the double electrical layer.

In ref.[55]) a study was made by us of the cathodic behaviour of lead and of alloys of the Pb-Ag and Pb-Sb-Ag system containing up to 10% of silver. The Sb content in lead-antimony-silver alloys amounted to ~4.5%. The hydrogen overvoltage was measured in 11.2N H_2SO_4 at 25°C in a range of current densities j = 10^{-7} -10^{-3} A/cm^2. The results of the measurements are shown in fig. 5.14.

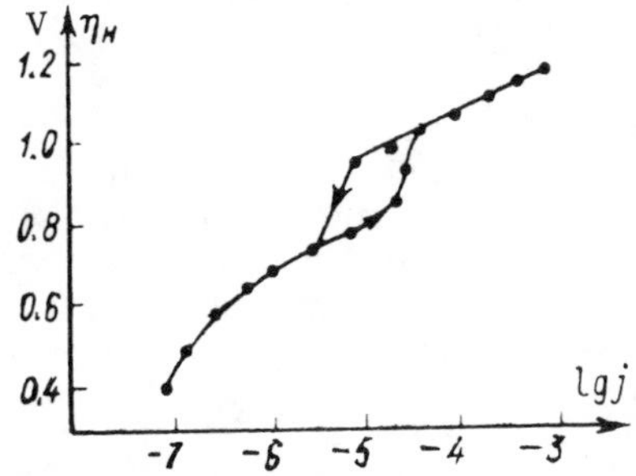

Fig. 5.13 Dependence of hydrogen overvoltage η_H on lead in 1N·H_2SO_4 on the logarithm of the current density.

From the data obtained it follows that the addition of 4.5% of antimony to the lead leads to a decrease in hydrogen overvoltage by approximately 50mV. The introduction of silver up to ~5% into a lead-antimony alloy also causes a decrease in the hydrogen overvoltage. Further increase in the silver content of the alloy does not lead to any marked change in the cathode potential. In the case of binary lead-silver alloys the depolarising effect of comparatively small additions of silver shows up somewhat more sharply. However, also in alloys of the Pb-Ag system, a rise in the concentration of silver from 3 to 9.5% does not cause any change in the hydrogen overvoltage.

It must be noted that the decrease in hydrogen overvoltage caused by

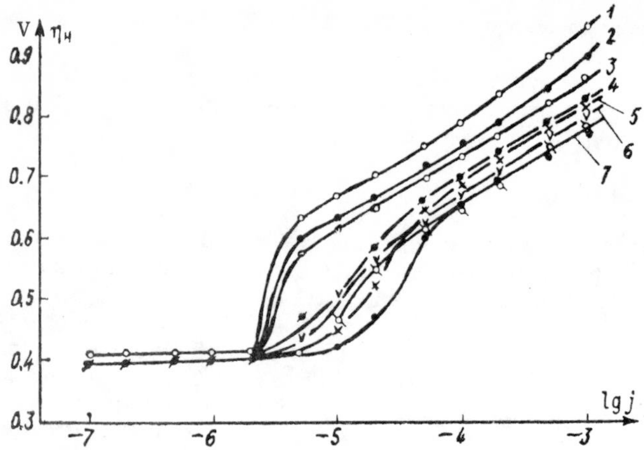

Fig. 5.14 Dependence of overvoltage of hydrogen evolution on the logarithm of the current density in 11.2N·H_2SO_4. 1 - Pb; 2 - Pb + 1.01% Ag; 3 - Pb + (2.94-9.87)% Ag; 4 - Pb + 4.5% Sb; 5 - Pb + 4.65% Sb + 0.95% Ag; 6 - Pb + 4.65% Sb + 3.04% Ag; 7 - Pb + 4.55% Sb + (4.94-9.47)% Ag.

the addition of silver to lead and lead-antimony alloy is markedly less in its value than the corresponding decrease in potential of the negative electrode of a battery caused by electro-deposition of silver on its surface. A possible reason for this difference is the high dispersibility of silver deposits obtained in electrolysis of a sulphuric acid solution. A certain role may also be played by a difference in the energy states of the metals coming into the composition of the alloy and deposited on the surface of the electrode.

According to the data obtained[55]), the semi-logarithmic graph of hydrogen overvoltage on lead in 11.2N H_2SO_4 in the range of current densities $j = 5 \cdot 10^{-6} - 10^{-4}$ A/cm² is described by the equation

$$\eta_H = 1.264 + 0.12 \lg j \qquad (5.42)$$

Judging by the results of the impedance measurements, the true surface of the electrodes under investigation exceeds by approximately 2 times their geometric surface (C_d = 35-40μm/cm² of visible surface). Therefore, if we calculate the current density per unit of the true surface, then the value of the first member in the right-hand part of equation (5.42) will be equal to 1.264 + 0.12 lg 2 = 1.30V. Thus equations (5.41) and (5.42) lead practically to one and the same result.

At $j > 10^{-4}$ A/cm² in the graph (η_H, lg) an increase in the coefficient of slope is observed for lead, which in the field of high current densities becomes equal to 0.16V. The increase in the pre-logarithmic coefficient, judging by the data from literature quoted above, may be explained by the gradual desorption of sulphate ions in the region of negative charge of the surface of the lead and by a decrease in the negative value of the ψ_1 potential. The absence of any sharp deflection in the graph (η_H, lg j) in the region of the point of zero charge of the lead is probably connected with the high concentration of the H_2SO_4 at which the adsorption of the sulphate ions may take place, not only with a positive charge on the surface of the electrode, but also with a small negative charge on it.

At a current density $j \leqslant 10^{-4}$ A/cm^2 clearly a limiting value is reached of the filling up of the surface with adsorbed particles, which is the reason for the normal coefficient of slope of the semi-logarithmic graph. The sharp decrease in the values of η_H at low current densities ($j < 10^{-5}$ A/cm^2) observed in fig. 5.14 can be explained by various depolarisers present in strong solutions of H_2SO_4 even with a fairly high degree of purification of these solutions [60]).

Finally, at $j = 5 \cdot 10^{-6} - 10^{-7}$ A/cm^2, as can be seen from fig. 5.14, the potential of the electrode in practice does not depend on the density of the polarising current. The value of the potential in this region accords well with the potential of the equilibrium $Pb \rightleftarrows PbSO_4$ measured in relation to a hydrogen electrode in the same solution, i.e. calculated according to formula (2.22). This result is fully in accord with the data of the work of Z A Joffe [60]).

The presence of silver in the alloy does not change the value of the potential in the region of low current densities under consideration, which confirms the data described earlier about the absence of an influence of silver on the potential of the equilibrium $Pb \rightleftarrows PbSO_4$.

The semi-logarithmic graphs of hydrogen overvoltage on alloys containing antimony are distinguished by several peculiarities. In the region of high polarisations there are no deflections in these graphs. This is obviously evidence of the fact that the graphs lie in the region of positive charge of the lead, when the surface of the electrode contains the limiting quantity of adsorbed sulphate ions. The slope of the graphs (η_H, lg j) is equal in the region of high current densities ($j \geqslant 10^{-4}$ A/cm^2) to 0.128V.

The sharp fall in overvoltage and the inflection in the semi-logarithmic graphs occurs in alloys containing antimony at higher current densities than in alloys without antimony. This phenomenon is obviously connected with the depolarising influence of the antimony ions appearing as a result of the interaction of the antimony with the hydrogen and the consequent partial decomposition of the antimony hydride forming then by the sulphuric acid. At low current densities the semi-logarithmic graphs for lead-antimony and lead-antimony-silver alloys, like the graphs for alloys without antimony, are practically parallel to the axis of the abscissae. Judging by the value of the potential on this section of the graph (η_H, lg j), the decisive role is played here by the equilibrium (equation 2.20). Some decrease in the cathode potential probably is connected with the influence of the equilibrium

$$Sb + H_2O \rightleftarrows SbO^+ + 2H^+ + 3e \quad (5.43)$$

The potential corresponding to the equilibrium (5.43), calculated in relation to a hydrogen electrode in the same solution, amounts to -0.252V, i.e. it lies at a more positive figure than the potential of the equilibrium $Pb \rightleftarrows PbSO_4$.

Judging by the results quoted above, the influence of antimony on the equilibrium potential of the lead-lead sulphate system is quite small. Therefore, the electrolytic transfer of Sb to the surface of a porous lead electrode has no influence on the potential of self-dissolution of lead in sulphuric acid.

The negative electrode of a lead acid battery can be considered as a multi-phase system consisting of lead and second phase additions of the electro-deposited components of the anode alloy. The concentration of these additions, which are characterised by relatively low hydrogen overvoltage, increases in the process of utilisation of the battery, leading to a decrease in the hydrogen evolution potential on the electrode. The quantitative examination of the dependence of hydrogen overvoltage on the phase composition of the electrode surface which was carried out by us in ref. [61]) is of interest.

Earlier it was shown by D S Nadyezhdny that the shift in potential of hydrogen evolution ($\Delta\varphi$) on metal 1 as a result of the addition to it of metal 2 under the condition of equipotentiality of the electrode surface can be calculated according to formula [62]):

$$\Delta\varphi = b_1 \ln \left[(A_{12} - 1) S_2 + 1 \right] \quad (5.44)$$

where $A_{12} = \exp\left(\frac{a_1 - a_2}{b_1}\right)$, a_1 and a_2 are constants in the Tafel's equation for metals 1 and 2, b_1 is the prelogarithmic coefficient, and S_2 is the part of the electrode surface occupied by the added metal 2.

From formula (5.44) it follows that the overvoltage of separation of hydrogen on a two-phase electrode $\eta_{2\phi}$ is equal to

$$\eta_{2\phi} = a_1 - b_1 \ln \left[(A_{12} - 1)S_2 + 1 \right] + b_1 \ln j \qquad (5.45)$$

If we introduce the symbol

$$a_{2\phi} = a_1 - b_1 \ln \left[(A_{12} - 1)S_2 + 1 \right] \qquad (5.46)$$

then the expression (5.45) takes on the ordinary form of a Tafel's equation for the hydrogen overvoltage on a two-phase electrode with the constant a which retains a dependence on the overvoltage on both phases A_{12}, and also dependence on the composition of the surface of the electrode S_2.

The invariance of the form of the Tafel's equation in respect to the change of phase composition of the electrode surface makes it possible to generalise equation (5.46) for calculation of the hydrogen overvoltage on an electrode representing systems with any number of phases [61]). Thus, for a three-phase system, according to (5.46) the constant a is determined by the equation

$$a_{3\phi} = a_{2\phi} - b_1 \ln \left[(A_{2\phi3} - 1)S_3 + 1 \right] = a_1 - b_1 \ln \left\{ \left[(A_{12} - 1) S_2 + 1 \right] \times \left[(A_{2\phi3} - 1)S_2 + 1 \right] \right\} \qquad (5.47)$$

where

$$A_{2\phi3} = \exp \left(\frac{a_{2\phi} - a_3}{b_1} \right) = \frac{\exp \left(\frac{a_1 - a_3}{b_1} \right)}{(A_{12} - 1)S_2 + 1} = \frac{A_{13}}{(A_{12} - 1)S_2 + 1} \qquad (5.48)$$

S_3 is the part of the surface occupied by phase 3.

For an electrode the surface of which contains an arbitrary number n of phases, the following formula was obtained by us [61])

$$a_{\pi\phi} = a_1 - b_1 \ln \prod_{i=2}^{n} \left[(A_{(i-1)\phi,i} - 1) S_i + 1 \right] \qquad (5.49)$$

Equations (5.46) and (5.47) represent special cases of (5.49) with n = 2 and n = 3. The coefficient $A_{(i-1)\phi,i}$ is determined by the recurrence formula

$$A_{(n-1)\phi,n} = \frac{A_{1n}}{\prod_{i=2}^{n} \left[(A_{(i-1)\phi,i} - 1) S_i + 1 \right]} \tag{5.50}$$

In equations (5.49) and (5.50) S_i represents the part of the surface of the electrode occupied by the i phase.

Obviously

$$\sum_{i=1}^{n} S_i = 1 \tag{5.51}$$

The equations shown are correct if the prelogarithmic coefficients in the Tafel's equation are alike for all phases of the given system, and this is observed fairly accurately in the majority of cases. An important condition for the applicability of formulae (5.46), (5.47) and (5.49) is the assumption that the simplest mechanism of hydrogen evolution on a multi-phase electrode, when all stages of the discharge of hydrogen occur in succession on each section of the electrode surface occupied by any i phase, is realised.

In ref.[63]) an attempt was made to generalise the results shown above for the case when separate phases of the electrode differ not only in the values of a in the Tafel's equation, but also in the values of the prelogarithmic coefficients. Allowing that the hydrogen overvoltage on a multi-phase electrode is subject to the relationship:

$$\eta_H = a_{n\phi} + b_{n\phi} \ln j \tag{5.52}$$

the author of ref.[63]) obtained the following formula for the constant a:

$$a_{n\phi} = a_1 - b_{n\phi} \ln \sum_{i=1}^{n} S_i \exp\left(\frac{a_1 - a_i}{b_i}\right) \tag{5.53}$$

At n = 2 the same prelogarithmic coefficients of formula (5.53), exactly like those of (5.49), leads to equation (5.46). However, at n = >2 the coincident results are obtained only in the case when the parts of the surface occupied by the additives (S_2, S_3 etc.) are small in comparison with the surface of the basic phase S_1. It must be noted that the use of the Tafel's relationship (5.52) for a multi-phase electrode with different prelogarithmic coefficients in its different parts gives rise to doubt. The method of calculation of the value of $b_{n\phi}$ in the work under consideration[63]) is only quoted for two-phase systems.

In the carrying out of the calculations of the hydrogen overvoltage on a multi-phase electrode, a known difficulty is presented by the determination of the value of S_i. For a porous lead electrode containing electro-deposited alloys *) on its surface, the most acceptable method is to assume that the relationship of the parts of the surface occupied by the different phases is equal to the relation of their total surfaces or to the relation of the volumes of the corresponding phases V_i to the power of $^2/_3$. In other words if this proposition is correct, it is possible to write for any two phases j and k

$$\frac{S_j}{S_k} = \left(\frac{V_j}{V_k}\right)^{2/3} = \left(\frac{m_j d_k}{m_k d_j}\right)^{2/3} \qquad (5.54)$$

where m_j and m_k are the amounts of the added metals by weight and d_j and d_k their densities. Simultaneous solution of equation (5.51) and the system of equations (5.54), the number of which for a n-phase system is equal to n-1, gives the possibility of determining the values of S_i (= 1, 2, . . . , n). In particular, for calculation of the surface concentration of antimony S_{Sb} on a negative electrode (in the absence of other additions) it is not difficult to obtain the following formula by the method described above.

$$S_{Sb} = \left[1 + 0.704\,(m_{Pb}/m_{Sb})^{2/3}\right]^{-1} \qquad (5.55)$$

With the use of a lead-antimony-silver alloy as an anode material, the concentration of the alloying metals on the surface of the negative electrode is determined by the equations

$$S_{Sb} = \left[1 + 0.704\,(m_{Pb}/m_{Sb})^{2/3} + 0.74\,(m_{Ag}/m_{Sb})^{2/3}\right]^{-1} \qquad (5.56)$$

$$S_{Sb} = \left[1 + 0.952\,(m_{Pb}/m_{Ag})^{2/3} + 1.352\,(m_{Sb}/m_{Ag})^{2/3}\right]^{-1} \qquad (5.57)$$

---

*) Deposition of alloying components of the anode alloy from a sulphuric acid electrolyte, where the solubility of the salts of these components is low, leads to the formation of spongy deposits, similar in their structure to the basic (Pb) phase.

The typical additions considered here, which are found on the surface of negative plates of a lead acid battery (Sb, Ag) are distinguished by a relatively low hydrogen overvoltage (compared with lead). We may therefore write:

$$\exp\left(\frac{a_{Pb} - a_i}{b_1}\right) \gg 1$$

where a_i is the constant in the Tafel's equation for the i-metal. The use of this inequality makes it possible to simplfy the formulae for the calculation of the change of hydrogen overvoltage on a negative electrode caused by electrolytic transfer of the alloying components of the anode alloy. Thus, according to (5.46), the transfer of antimony causes a shift of the constant a in the Tafel's equation equal to

$$\Delta a_{(Sb)} = b_1 \ln\left(S_{Sb} e^{\frac{a_{Pb}-a_{Sb}}{b_1}} + 1\right) \quad (5.58)$$

According to (5.47) simultaneous transfer of silver and antimony leads to a displacement of the hydrogen overvoltage equal (at $S_{Ag} \ll 1$) to

$$\Delta a_{(Sb+Ag)} = b_1 \ln\left(1 + S_{Sb} e^{\frac{a_{Pb}-a_{Sb}}{b_1}} + S_{Ag} e^{\frac{a_{Pb}-a_{Sb}}{b_1}}\right) \quad (5.59)$$

In the carrying out of the calculation according to formulae (5.58) and (5.59) we used the following numerical values: $b_1 = 0.05V$; $a_{Pb} = 1.31V$; $a_{Ag} = 0.95V$; $a_{Sb} = 0.93V$. The values of S_{Ag} and S_{Sb} were calculated according to formulae (5.55)-(5.57), in which the concentration by weight of silver and antimony in the negative active mass determined by the analytical method were substituted. The results of the calculation show that the dependence of the shift of the final charge potential of the negative electrode on the concentration of the above-mentioned metal additions is described satisfactorily by the equations mentioned. The calculated and experimental values of Δa coincide with an accuracy of $\pm$15-20%. Obviously, the error is caused by the not completely strict determination of S_{Sb} and S_{Ag}, since the formulae used for the calculation of these values (5.55)-(5.57) do not take into account the unevenness of the distribution of the admixture along the thickness of the electrode. It is also possible that the presence of a definite potential gradient along the thickness, peculiar to porous electrodes, may be observed.

Thus, the equations obtained may be used for approximate calculation of the change of hydrogen overvoltage caused by the transfer of the components of the anode alloy to the negative electrode. The use of formula (5.34) makes it possible to evaluate the corresponding change in the rate of self-discharge of the electrode under consideration.

Substituting the value of Δa (5.58) in formula (5.34) we have

$$\frac{\Delta V}{V} = S_{Sb} \exp\left[\frac{\alpha F}{RT}(a_{Pb} - a_{Sb})\right] \tag{5.60}$$

where $\Delta V = V' - V$ is the increase in the volume of hydrogen as a result of the addition of antimony. Equation (5.60) shows that the relative change in the rate of self-discharge of the negative electrode caused by electrolytic transfer of antimony is directly proportional to the surface concentration of this metal.

In the case of a ternary anode alloy containing silver along with antimony, the relative increase in the rate of self-discharge, according to (5.59) and (5.34), will be determined by the formula

$$\frac{\Delta V}{V} = S_{Sb} \exp\left[\frac{\alpha F}{RT}(a_{Pb} - a_{Sb})\right] + S_{Ag} \exp\left[\frac{\alpha F}{RT}(a_{Pb} - a_{Ag})\right] \tag{5.61}$$

Since $a_{Sb} \approx a_{Ag}$ (= a') equation (5.61) can be rewritten in the form

$$\frac{\Delta V}{V} = (S_{Sb} + S_{Ag}) \exp\left[\frac{\alpha F}{RT}(a_{Pb} - a')\right] \tag{5.62}$$

From the formula (5.62) it follows that the relative increase in the rate of self-discharge is directly proportional to the total content of the added elements in the total mass of the negative electrode (in the event of the additions being characterised by the same values of hydrogen overvoltage). In the more usual case $\Delta V/V$ is determined by the formula

$$\frac{\Delta V}{V} = \exp\left(\frac{\alpha F}{RT} a_{Pb}\right) \sum_{i=1}^{n} S_i \exp\left(-\frac{\alpha F}{RT} a_i\right) \tag{5.63}$$

where n is the number of different phases on the surface of the electrode.

Inhibitors of self-discharge of the negative electrode

It has been shown above that in current lead acid batteries the lowering of the rate of electrolytic transfer of alloying components of the anode alloy presents considerable difficulties. The most effective method of decreasing the rate of self-discharge of the negative electrode must be reckoned to be the use of special surface-active additives which have received the name of inhibitors of self-discharge[64]). Owing to the fact that the negative electrode of a battery represents a multi-phase system, the basic significance of such substances resides in their adsorption on the phase admixtures with a relatively low hydrogen overvoltage. The result of the adsorption must be an increase in the overvoltage of separation of hydrogen on the surface of the electrode and a decrease owing to this in the rate of self-dissolution of lead.

Many of the surface-active substances used in practice do not show any tendency to specific adsorption except on definite metals[16]). Therefore it is natural that the introduction of organic inhibitors to the battery may lead to the adsorption of particles not only on metal admixtures electro-deposited on the surface of the negative plates, but also to adsorption on lead. The successful use of such substances, as has been shown by L I Antropov, is possible only in the case when they suppress the acid corrosion of the lead on account of the arresting of the cathode process ($H^+ \rightarrow H_2$), without having any influence on the rate of the anode reaction ($Pb \rightarrow Pb^{2+}$)[65]).

From the data quoted at the beginning of this chapter it follows, however, that a number of organic substances show a known influence on the processes of ionisation and anodic passivation of lead. It is clear that the use of self-discharge inhibitors, which lead to the consolidation of the passivating sulphate layer, is possible only with the simultaneous introduction into the battery of effective depassivators (expanders). If this is not done many self-discharge inhibitors cause a marked decrease in the discharge capacity of the negative electrode, as was shown above.

The multi-phase structure of the electrode under consideration makes it possible to carry out the selection of effective self-discharge inhibitors by means of a study of the influence of the surface-active substances on the hydrogen overvoltage on metals which are typical additions. Among such metals are antimony, silver and also copper. The basic results obtained by us in the measurement of hydrogen overvoltage on the metals mentioned in the presence of different organic additives[26])[52])[64])[66]), are set out below.

The principal object of experimental research was the organic substances used in the battery industry as expanders (depassivators) of the negative electrode and inhibitors of atmospheric oxidation of lead. Among such substances were: humic acid (HA), the sodium salt of lignosulphonic acid (SA), tanning agent No. 4 (T-4), tanning agent BNF, disperser NF, casting strengthener (CS), α oxynaphthalic acid, (α ONA). A study was also made of compounds of the naphthalene series (α naphthol, β naphthol, α nitrose-β naphthol, β nitrose-α naphthol, acenaphthene etc.). Some of these compounds appear as semi-products in the synthesis of substances used as organic expanders. A study was made of a number of organic dyes of the naphthalene series. Organic acids were studied which influence the electro-crystallisation of silver from a nitric acid solution, i.e. those tending to adsorb on silver, and also a number of organic products used in electroplating (naphthalene disulphonic acid, OP-7, sulphanol, gelatine, joiner's glue and others).

The measurement of the cathode potentials was carried out in solutions of H_2SO_4 with a density of 1.32 (11.2N), 1.36 (12.9N), and 1.38 (13N), at a temperature of 20 ± 1°C. The range of current densities investigated ranged from approximately $0.5\text{-}5 \cdot 10^{3}$ A/cm^2 of geometric surface of the electrode.

Surface-active additives were introduced into the electrolyte, from a calculated 1% solution, after the establishment of stable values of potential in "pure" acid. The results obtained are partially shown in figs. 5.15 and 5.16. The potential is shown relative to a Hg/Hg_2SO_4 electrode in the same electrolyte as the electrode under investigation.

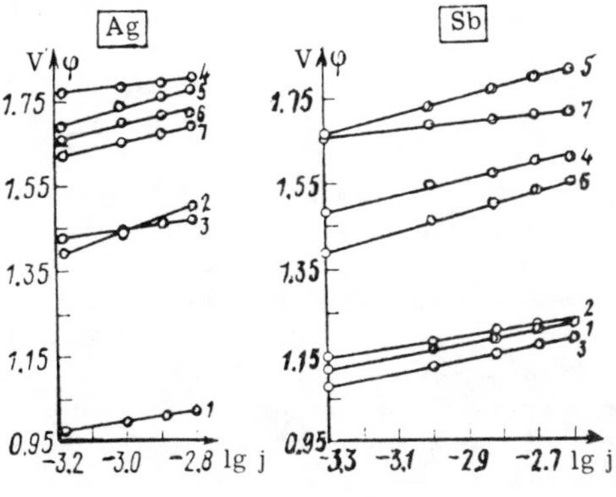

Fig. 5.15 The influence of surface-active substances on the hydrogen overvoltage on silver and antimony in a H_2SO_4 solution of density 1.32. 1 - electrolyte without additives; 2 - HA added; 3 - T-4 added; 4 - α-ONA added; 5 - α-naphthol added; 6 - β-ONA added; 7 - β-nitrose-α-naphthol added.

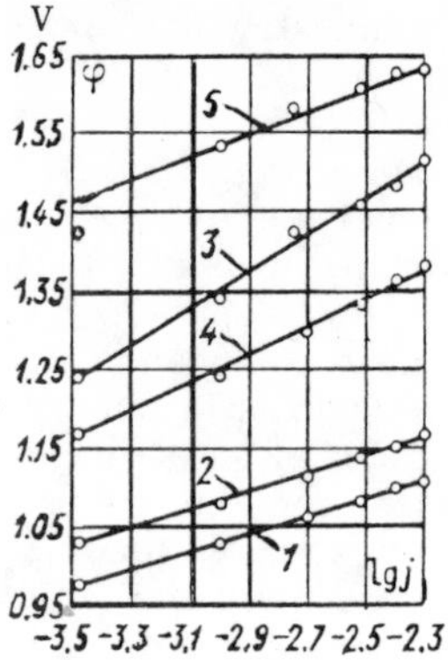

Fig. 5.16 The influence of surface-active substances on the hydrogen overvoltage on copper in a H_2SO_4 solution (density 1.32). 1 - electrolyte without additives; 2 - T-4 added; 3 - HA added; 4 - SA added; 5 - β-ONA added.

The data obtained bear witness to the fact that the dependence of the hydrogen overvoltage on the log of the current density is in almost every case characterised by a straight line, which can be described by a Tafel's equation. The influence of the organic additives leads to a change in the coefficients in this equation, with particularly substantial changes being suffered by the constant a. The prelogarithmic coefficient of the Tafel's equation in the presence of the majority of additives amounts to 0.13-0.18V.

Among the substances studied, the greatest increase in hydrogen overvoltage on the metals under investigation is caused by the group of compounds of the naphthalene series. Among this group are α and β naphthol, α nitroso-β naphthol, β nitroso-α naphthol, α and β oxynaphthalic acid. The increase in cathode potential in the presence of these substances was 0.5-0.7V. In principle, these compounds may be used as quite effective inhibitors of self-discharge of the negative electrode of a battery in which the grids of the positive plates are made from a corrosion-resistant lead-antimony-silver alloy, and the foundations of the negative plates are made of copper. It may be assumed that adsorption of the compounds of the naphthalene series basically bears the character of specific interaction of the metal with the molecules of the adsorbed substance, which does not depend much on the sign of the charge of the electrode surface.

It must be noted that the influence of α-oxynaphthalic acid on the hydrogen overvoltage depends substantially on the degree of purification. of this compound. The difference observed between the technical and the specially purified product is obviously connected with the change in the content in it of α-naphthol, which is the basic constituent in making technical α-oxynaphthalic acid.

Interest is attracted by the fact that, in the presence of substances that strongly increase the hydrogen overvoltage, a stable value of the potential is only established after long cathodic polarisation. The gradual rise in potential in the presence of such compounds is accompanied by a decrease in the slope of graphs (φ, lg j). In this case, the hydrogen overvoltage values showed hardly any change with a change in current nt density of even a decrease with an increase in the current[64]).

The influence of the naphthalene products under consideration on the kinetics of the separation of hydrogen is probably connected principally with the impeding of the discharge of H^+ ions on the most active parts of the surface of the electrode, as a result of the filling up of it with the inhibitor molecules being adsorbed. From this point of view, the slow increase of cathode potential in time is evidence of the gradual increase in the degree of filling up of the electrode surface. The rate of this process may be subject to equation (5.8). Obviously, the possibility of the formation of multi-layer adsorption films which also occurs at a low rate is not excluded. The slight dependence of the cathode on current may be explained by partial desorption of surface-active substances at considerable cathodic polarisation of the electrode. As a result of the desorption there is an increase in the active surface of the electrode and a decrease in true current density, which, naturally, leads to a decrease in overvoltage.

From the data shown in figs. 5.15 and 5.16 it follows that the most effective depassivators, as for example, humic acid and tanning agent T-4, considerably increase the hydrogen overvoltage on a silver cathode (by approximately 0.4V) and, in practice, have no influence on the cathode potential of antimony. Sodium lignosulphonate substantially increases the hydrogen overvoltage on copper. Let us note that this substance disperses electrolytic deposits of copper obtained from sulphuric acid electrolytes, which is evidence of the adsorption of lignosulphonic acid (SA) on a copper cathode[67]). The favourable influence of SA on the electro-crystallisation of copper, and also the decrease in the presence of SA of the rate of separation of hydrogen, is the reason for the usefulness of employing this substance as an additive to the negative active mass of a copper-lead battery[67]).

A considerable increase in hydrogen overvoltage on silver (~0.5V) is caused by the addition to the solution of sulphanol. This substance is introduction as a wetting agent into the material of the synthetic separators. The action of sulphanol on an antimony electrode is shown to be less important.

Owing to the necessity of simultaneous introduction of a self-discharge inhibitor and a depassivator into the battery, a study was made of the combined influence of effective inhibitors (α-ONA and α-naphthol) with a depassivator-tanning agent No. 4. The results obtained in this are evidence of the fact that the presence of T-4 shows no substantial influence on the inhibiting properties of these substances: the presence of α-ONA and α-naphthol in the electrolyte ensures a high value of cathode potential of silver and antimony. Thus, the combined use of depassivators and inhibitors should lead to a substantial decrease in the rate of self-discharge of the negative electrode of a lead acid battery.

Let us also note that an increase in the concentration of H_2SO_4 within the limits studied does not decrease the inhibiting effect of α-naphthol, α-ONA and a number of other compounds on the process of hydrogen evolution on silver and antimony.

Let us consider the results obtained in a study of the influence of a number of organic additives on the cathodic behaviour of lead[68]). Experiments were carried out with thin coated electrodes (of 1mm thickness), the grids of which were cast from lead. The electrodes were subjected to cycling at a current density $j = 2.5 mA/cm^2$. After the carrying out of 7-9 cycles, the electrodes were subjected cathodically to the same current until a constant potential was attained. The additive under investigation was introduced then into the electrolyte. Measurement of the hydrogen overvoltage was carried out over the current density range $0.5\text{-}5 \cdot 10^{-3} A/cm^2$. These values are comparable with the charge currents in a battery. After stable hydrogen overvoltage values were attained (in 10-12 days), cycling was again carried out (5-6 cycles) under the conditions indicated above. Such a method made it possible in one experiment to determine the influence of surface-active substances on the hydrogen overvoltage and on the anodic passivation of a spongy lead electrode. The small thickness of the electrodes under investigation made it possible to reckon polarisation as being even over the whole surface.

The influence of the additives studied on the hydrogen overvoltage is shown in fig. 5.17. As can be seen from the diagram, the introduction into the electrolyte of organic substances does not cause any considerable change of the slope of graphs (φ, lg j) whatsoever. The prelogarithmic coefficient amounts to 0.10-0.12V. The maximum increase in hydrogen overvoltage is observed in the presence of **α-nitroso-β-**naphthol and **β**-nitroso-**α**-naphthol, which increase the potential of lead by approximately 0.4V. These substances are of interest as inhibitors of self-discharge of pure lead. Similar compounds may find application for batteries intended for long-term storage in a charged state with electrolyte.

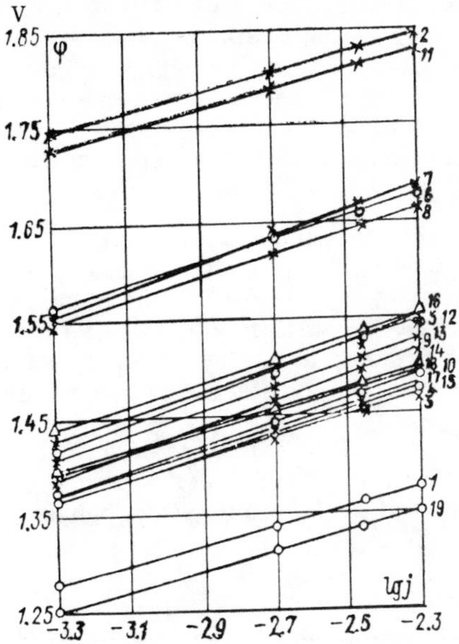

Fig. 5.17 The effect of surface-active substances on the potential of separation of hydrogen on lead. 1 - electrolyte without additives (density 1.38); 2 - α-nitrose-β-naphthol added; 3 - nitrol ANF added; 4 - tanning agent BNF added; 5 - casting strengthener added; 6 - β-naphthol added; 7 - β-ONA added; 8 - α-naphthol added; 9 - sulphanol added; 10 - α-ONA added; 11 - β-nitrose-α-naphthol added; 12 - disperser NF added; 13 - T-4 added; 14 - HA added; 15 - SA added; 16 - tanning agent No. 2 added; 17 - slovatone added; 18 - sulphite liquor added; 19 - cuboid golden yellow ZhKh added.

The addition to the solution of α and β-naphthol, and also of β-oxynaphthalic acid causes an increase in the cathode potential of the lead by approximately 0.3V. All the remaining additives are shown to be, as can be seen from fig. 5.17, of comparatively little effect.

The organic substances under investigation show no effect on the character of the change of potential at discharge and charge of the electrode. The potential of the electrode during the course of practically the whole time of discharge (excluding the initial and final periods) remains practically constant. The value of the discharge potential is approximately 20mV more positive than the equilibrium potential of the system $Pb \rightleftarrows PbSO_4$.

The discharge capacity of an electrode not containing organic additives decreases in the process of cycling, which is naturally connected with the deposition of spongy lead causing a decrease in the active surface (fig. 5.18). The introduction into the solution of expander additives causes an increase in capacity. At the same time, in accordance with the data quoted above, effective self-discharge inhibitors cause a decrease in the discharge capacity of a lead electrode.

It must be mentioned that although the nature of the effect of surface-active substances on the cathode potential of a spongy lead electrode is similar to that observed for smooth electrodes; however, in absolute value the shift in potential of a lead electrode is less than the value obtained in the testing of the same substances with smooth electrodes. This difference can be explained principally by the considerable magnitude of the true surface of a spongy electrode. The peculiarities of the influence of additives introduced into the electrolyte is known to be connected with the difficulty of diffusion of the molecules of surface-active substances into the pores of the electrolyte.

In fig. 5.19 data are shown characterising the influence of two self-discharge inhibitors (α-naphthol and α-ONA) on the cathodic potential of a negative electrode in the process of electrolytic transfer of silver and antimony. The electrode under investigation represented a RG type coated plate with a lead grid. The electrode was polarised until a constant hydrogen overvoltage was obtained with positive lead plates. Then, the lead anodes were replaced by plates with grids made of lead-antimony-silver alloy (Pb + 5% Sb + 1% Ag).

As can be seen from fig. 5.19, the introduction of α-naphthol into the electrolyte, with the polarisation of the electrode under investigation, leads with lead anodes to an increase in the hydrogen overvoltage of approximately 0.2V; α-ONA in these conditions is less effective. Replacing the lead anodes by plates with lead-antimony-silver alloy grids (in a cell containing α-naphthol) there is observed initially an increase in cathode potential. This phenomenon is obviously connected with the considerable adsorption of α-naphthol on silver and antimony, which are settling intensively on the cathode in this period. Afterwards the potential decreases and later, in the course of a long period of polarisation, it does not change. Only after the transmission of ~200 Ah of electricity is a sharp fall in potential observed. This fall in potential is obviously caused by the sharp rise in the rate of

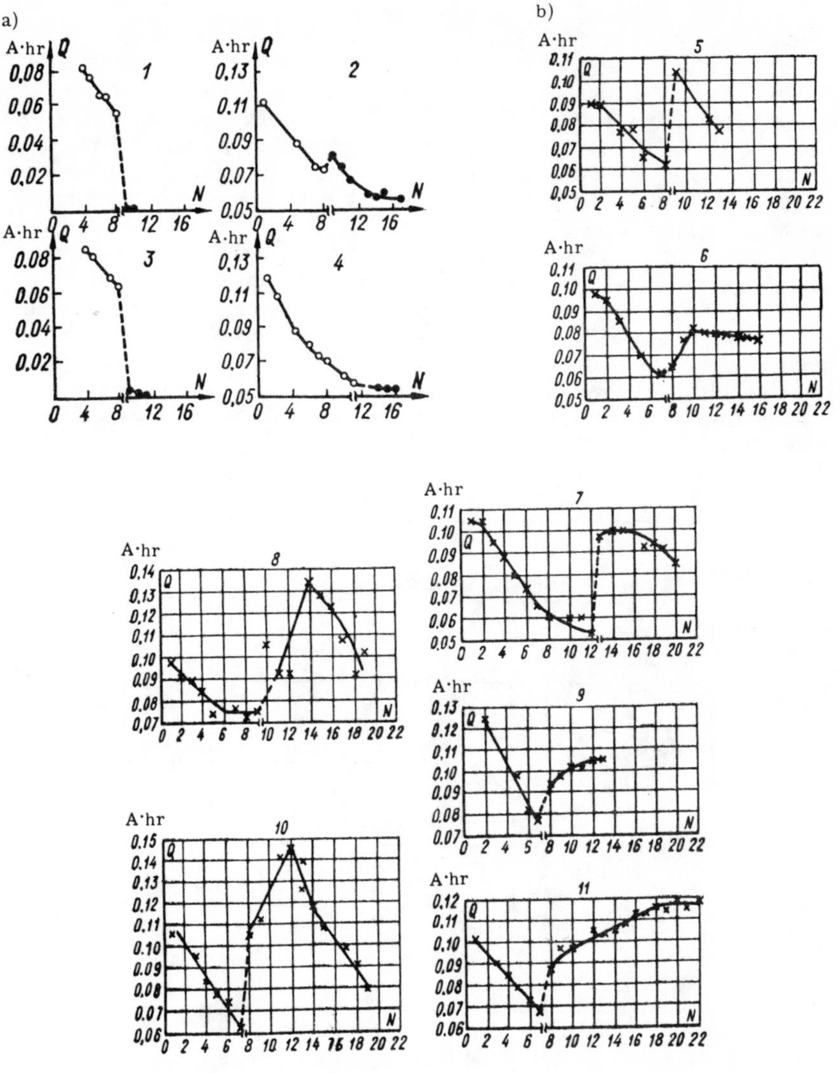

Fig. 5.18 Change in discharge capacity of a porous lead electrode with the introduction of organic additives into the solution: inhibitors (a) and expanders (b). 1 - **α-nitroso-β-naphthol**; 2 - α-oxynaphthalic acid; 3 - **β-nitroso-α-**naphthol; 4 - β-oxynaphthalic acid; 5 - casting strengthener; 6 - tanning agent BNF; 7 - humic acid; 8 - sulphite liquor; 9 - tanning agent No. 4; 10 - sodium lignosulphonate; 11 - dispersant NF.

transfer of silver and antimony owing to the great deterioration of the grids of the positive plates. There may turn out to be insufficient α-naphthol present in the solution for adsorption on the surface of electro-deposited Ag and Sb, all the more so since, as was mentioned before, the rise in the hydrogen overvoltage on silver and antimony under the influence of the adsorption of α-naphthol, takes place quite slowly. Therefore, with a high rate of electrolytic transfer of the components of the anode alloy on the surface of the negative electrode, there may be particles of silver and antimony characterised by relatively low values of potential at any moment of time, which causes a decrease in the potential of the whole electrode. In addition, partial oxidation or reduction of α-naphthol on the surface of the electrode is possible. With the introduction of a new portion of α-naphthol into the electrolyte, as can be seen from fig. 5.19, a sharp rise in the cathode potential and a subsequent retardation of its decrease is observed.

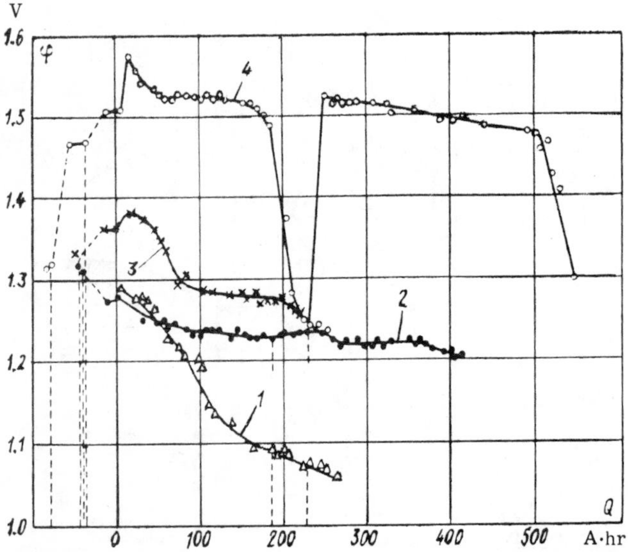

Fig. 5.19 Dependence of the potential of the negative electrode on the amount of electricity transmitted. The vertical line from the abscissa 0 corresponds to the replacement of the lead anodes by plates with grids of the alloy Pb + 5% Sb + 1% Ag, and the dotted lines to the introduction of an additive into the electrolyte. 1(Δ) - electrolyte without additives (H_2SO_4 solution, density 1.32); there were added to the electrolyte; 2(●) - α-ONA (pure); 3(X) - α-ONA (technical); 4(O) - α-naphthol. Current density $1.5 \cdot 10^{-3} A/cm^2$ of visible surface. Potential measured against a Hg/Hg_2SO_4 electrode.

From the data quoted it follows that α-ONA is inferior in its inhibiting effect to α-naphthol. In addition, an increase in the degree of purity of the α-ONA decreases the effectiveness of the given inhibitor's action.

The selection of two organic substances (an expander and an inhibitor) intended for simultaneous introduction into the battery presents difficulties. In a number of cases the introduction of a self-discharge inhibitor causes marked decrease in the discharge capacity of the negative electrode. This generally occurs if the substances serving as depassivator and inhibitor are substantially different in their structure. On the other hand, as a rule, substances which are close in their chemical nature can be simultaneously used in a battery as additives intended for a different purpose [68]).

The reason for the different "combinability" of organic additives is not completely clear. It may be assumed that there occurs between heterogeneous molecules in the adsorption layer a stronger attraction interaction than between molecules which are close to each other in structure. In that case the formation of a dense adsorption film, which hinders the occurrence of the discharge process ($Pb \rightarrow PbSO_4$) and, as a result of this, decreases the discharge capacity of a lead electrode, is possible. Let us note that the use of two surface-active additives of a different nature also has a negative effect on the structure of electrolytic deposits of lead [42]).

As an illustration of what has been said we may use the results quoted below, of a comparative study of two expanders: humic acid and tanning agent No. 4. Tests were carried out with coated plates of the RG type the grids of which were cast from lead. The expanders under investigation were introduced into the active mass simultaneously with barium sulphate. The electrodes were tested by the method of cycling with a 5-hour discharge regime in an electrolyte of 1.32 density. In the process of testing, measurements were taken of the values of final charge potential (against a Hg/Hg_2SO_4 reference electrode), discharge capacity and the volume of hydrogen separating at self-discharge was determined periodically. Use was also made of RG type plates as positive electrodes, but with grids of lead-antimony-silver alloy (Pb + 5% Sb + 1% Ag). After a considerable fall in the final charge potential (63 cycles) α-naphthol was introduced into the solution. The results obtained are shown in fig. 5.20. The moment of introduction of α-naphthol is shown by a dotted line.

From fig. 5.20 it follows principally that the capacity of the plates with tanning agent No. 4 is higher throughout the whole experiment than the capacity of the plates containing humic acid (HA) in the active mass. In addition, for electrodes with HA, a characteristic feature is

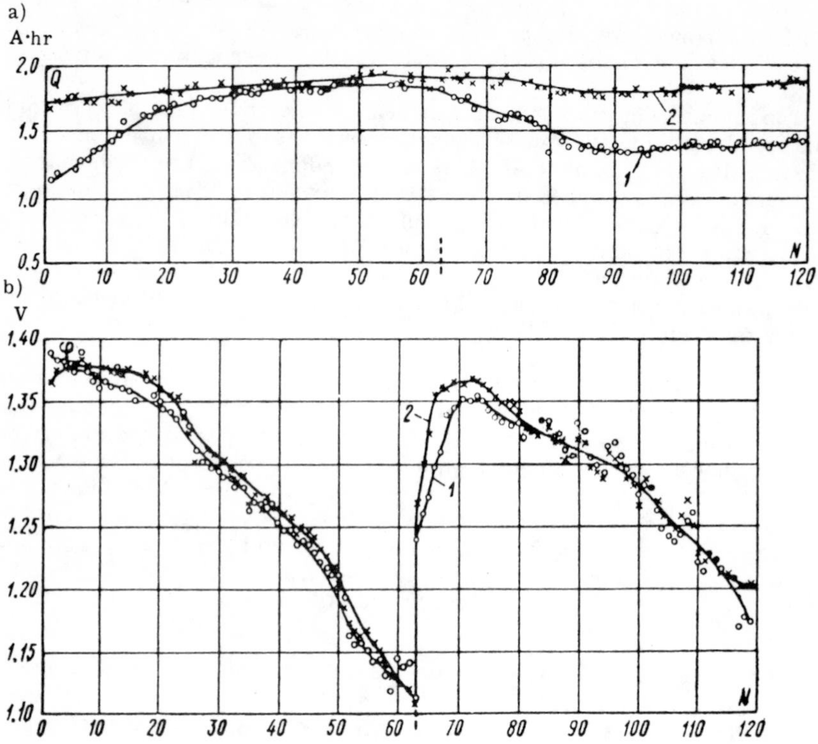

Fig. 5.20 Change in discharge capacity (a) and final charge potential (b) of a negative electrode in the process of cycling. 1(o) - 1% HA is introduced into the paste; 2(x) - 0.6% T-4 is introduced; ---- α-naphthol is introduced into the electrolyte.

a slow increase in capacity at the beginning of the experiment, while the capacity of plates with T-4 is quite large from the very first cycles and in the process of testing it changes comparatively little.

It is essential to mention that the introduction of α-naphthol into the electrolyte caused a decrease in discharge capacity of electrodes with HA. A similar result was obtained in the investigation of the effect of α-naphthol, and also of α-ONA, on the characteristics of batteries where HA was used as an expander. Whilst, as can be seen from fig. 5.20, the introduction into the solution of α-naphthol in the presence of T-4 in the active mass of the negative electrode, does not cause any change in the discharge capacity. This result obviously is due to a certain similarity in the structure of tanning agent No. 4, which is a condensation product of β-naphthol sulphonic acids and phenols with formalin, and the self-discharge inhibitors compounds of the naphthalene series.

The course of the change of final charge potential (FCP) in the process of cycling is perfectly similar for electrodes with HA and T-4 (fig. 5.20). Both the expanders show an almost identical influence on the cathode potential of a spongy lead electrode, both with a "pure" surface and that containing additions of silver and antimony. A comparison of the results shown in fig. 5.20 shows that electrolytic transfer of Sb and Ag, causing a decrease of FCP of a negative electrode, has no effect on its discharge capacity. As can be seen from fig. 5.20, the introduction of α-naphthal into the solution causes a sharp shift of FCP in the negative direction towards its original value. At the same time there is a substantial fall in the rate of self-discharge of the electrodes under investigation, determined by the volume of hydrogen separating at the self-dissolution of lead.

Thus a combination of T-4 with α-naphthol can be used in batteries with a limited rate of self-discharge. The latter result opens up the possibility of using lead alloys compounded with silver, which are distinguished by high corrosion resistance, in batteries employed in sealed or badly ventilated locations.

Further investigations[68]) showed that besides α-naphthol and α-ONA, self-discharge inhibitors such as α-nitrose-β-naphthol, β-ONA and some dyes of the naphthalene series may be used. In all cases on the introduction of the inhibitor a sharp fall in the rate of self-discharge of the negative electrode is observed, whilst the capacity of the electrode is practically unchanged (in particular cases a certain increase in discharge capacity even takes place on the introduction of the inhibitor).

The use of naphthalene products as a self-discharge inhibitor is possible if substances such as tanning agent BNF and disperser NF are depassivators. These products are similar in their structure to tanning agent No. 4. The results described were obtained by us in the testing of electrodes in an electrolyte with a density of 1.32 and 1.36. The possibility was also demonstrated of the introduction of an inhibitor along with a corresponding expander (depassivator) into the active mass of the negative electrode.

Sodium lignosulphonate (SA) is quite an effective depassivator of the negative electrode. The introduction of this substance into the active mass ensures that a high discharge capacity is obtained, particularly under long-term discharge conditions. At the same time SA does not

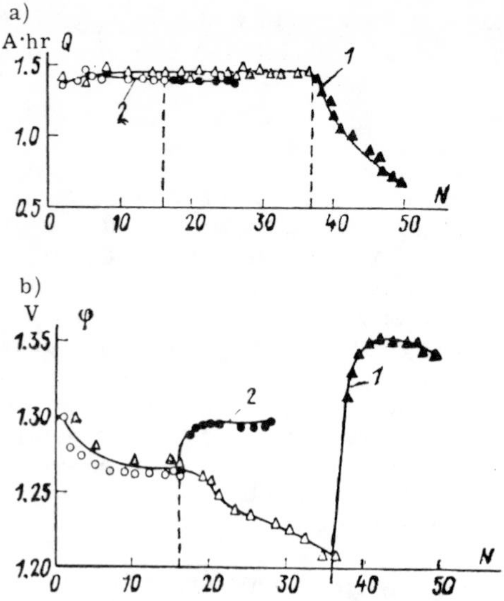

Fig. 5.21 The effect of α-naphthol (1) and sulphanol (2) on the discharge capacity (a) and on the final charge potential (b) of a negative electrode containing SA in the active mass. ---- an inhibitor is introduced into the electrolyte.

possess any marked inhibiting properties, therefore electrodes with this expander are distinguished by an increased rate of self-discharge.

In fig. 5.21 it is shown how discharge capacity and FCP of a negative electrode, containing in the active mass 0.5% of SA, are influenced by the self-discharge inhibitors α-naphthol and sulphanol in the process of cycling positive electrodes, the grids of which are made from a lead-antimony-silver alloy. It can be seen from fig. 5.21 that the introduction into the electrolyte of α-naphthol and sulphanol leads to an increase in FCP of the negative electrodes containing SA in the active mass. The value of the potential achieved in this corresponds in the case of the introduction of sulphanol to the original value. A second introduction into the electrolyte of this substance does not show any influence on the FCP of the negative electrode.

In the presence of α-naphthol a more pronounced shift of FCP of the electrode in a negative direction is observed. This difference in the behaviour of the inhibitors under consideration is explained by the fact that sulphanol substantially increases the hydrogen overvoltage, most of all on silver, while α-naphthol causes a considerable shift in potential of all three components of the electrode: lead, antimony and silver.

As can be seen from fig. 5.21, the introduction of α-naphthol into the electrolyte in the presence of SA in the active mass of the negative electrode causes a decrease in the discharge capacity. The introduction of sulphanol does not lead to a change in the capacity of the electrode. This result confirms what has been said above on the subject of the influence of the similarity of chemical structure on the possibility of simultaneous introduction of additives intended for different purposes. In fact, sodium lignosulphonate and sulphanol are similar in chemical structure to a certain extent: both substances contain benzene rings and sulpho groups. Simultaneous use of SA and sulphanol is undoubtedly of practical interest. They are often used especially for batteries whose positive grids are made of an alloy containing silver.

Some evidence about the character of the adsorption of surface-active substances on the negative electrode and their influence on the active surface of the electrode may be obtained by means of a comparison of the values of the capacity of the electrical double layer C_d and the discharge capacity Q of the electrode in the presence of one compound or another[26]. The values of the capacity of the double layer corresponding to the minimum of the graph (C_d, φ) also the values of Q obtained at discharge at a 3-cycle 5-hour regime (table 5.1) are given below.

Table 5.1: The influence on the capacity of the double layer (C_d) and the discharge capacity of an electrode (Q)

Additive to the active mass *)	Q		C_d	
	A·hr/g	%	A·hr/g	%
Without additives	0.054	100	40	100
$BaSO_4$	0.061	113	52	130
T-4	0.101	187	35	88
HA	0.099	183	22	55
Tanning agent BNF	0.092	170	26	65
Disperser NF	0.090	167	48	120
SA	0.075	139	31	78
Sulphite liquor	0.075	139	43	108
β-nitrose-α-naphthol	0.048	89	26	65

*) All organic additives were introduced simultaneously with $BaSO_4$.

The introduction of $BaSO_4$ into the active mass of the negative electrode (in the absence of organic additives) leads to a known expansion of the surface of the electrode which is not connected with adsorption. This is evidenced by an increase both of capacity of the double layer and of the discharge capacity under the influence of $BaSO_4$. The majority of depassivators, as can be seen from the data quoted, cause a fall in the value of C_d and a rise in Q. A particularly marked decrease in C_d is observed in the presence of HA.

The addition of T-4 and SA obviously causes a marked increase in the true surface of a spongy lead electrode: the values of C_d with the presence in the active mass of these substances are higher than in an electrode with HA. Sulphite liquor works in a similar way, and so especially does disperser NF, which causes a considerable expansion of the surface of the electrode.

The introduction of **β-nitroso-α-naphthol - an effective self-discharge** inhibitor - into the active mass causes a considerable decrease in the capacity of the double layer and in discharge capacity. Adsorption of this substance leads to a decrease in the active surface of the electrode, which may be the reason for the decrease in the value of Q. Other inhibitors which are naphthalene products act in a similar way.

Bench tests of batteries containing T-4 or BNF (0.25-0.3%) in the active mass as an expander and α-naphthol or **β-nitroso-α-naphthol** (0.1-0.12%) as an inhibitor showed the possibility of a 2-3-fold decrease in the rate of self-discharge of the negative electrode with the maintenance of a high discharge capacity.

The effect mentioned, caused by the action of the self-discharge inhibitors, is observed in batteries with a production anode alloy and, in particular, with the use of a lead-antimony-silver alloy. As was shown by tests, the inhibitor may also be introduced into the electrolyte of a battery in use with the aim of decreasing the rate of self-discharge, which rises considerably towards the end of the service life.

The use of arsenic as an alloying compound of the anode alloy does not lead to a change in the characteristics of the negative electrode of a battery. As has already been mentioned, arsenic does not accumulate in any noticeable quantity on the surface of the electrode. Therefore, the inhibitors of self-discharge described above can be used in batteries with the grids of the positive electrode cast from alloys compounded with arsenic.

Sulphation of the negative electrode and methods of combating it

By sulphation we understand the condition of the battery plates when they do not charge when the normal charging current is passed for the normal interval of time. In the literature this phenomenon is sometimes called "irreversible sulphation", thereby emphasising how it differs from the formation of sulphate in normal discharge. Such a term, however. may not be considered justified owing to the fact that, as will be shown below, quite effective methods exist for reducing the sulphated plates. Characteristic signs of sulphation of the battery plates are the higher voltage and large-scale gassing observed at the very beginning of the charge.

It is generally considered that the cause of sulphation and of the decreased capacity connected with it, is a decrease in the solubility of the lead sulphate, caused by its recrystallisation. As was shown by Barret, a normal negative plate of a battery in the discharged state contains basically finely-crystalline lead sulphate, the dimensions of the crystals of which do not exceed 10^{-3}-10^{-5} cm. Only 7-10% of the lead sulphate has a crystal size of the order of 10^{-2} cm. The sulphated plates consist only of large crystals of $PbSO_4$.

Recrystallisation of the $PbSO_4$, leading to an enlargement of the crystals, is the result of the polycrystalline system striving towards a decreasing of free surface energy. This process takes place as a result of the fact that the solubility of the fine crystals markedly exceeds the solubility of the large ones (in accordance with the well-known Thomson's equation), therefore, in favourable conditions an increase in the separate $PbSO_4$ crystals may take place owing to the dissolution of the finer crystals lying nearby.

A somewhat different view on the nature of the sulphation of the negative electrode of a lead acid battery has been developed from the experimental work of T I Popova and B N Kabanov[69]). According to the data of these authors, the basic cause of the decrease in the rate of solution of the lead sulphate is the adsorption on it of surface-active substances present as an addition to the sulphuric acid electrolyte and also leached from the separators, active masses and other materials in contact with the electrolyte. In ref.[69]) it is shown that long-term storage (for a period of 8 months) of discharged negative electrodes in a solution of H_2SO_4 thoroughly purified from any additives whatever, caused no difficulties in subsequent charging, although recrystallisation and enlargement of the $PbSO_4$ crystals took place. The authors assume that the adsorbed additives sharply increase the overvoltage of the process of reduction of the lead ions. It is known that the positive electrode of a lead acid battery is considerably less subject to sulphation than the negative one. This phenomenon is explained by T I Popova and B N Kabanov by the fact that as a rule surface-active substances are oxidised at potentials realised on a lead dioxide electrode to water and carbon dioxide and therefore cannot have any marked deleterious effect.

It is possible to distinguish the following basic causes of sulphation[70]:

1. The battery is kept for a long time in a discharged or not fully charged state. In this case, in the active mass a considerable amount of $PbSO_4$ crystals occurs which are not subjected to electro-chemical reduction. These crystals are capable of growing and, in addition, considerable adsorption of organic particles can take place on their faces. These conditions, as has been shown above, lead to sulphation of the plates. From what has been said it follows that accumulator batteries must be kept only in the charged state, avoiding long-term storage in a discharged or not fully charged form.

2. Systematic prolonged discharges down to $\leqslant$1.75-1.80V leads to the accumulation of marked quantities of lead sulphate in the active mass, which is not reduced in subsequent charged.

3. Systematic incomplete charging of the battery leads to similar consequences being a frequent cause of sulphation. It is necessary, therefore, to check thoroughly the carrying out of the charging process, particularly in the event of prolonged discharge of the battery preceding the charge.

4. An increase in the concentration of the electrolyte leads to a speeding up of the self-discharge of the negative electrode, especially if the battery is stored after carrying out a considerable number of charge-discharge cycles, when the surface of the negative plates contains a large amount of antimony transferred from the anode. In that case an accumulation is also possible of large $PbSO_4$ crystals in the active mass, containing on their surface adsorbed additives which is a direct cause of sulphation, as has been said above. The concentration of the battery electrolyte as a rule, must not exceed the level necessary for ensuring the given discharge characteristics.

5. Keeping batteries at elevated temperatures causes a speeding up of the process of recrystallisation of lead sulphate and also of the self-discharge of the negative electrode, which favours sulphation of the plates. Sudden variations in temperature have an adverse effect on the condition of the plates. The best conditions for keeping lead acid batteries must therefore be considered to be at the lower temperatures.

6. The development of sulphation is caused by systematic charging at an accelerated rate, i.e. at relatively high current densities. Here, owing to the specific quality of porous electrodes, the deep-down layers of the active mass may be systematically not fully charged, which causes gradual accumulation of lead sulphate in the active mass. In addition,

sudden variations in the concentration of the electrolyte in the pores at charging with large currents causes recrystallisation of $PbSO_4$. In the literature charging with periodic pauses is recommended, which produces an equalisation of the concentration of the electrolyte.

7. One of the causes of sulphation is the appearance of short circuits at the edges of the plates and through the separators. This is basically connected with an accumulation of sludge at the bottom of the battery tank, owing to dissolution of the positive active mass. Sludge particles are transferred electrophoretically to the negative plates and, in being reduced, lead to the appearance of bridges round the separators. In a number of cases short circuits occur as a result of the swelling of the negative active mass, which penetrates the pores of the separators if the dimensions of the pores are sufficiently large.

Short circuits cause sulphation of the plates, both as a result of accelerated self-discharge (more accurately, the occurrence of discharge through areas of short circuit), and also as a result of incomplete charging of the battery, since part of the charge current is expended not on the carrying out of the charging process but on warming up the battery.

An effective measure for prevention of short circuits is an improvement of the quality of the separators, the use of separator jackets pulled over the plates of common polarity. Naturally, the methods of decreasing the rate of deterioration and dissolution of the positive active mass considered in Chapter 4 are at the same time important methods of combating the appearance of short circuits in the process of utilisation of the battery.

A number of methods have been worked out for the elimination of sulphation of battery plates which are widely described in literature [e.g. see ref.[71]]. As a rule, these methods are based on increasing the solubility of the lead sulphate by means of a change in the composition of the electrolyte. One of the widely used methods of treatment of sulphatted plates consists of replacing the battery electrolyte by distilled water *) and charging being carried out at low current density, i.e. approximately 0.1 of the normal charge current. After the beginning of large-scale gassing and an increase in the density of the electrolyte to 1.1g/cm^3 the charge is stopped, the acid that has formed is again replaced by water and a repeated charge is effected at the same current. This operation is repeated sometimes several times, correcting the electrolyte to the necessary composition after its density ceases to in-

---

*) The solubility of $PbSO_4$ in water at 25°C is 44.5mg/l, but in a 20-40% H_2SO_4 solution only 1.2mg/l[71].

crease in the charge process.

A method exists of removing sulphate with the aid of NaOH solution[71], and also by means of the introduction of special additives (sulphate of ammonia etc.) into the electrolyte.

In accordance with the adsorption theory of the appearance of sulphation of the negative electrode, T I Popova and B N Kabanov have proposed an effective method of eliminating sulphation of the plates, which consists in the desorption of organic additives from their surface in the presence of a quite strong cathodic polarisation. The density of the polarising current should amount to approximately 100mA/cm^2, i.e. 10 tens higher than a normal charging current. It must be noted that widespread use of this method of desulphation is at present hampered by the insufficient power of the charging devices used in practice.

The kinetics of separation of stibine in the charging of a lead acid battery

In the process of charging lead acid batteries having lead-antimony alloy grids as the negative electrode, along with hydrogen there occurs liberation of stibine. Stibine is distinguished by high toxicity, therefore, a study of the laws of SbH_3 formation with the aim of finding methods of maximum reduction of the rate of this process is of great interest, especially in relation to batteries used in sealed or badly ventilated lŏcations.

Stibine is formed basically from antimony which has passed into the solution as a result of corrosion of the positive grids and electrodeposited on the surface of the negative plates[72]. Separation of SbH_3 is observed mainly at the end of the charge (in the period of overcharge), when the tension of the battery exceeds 2.45V[73].

Holland[73] established that the concentration of SbH_3 in the gaseous mixture separating from the battery during charge is an exponential function of the charge tension. This dependency obviously has an effect on the electro-chemical mechanism of the formation of stibine[74][75].

The potential corresponding to the equilibrium

$$Sb + 3H^+ + 3e \rightleftarrows SbH_3 \qquad (5.64)$$

constitutes

$$\varphi_{Sb/SbH_3} = -0.510 + \nu \lg a_{H^+} \approx -0.510 + 0.059 \lg a_{H^+} \qquad (5.65)$$

In electrolyte of density 1.3g/cm^3, m = 6.5 and $\gamma_\pm$ = 0.285, whence $\alpha_\pm = \sqrt[3]{4m\gamma_\pm}$ = 2.94 and, according to (5.65), φ_{Sb/SbH_3} ≈ -0.48V (in relation to nve).

The value of the final charge potential of the negative electrode of a lead acid battery reaches $\varphi_{f.c.}$ = -0.60V (nve). A comparison of the values quoted shows that $\varphi_{f.c.} < \varphi_{Sb/SbH_3}$. Thus, the formation of stibine by means of electrode oxidation of antimony by hydrogen ions is thermodynamically possible. This process can occur only at sufficiently high cathodic potential of the negative electrode (< -0.48V), attained in the final period of charge. It is namely in this period, as was mentioned above, that separation of SbH_3 is also observed.

Since the most probable processes are ones involving an electron, it may be assumed that the stage limiting the rate of formation of SbH_3 on the cathode is described by the equation

$$Sb + H^+ + e \rightarrow SbH \tag{5.66}$$

and leads to intermediate formation of the radical SbH. Witness is borne in favour of this proposition by the evidence existing in literature of the appearance in the process of electrolysis on an antimony cathode of the solid hydrate Sb_2H_2, which can be considered as a product of the dimerisation of the SbH radical.

A further stage of the process of formation of stibine may occur, e.g. according to the scheme

$$SbH + H_2 \rightarrow SbH_3 \tag{5.67}$$

The possibility is also not excluded of an electro-chemical mechanism of this reaction (with the participation of hydrogen ions).

Passing through the H_2SO_4 solution, the stibine is partially decomposed according to the scheme

$$SbH_3 + 3H^+ \rightarrow Sb^{3+} + 6H_2 \tag{5.68}$$

with the speed of decomposition increasing with an increase in the concentration of the solution.

The rate of separation of stibine ν, in the event of its formation being limited by the single electron cathodic reaction occurring on sections of the electrode occupied by antimony, is determined by the equation

$$\nu = k\chi S_{Sb} a_{H^+} e^{-\frac{\alpha F\phi}{RT}} e^{-\frac{\beta F\phi_1}{RT}} \qquad (5.69)$$

where: k is a constant of the rate, S_{Sb} the portion of the electrode surface occupied by antimony, χ a coefficient ($\chi < 1$) characterising the part of the total amount of stibine formed which has not reacted with the sulphuric acid according to the reaction (5.68), a_{H^+} the activity of the hydrogen ions in the solution, ψ_1, α, β, R, T and F have the usual meaning.

From the formula (5.69) it follows that the rate of separation of SbH_3 increases with an increase in cathode potential according to the exponential law, which accords with the data of the work[73]) quoted above. The concentration of the electrolyte should have little influence on the value of ν, since with a change in the concentration of H_2SO_4 the values of a_{H^+} and χ change in opposite directions. The rate of separation of SbH_3, according to (5.69), increases with adsorption on the electrode of anionic compounds which shift the ψ_1 potential in a negative direction, and it decreases as a result of the adsorption of cationic substances. Naturally the adsorption of organic compounds may show an influence not only on the value of the ψ_1 potential, but it may also lead to the insulation of part of the electrode surface. In this case adsorption on antimony should cause an arresting of the process under consideration, decreasing the value of S_{Sb}. Thus, the adsorption of organic substances may influence the rate of separation of stibine differently. The character of this influence depends on the degree of change, as a result of adsorption, of the double electrical layer and the dimensions of the active surface of the electrode. We shall discuss this problem in more detail at the end of the present chapter.

The potential of the electrode may be expressed by the formula

$$\varphi = \varphi^0 + \frac{RT}{F} \ln a_{H^+} - \eta \qquad (5.70)$$

where: η is the overvoltage of the process (5.66), φ^0 the standard value of the equilibrium potential corresponding to this process.

Substituting (5.70) in equation (5.69) we have

$$\nu = k_1 \chi S_{Sb} a_{H^+}^{\beta} e^{\frac{\alpha F\eta}{RT}} e^{-\frac{\beta F\psi_1}{RT}} \qquad (5.71)$$

where: $k = k \exp(-\alpha F\varphi^0/RT)$. The values of η and ψ_1 in equation (5.71) are functions of the composition of the electrode surface. Considering the negative electrode as a 2-phase system, it is possible, according to formula (5.58), to write that

$$\eta = \eta_{Pb} - \frac{RT}{\alpha F} \ln \left(S_{Sb}\, e^{\frac{(\eta_{Pb}-\eta_{Sb})\alpha F}{RT}} + 1 \right) \qquad (5.72)$$

The dependence of the value of the ψ_1 potential on the composition of the electrode surface at low surface concentrations of antimony may clearly be represented in the form of a linear function from S_{Sb} :

$$\psi_1 = \psi_1^{(Pb)} (1 - S_{Sb}) + \psi_1^{(Sb)} S_{Sb} = \psi_1^{(Pb)} + (\psi_1^{(Sb)} - \psi_1^{(Pb)}) S_{Sb} \qquad (5.73)$$

The upper and lower indices (Pb and Sb) in formulae (5.72) and (5.73) point to dependence on the corresponding amounts **of antimony or lead.**

Substituting the expressions (5.72) and (5.73) in equation (5.71), we obtain a formula characterising the dependence of the rate of separation of stibine on the negative electrode of a lead acid battery on the antimony content on the electrode surface:

$$\nu = \frac{A_c S_{Sb} e^{-\psi S_{Sb}/b_2}}{1 + B_c S_{Sb}} \qquad (5.74)$$

$$A_c = k_1 \chi a_{H^+}^{\beta} \exp \left[\frac{F}{RT} (\alpha \eta_{Pb} - \beta \psi_1^{(Pb)}) \right] \qquad (5.75)$$

$$B_c = \exp \left[\frac{(\eta_{Pb} - \eta_{Sb}) \alpha F}{RT} \right] \qquad (5.76)$$

$$\psi = \psi_1^{(Sb)} - \psi_1^{(Pb)} \qquad (5.77)$$

$$b_2 = RT/\beta F \qquad (5.78)$$

Since the surface of the lead is charged positively at the potentials realised on the negative electrode of a battery, adsorption of sulphate ions (in the absence of surface-active additives) causes a shift in the ψ_1 potential in a negative direction, i.e. $\psi_1^{(Pb)} < 0$. The surface of the antimony in these conditions is negatively charged, consequently $\psi_1^{(Sb)} \geqslant 0$. Hence, according to formula (5.77) $\psi > 0$.

Equation (5.74) characterises the limiting dependence of ν on S_{Sb}. The extreme value of $S_{Sb}(S_m)$ can be found by logging (5.74), differentiating the result by S_{Sb} and equating the expression obtained to zero:

$$\frac{\partial \lg \nu}{\partial S_{Sb}} = \frac{1}{S_m} - \frac{\psi}{b_2} - \frac{B_c}{1 + B_c S_m} = 0 \qquad (5.79)$$

Solving (5.79) in relation to S_m, we shall have

$$S_m = \frac{1}{2B_c} + \sqrt{\frac{1}{4B_c^2} + \frac{b_2}{B_c \psi}} \qquad (5.80)$$

It is not difficult to show that the second product $d^2 \ln \nu / dS^2_{Sb}$ is a negative value, i.e. the function $\nu(S_{Sb})$ at $S_{Sb} = S_m$ goes through a maximum.

According to formula (5.76), $B_c \gg 1$, which gives a basis for simplification of equation (5.80), which can be rewritten in the form

$$S_m \cong \sqrt{\frac{b_2}{B_c \psi}} \qquad (5.81)$$

The value of S_m according to (5.80) or (5.81), over a wide range of charge currents does not depend on the current, since in practice B_c does not depend on the current, and the value of ψ can only change (in sufficiently concentrated H_2SO_4 solutions) at quite considerable polarisations. The adsorption of surface active substances on lead and antimony, causing a shift in the values of $\psi_1^{(Pb)}$ and ψ_1^{Sb} may change the value of S_m as a result of the change in ψ. The adsorption of anionic compounds on lead, causing a shift in the ψ_1 potential in a negative direction, i.e. an increase in the value of ψ, must, according to formulae (5.77) and (5.81), lead to a decrease in S_m, i.e. to a displacement of the maximum rate of separation of stibine in the direction of the initial period of testing or utilisation of the battery.

In the process of cycling the battery, the concentration of antimony on the surface of the negative electrode increases, causing a fall in the final charge potential (hydrogen overvoltage) and a rise in the rate of self-discharge. The dependence of the rate of evolution of SbH_3 on the number of cycles observed in the experiment, often goes through a maximum which corresponds to the result obtained above (fig. 5.22). Naturally, if the concentration of antimony in the active mass of the negative electrode does not reach a value equal to S_m, in the process of battery testing or use, then we shall observe only a uniform in-

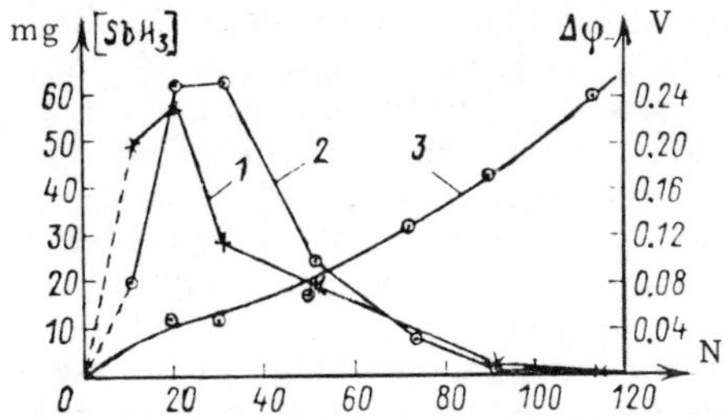

Fig. 5.22 Dependence of the amount of SbH_3 separating at charge of the battery and shift of the final charge potential of the negative electrode ($\Delta\varphi$-) on the number of cycles N. 1 and 3 - anode alloy Pb + 6.5% Sb; 2 - anode alloy Pb + 4.7% Sb + 0.37% As; 1 and 2 - amount of SbH_3; 3 - $\Delta\varphi$- V.

crease in the concentration of SbH_3 from cycle to cycle, which also sometimes happens.

It is possible to use the following values for an estimate of the value of S_m according to formula (5.81): $b_2 = 0.05V$, $\eta_{Pb} - \eta_{Sb} \cong 0.4V$ and $\psi_1^{(Pb)} \approx 0.15V$. According to the equation (5.76) $B_c = 2\,980$ and according to (5.81) $S_m \approx 0.106 \approx 1\%$. The weight concentration of antimony in the negative active mass corresponding to the maximum rate of evolution of stibine may be estimated, starting out from formula (5.55), according to which (at $S_{Sb} \ll 1$).

$$\frac{m_{Sb}}{m_{Pb}} \cong (0.704 S_m)^{3/2} = 0.000644 \approx 0.06\%$$

Thus, if the concentration of antimony in the active mass of the negative electrode exceeds ~0.06%, then this should lead to a decrease in the rate of separation of SbH_3 with further increase in the value of S_{Sb}.

As is shown by the results of chemical analysis, the concentration of Sb in the active mass of the negative plates at the end of the service life of a battery oscillates within the limits 0.02-0.2%. The concentration of Sb calculated above, corresponding to the maximum rate of evolution of SbH_3, is in this range. It may thus be considered that in many cases the dependence of the rate of separation of SbH_3 on the number of cycles must pass through the maximum, which is confirmed in the experiment.

It must be mentioned that the character of the change in concentration of the antimony in the negative active mass of a battery in use has not been studied in detail. Although, as has been shown above, there is no doubt that S_{Sb} increases with the number of cycles N, however, there are no reasons for assuming that S_{Sb} increases in proportion to N. A possibility is the complicated character of the function $S_{Sb}(N)$, which is determined by the cycling regime, type and construction of the battery, form and rate of corrosion of the positive grids, properties of the separation, etc. The removal of antimony in form of stibine leads to a decrease in the concentration of Sb in the active mass of the negative electrode, thus arresting an increase in S_{Sb} in the process of cycling. On the other hand, the partial decomposition of the SbH_3 by sulphuric acid and the subsequent electrodeposition of Sb by means of the discharge of the Sb^{3+} ions thus formed, must lead to some increase in S_{Sb}. **From what has been said** it is clear that the theoretical function $\psi(S_{Sb})$, expressed by equation (5.74) only reflects qualitatively the function $\psi(N)$ observed in the usual experiments.

A change in concentration of the antimony in the negative active mass shows up most of all in the corresponding shift of the final charge potential of the negative electrode. In this connection an interesting point is the establishment of a relationship between the rate of separation of SbH_3 and the shift of the final charge potential (hydrogen overvoltage) from the original value. The subsequent value is equal to $\Delta\eta = \eta_{Pb} - \eta$. According to equation (5.72) taking into account (5.76)

$$S_{Sb} = \frac{e^{\Delta\eta/b_2} - 1}{B_c} \tag{5.82}$$

Substituting this expression in equation (5.71) and assuming for simplicity that $\alpha = \beta$, we then have

$$\nu = k_1 \chi a^{\beta}_{H^+} e^{\frac{\eta_{Sb}}{b_2}} \left(1 - e^{-\frac{\Delta\eta}{b_2}}\right) e^{-\frac{\psi_1}{b_2}} \tag{5.83}$$

From equation (5.83) it follows that, if we neglect the change in ψ_1 potential, the rate of evolution of SbH_3 increases with an increase in $\Delta\eta$ from 0 (at $\Delta\eta = 0$) to

$$\nu = k_1 \chi a^{\beta}_{H^+} e^{\frac{\eta_{Sb}}{b_2}} \left(1 - e^{-\frac{\eta_{Pb}-\eta_{Sb}}{b_2}}\right) e^{\frac{\psi_1}{b_2}} \tag{5.84}$$

at $\Delta\eta = \eta_{Pb} - \eta_{Sb}$, i.e. at $\eta = \eta_{Sb}$. To characterise the influence of the composition of the surface on the value of the ψ_1 potential let us use equation (5.73), which, taking into account equations (5.82) and (5.76) to (5.78) may be rewritten in the form

$$\psi_1 = \psi_1^{(Pb)} + \frac{\psi}{B_c}(e^{\Delta\eta/b_2} - 1) \tag{5.85}$$

According to (5.83) and (5.85)

$$\nu = k_1 \chi a_{H^+}^{\beta} \exp\left(\frac{\eta_{Sb} - \psi_1^{(Pb)}}{b_2}\right)\left[1 - \exp\left(-\frac{\Delta\eta}{b_2}\right)\right] \cdot \exp\left\{-\frac{\psi}{B_c b_2}\left[\exp\left(\frac{\Delta\eta}{b_2}\right) - 1\right]\right\} \tag{5.86}$$

Taking logarithms and differentiating equation (5.86), we shall have

$$\frac{\partial \ln \nu}{\partial \Delta\eta} = \frac{1}{b_2\left(e^{\frac{\Delta\eta}{b_2}} - 1\right)} - \frac{\psi}{B_c b_2^2} e^{\frac{\Delta\eta}{b_2}} \tag{5.87}$$

$$\frac{\partial^2 \ln \nu}{\partial \Delta\eta^2} = \frac{1}{b_2^2\left(e^{\frac{\Delta\eta}{b_2}} - 1\right)^2} - \frac{\psi}{B_c b_2^3} e^{\frac{\Delta\eta}{b_2}} \tag{5.88}$$

It follows from (5.88), $d^2 \log_e \nu / d\,\Delta\eta^2 < 0$, i.e. the function $\nu(\Delta\eta)$ has a maximum. The corresponding value of the shift of final charge potential of the negative electrode $\Delta\eta_m$ is determined, in accordance with (5.87), by the equation

$$\Delta\eta_m = b_2 \ln\left(\frac{1}{2} + \sqrt{\frac{1}{4} + \frac{B_c b_2}{\psi}}\right) \approx \frac{b_2}{2} \ln \frac{B_c b_2}{\psi} \tag{5.89}$$

With $b_2 = 0.05V$, $\psi = 0.15V$ and $B_c = 2\,980$, $\Delta\eta_m = 0.172V$. Let us note that equation (5.89) can be obtained also by means of substitution of the value of S_m (5.81) in the formula (5.72).

From equation (5.89) it follows that adsorption of anionic compounds on lead, causing a shift in the value of ψ_{1Pb} in a negative direction, i.e. in accordance with (5.77), increasing the value of ψ leads to some decrease in the value of $\Delta\eta$, i.e. to a displacement of the maximum rate of SbH_3 evolution to the initial cycles, which corresponds to the result described above.

As a rule, experimental values of the shift of final charge potential of the negative electrode of a lead acid battery $\Delta\varphi_{f.c.}$ at which the maximum rate of separation of stibine is observed are somewhat less than the calculated value. This is explained principally by the anionic nature of the expanders used. In addition, we must take into account the fact that in the process of cycling, growth of the electrode surface occurs, causing a definite drop in the final charge potential as a result of a decrease in the true current density. Finally, electrolytic transfer of antimony in the process of charging the plates leads to an increase in the initial value of the charge potential of the negative electrode, i.e. to a decrease in the value of $\Delta\varphi_{f.c.}$.

Substituting formula (5.81) in equation (5.74), we obtain the expression for the maximum rate of SbH_3 evolution:

$$\nu_{max} = \frac{A_c\sqrt{\frac{b_2}{B\,\psi}}\,e^{-\sqrt{\frac{\psi}{B_c b_2}}}}{1+\sqrt{\frac{B_c b_2}{\psi}}} \approx \frac{A_c}{B_c}\,e^{-\sqrt{\frac{\psi}{B_c b_2}}} \qquad (5.90)$$

Since the value of $\sqrt{\psi/(B_c b_2)}$ is quite small *), it is possible with a fairly good approximation to assume that

$$\nu_{max} \cong \frac{A_c}{B_c} \qquad (5.91)$$

or, taking into account (5.75) to (5.77) at $\alpha = \beta = 0.5$.

$$\nu_{max} \cong k_1 \chi \sqrt{a_{H^+}}\,\exp\left(\frac{\eta_{Sb} - \psi_1^{(Pb)}}{b_2}\right) \qquad (5.92)$$

From equation (5.92) it follows that the value of ν_{max} depends little on the concentration of the electrolyte and increases with an increase in current (since here the value of η_{Sb} increases). The adsorption on lead of anionic compounds, which shift the $\psi_1^{(Pb)}$ potential in a negative direction, leads to an increase in ν_{max}.

---

*) At $\psi = 0.15V$, $b_2 = 0.05V$ and $B_c = 2980$, $\sqrt{\psi/B_c b_2} = 0.03$ and $e^{-0.03} = 0.97$.

However, it must be mentioned that with a considerable shift of $\psi_1^{(Pb)}$ i.e. an increase in the value of ψ, it is necessary to use formula (5.90) instead of formula (5.92). Here the influence of the value of ψ on the maximum rate of stibine evolution will show up to a somewhat lesser degree.

The methods which are mainly suitable for decreasing the rate of formation of stibine in a lead acid battery, are those directed towards a decrease in the charge potential of the negative electrode, and also towards a substantial decrease in the antimony content in the negative active mass *).

A quite effective means of decreasing the concentration of SbH_3 in the gas separating from the battery is when charging at a constant and relatively low voltage. The potential of the negative electrode should not exceed an absolute value of 0.45-0.5V (in relation to nve). In this case the formation of SbH_3 becomes thermodynamically impossible or occurs at quite a low rate. However, since constant voltage charging is linked with the prolongation of the cycle, which is not always allowable, methods worthy of serious interest are those which are directed towards a marked lowering of the surface concentration of the Sb in the active mass of the negative plates. Among such methods is the addition of metals to the anode alloy that increase its corrosion resistance and consequently decrease the rate of anionic dissolution of antimony.

The concentration of Sb in the negative active mass decreases particularly with the use of positive grids of a lead-antimony-silver alloy, which is distinguished by high corrosion resistance. Naturally, all the methods of decreasing the rate of electrolytic transfer of the components of the anode alloy examined in the section under "Self-discharge of the negative electrode", should cause a decrease in the surface concentration of antimony on the negative electrode.

A point of considerable interest is the use of inhibitors (such as α-naphthol and several other compounds of the naphthalene series), which being adsorbed on antimony, decrease its active surface and arrest the process of interaction of the antimony with the hydrogen ions. If adsorption leads to partial screening of the surface of the electrode, then equation (5.74) must be replaced by the following expression

---

*) Naturally an increase in S_{Sb}, also leading to a decrease in the value of ν, cannot be used as a means of decreasing the concentration of stibine in the gaseous mixture separating from the battery, since then a considerable increase in the rate of self-discharge of the negative electrode will occur and also a decrease in the efficiency of utilisation of the charging current.

$$\nu = \frac{A_c S_{Sb}(1-\Theta) e^{-\frac{\psi S_{Sb}(1-\theta)}{b_2}}}{1 + B_c S_{Sb}(1-\Theta)} \tag{5.93}$$

where: Θ is the degree of filling up of the surface with adsorbed particles. Equation (5.74) is a special case of (5.93) at $\Theta = 0$. According to (5.93) $\lim_{\Theta \to 0} \nu = 0$. From formula (5.93) it follows further that the relative decrease in the rate of separation of stibine, caused by the screening of the antimony, which is electro-deposited on the surface of the negative electrode, is equal to

$$\frac{\nu}{\nu_{\theta=0}} = \left[1 - \frac{\Theta}{1 + B_c S_{Sb}(1-\Theta)}\right] e^{\frac{\psi S_{Sb}\theta}{b_2}} \tag{5.94}$$

According to (5.94) the ratio $\nu/\nu_{\Theta=0}$ increases, i.e. the difference between ν and $\nu_{\Theta=0}$ decreases with an increase in the value of S_{Sb}. Therefore, it may be assumed that adsorption of organic substances, connected with the decrease in the active surface of the electrode, must lead to a decrease in the rate of separation of stibine, principally at low surface concentrations of antimony. Hence, it follows that an effective method of decreasing the rate of separation of stibine may be the simultaneous use of a corrosion-resistant anode alloy and surface-active additives which are predominantly adsorbed on antimony.

As was shown by bench tests, the use of positive grids made of lead-antimony-silver alloy in a battery, with simultaneous introduction of an α-naphthol addition, causes a substantial decrease in the concentration of SbH_3 in the gaseous mixture separating on charging.

It must be noted that the use of silver as an alloying component of the anode alloy leads to a decrease in the rate of stibine evolution even in the event of the concentration of antimony in the negative active mass not changing. With the presence of silver on the surface of the negative electrode instead of formula (5.58) we must use formula (5.59), according to which

$$\eta \approx \eta_{Pb} - \frac{RT}{\alpha F} \ln\left(S_{Sb} e^{\frac{(\eta_{Pb}-\eta_{Sb})\alpha F}{RT}} + S_{Ag} e^{\frac{(\eta_{Pb}-\eta_{Ag})\alpha F}{RT}} + 1 \right) \tag{5.95}$$

Here S_{Ag} is the surface concentration of silver, η_{Ag} is the overvoltage of hydrogen evolution on silver. For calculation of the ψ_1 potential we may use the following equation

$$\begin{aligned}\psi_1 &= \psi_1^{(Pb)}(1 - S_{Sb} - S_{Ag}) + \psi_1^{(Sb)} S_{Sb} + \psi_1^{(Ag)} S_{Ag} \\ &= \psi_1^{(Pb)} + S_{Ag}(\psi_1^{(Ag)} - \psi_1^{(Pb)}) + S_{Sb}(\psi_1^{(Sb)} - \psi_1^{(Pb)})\end{aligned} \tag{5.96}$$

Substituting (5.95) and (5.96) in equation (5.71), we have

$$\nu' = \frac{A_c' S_{Sb}\, e^{-\frac{\psi S_{Sb}}{b_2}}}{B_c' + B_c S_{Sb}} \tag{5.97}$$

where

$$A_c' = A_c \exp\left[-\frac{S_{Ag}(\psi_1^{(Ag)} - \psi_1^{(Pb)})}{b_2}\right] \tag{5.98}$$

$$B_c' = 1 + \psi_{Ag} \exp\left[\frac{(\eta_{Pb} - \eta_{Ag})\alpha F}{RT}\right] \tag{5.99}$$

According to equations (5.98) and (5.99) $A_c' < A_c$, but $B_c' > B_c$, therefore, as is shown by comparison of equations (5.74) and (5.97), $\nu' < \nu$, i.e. the electrolytic transfer of silver leads to a decrease in the rate of stibine evolution. The effect mentioned can be qualitatively evaluated, starting out from equations (5.74) and (5.97). From these equations it follows that

$$\frac{\nu}{\nu'} = \frac{A_c}{A_c'} \frac{B_c' + B_c S_{Sb}}{1 + B_c S_{Sb}} \tag{5.100}$$

Taking into account the closeness of the potentials at zero charge of lead and silver, it may be assumed as a reasonable approximation that $\psi_1^{(Pb)} \approx \psi_1^{(Ag)}$. In that case $A_c \approx A_c'$. Further $\eta_{Ag} \approx \eta_{Sb}$, i.e. $B_c' \approx 1 + B_c S_{Ag} \approx B_c S_{Ag}$ ($B_c S_{Ag} \gg 1$). Taking into account all these approximations we may write

$$\frac{\nu}{\nu'} \simeq 1 + \frac{S_{Ag}}{S_{Sb}} \tag{5.101}$$

If we use equation (5.54), then equation (5.101) takes the form

$$\frac{\nu}{\nu'} \simeq 1 + 0.74 \left(\frac{m_{Ag}}{m_{Sb}} \right)^{2/3} \tag{5.102}$$

From formula (5.102) it follows that with an increase in the concentration of silver in the negative active mass the rate of separation of stibine decreases, and with a rise in the concentration of antimony it increases. Naturally, the addition of silver to the anode alloy, leading to a rise in the value of m_{Ag} and a decrease in m_{Sb}, causes a decrease in the rate of SbH_3 evolution.

Equation (5.92), like (5.74), describes the limiting function $\nu'(S_{Sb})$. The maximum value of ν' should be observed in this case with a surface concentration of antimony in the active mass of the negative electrode equal to

$$S'_m \cong \sqrt{\frac{B'_c b_2}{B_c \psi}} \tag{5.103}$$

Since $B_c' \gg 1$, $S_m' > S_m$, i.e. the electrolytic transfer of silver should lead to a considerable shift in the maximum rate of SbH_3 evolution in the direction of the final period of use or testing of the battery.

Bibliography

Chapter 1

1) G Vinel: "Storage batteries" Gosenergoizdat 1960, 480 pp.
2) L D Belkind, A N Mokeyev and A E Tveritinov: "Yevgenii Pavlovich Tveritinov" Gosenergoizdat 1962, 119 pp.
3) E P Tveritinov: "Electric batteries" SPb 1886, 152 pp.
4) V N Chikolev: "Electric batteries" SPb 1886, 184pp.
5) "Ten years of TsAL 1925-1935". Collection of scientific research papers on Chemical sources of Current: Vol. 1 TsAL 1935, 5-16.
6) V F Fedorov: "The Soviet battery industry over 50 years". Collection of papers on Chemical sources of Current, Vol. 3 Energiya 1968, 3-10.
7) A N Mokeyev: "From the history of the Central Accumulator Laboratory (1925-1946)" ibid 11-18.
8) N S Lidorenko: "Chemical sources of current and physical energy converters" Collection - "The electro-technical industry of the USSR", Informstandart-elektro 1967, 76-92.
9) M A Dasoyan and I A Aguf: "The development of the theory of the lead acid battery in the publications of Soviet electro-chemists": Collection of papers on Chemical sources of Current, Vol. 3 Energiya 1968, 21-46.
10) M A Dasoyan: "Chemical sources of current", Energiya 1969, pp. 587.
11) M F Afanasyev and S Kh Pastushkov: "The state and perspective development of tractive batteries". Collection - Research in the field of Chemical sources of Current, Vol. 2 Publ. Saratov University 1971, 3-15.
12) S U Falc and A J Salkind: "Alkaline storage batteries" John Wiley & Sons Inc., N.Y. 1969, 656 pp.

Chapter 2

1) M A Dasoyan, I A Aguf and A I Rusin: "What's new in the lead acid battery industry" Vol. 1 Informstandartelektro 1970, 67pp.
2) P Delahay, M Pourbaix and P van Rysselberghe: "Diagram of the potential-pH for Pb and its application to the study of lead acid batteries" J. Electrochem. Soc. 1951, **98**, (2), 57-64.
3) V M Latimer: "Oxidation conditions of cells and their potentials in aqueous solutions" Foreign Literature Publishing House 1954, pp. 400.
4) V P Vasilyev and S R Glavina: "The thermodynamic character of the Pb^{2+} ion in an aqueous solution" Elektrokhimia 1971, **7**, (9), 1395.
5) P Ness: "The current state of works in the field of the positive electrode of a lead acid battery" Electrochem. Acta 1967, **12**, (2), 161-178.
6) H Bode and E Voss: "Basic lead sulphate and its formation on the electrode of a lead acid battery" Electrochem. Acta 1959, **1**, (4), 318-325.
7) A K Covington, J V Dobson and Lord Wynne-Jones: "Stoichiometric coefficients of activity and standard potential of $PbO_2/PbSO_4$ and Hg/Hg_2SO_4" Trans. Faraday Soc. 1965, **61**, (513), 2050-2056.
8) W L Marshall and E V Jones: "The second constant of dissociation of H_2SO_4 at 25-350°C determined by soluble $CaSO_4$" J. Phys. Chem. 1966, **70**, (12), 4028-4040.

9) L A Pavlyuk, B S Smolyakov and P A Kryukov: "The second constant of ionisation of H_2SO_4 in the temperature range 25-175°C" Izv. Sib. Otd. an SSSR - Seria Khimiya Akad. Nauk 1972, (3), 3-7.
10) J D Esdaile: "The PbO-$PbSO_4$ system" J. Electrochem. Soc. 1966, **113**, (1), 71-75.
11) P Rüetschi and R T Angstadt: "Anodic oxidation of Pb at constant potential" J. Electrochem. Soc. 1964, **111**, (12), 1323-1330.
12) D Pavlov: "The mechanism of anodic oxidation of Pb in H_2SO_4 solutions" Report of the Federal Society for Physical Chemistry 1967, **71**, (4), 398-404.
13) H E Wirth: "Coefficients of activity in solutions of H_2SO_4 and H_2SO_4+Na_2SO_4" Electrochem. Acta 1971, **16**, (9), 1345-1357.
14) L V Vanyukova, M M Isayeva and B N Kabanov: "Solubility and the mechanism of dissolution of quadrivalent lead" Dokl. An. SSSR 1962, **143**, (2), 377-379.
15) H W Billhardt: "New data about basic lead sulphates" J. Electrochem. Soc. 1970, **117**, (5), 690-695.
16) N N Milyutin and N N Ozhiganova: "The electro-chemical behaviour of Pb in sulphuric acid solutions" Journal of Applied Chemistry 1970, **43**, (8), 1686-1693.
17) R Robinson and R Stokes: "Electrolyte solutions" Foreign literature Publishing House 1963, 646 pp.
18) W J Hamer: "The potential of a PbO_2-$PbSO_4$ electrode at different temperatures" J. Amer. Chem. Soc. 1935, **57**, (1), 9-15.
19) W H Beck, K P Singh and W F K Wynne-Jones: "The potential of a PbO_2/$PbSO_4$ electrode" Trans. Faraday Soc. 1959, **55**, (2), 331-338.
20) S J Bone, K P Singh and W F K Wynne-Jones: "The potential and conversion of α-PbO_2" Electrochem. Acta 1961, **4**, (7-8), 288-293.
21) W L Lardner, R E Mitchell and J W Cobble: "Electrode potentials of electrodes with sulphate ions" J. Phys. Chem. 1969, **73**, (6), 2021-2024.
22) I G Kiseleva and B N Kabanov: "On the formation and electro-chemical properties of the crystalline modifications of PbO_2" Dokl. Akad. Nauk An. SSSR 1958, **122**, (6), 1042-1046.
23) R T Angstadt, C J Venuto and P Rüetschi: "Electrode potentials and thermal decomposition of α and β--PbO_2" J. Electrochem. Soc. 1962, **109**, (3), 177-184.
24) V A Kirkinsky: "Polymorphic modifications of PbO_2" Zhur. Neorg. Khim. 1965, 10, (9), 1966-1970.
25) W B White, F Dachille and R Roy: "Polymorphism of lead oxides at high pressures and temperatures" J. Amer. Ceram. Soc. 1961, **44**, (4), 170-174.
26) J Syano and S Akomoto: "Synthesis of PbO_2 of the fluorite type at high pressure" Mat. Res. Bull. 1968, **3**, (2), 153-155.
27) H S Harned and W J Hamer: "Normal electrode potentials and the electromotive force of lead acid batteries at temperature of 0-60°C" J. Amer. Chem. Soc. 1935, **57**, (1), 33-35.
28) B A Kosobryukov: "On the problem of the thermodynamics of lead acid batteries" Collection of scientific research works on Chemical sources of Current Vol. 2 TsAL 1935, 28-40.
29) B N Kabanov: "On the theory of the lead acid battery" Collection of scientific research papers on Chemical sources of Current Vol. 3 TsAL 1938, 41-57.
30) A K Lorenz: "The problem of the thermodynamics of the foundation of a theory of double sulphation" Collection of scientific research papers on Chemical sources of Current Vol. 4 TsAL 1939, 35-54.
31) D N Craig and G W Vinal: "The thermodynamic properties of H_2SO_4 solutions and their connection with the emf and the heat of reaction in lead acid batteries" J. Res. Nat. Bur. Stand. 1940, **24**, 475-490.

32) J A Dulsman and W F Giaque: "The thermodynamics of the lead acid battery. The heat capacity and entropy of PbO_2 at 15-318°K" J. Phys. Chem. 1968, **72**, (2), 562-573.
33) J Basquet, J M Blanchard and J C Remy: "Research on the purity of α and β-PbO_2 depending on the method of preparation" Bul. Soc. Chim. Fr. 1968, (8), 3206-3210.
34) P V V Rao and H V K Udupa: "Coulometric determination of oxygen in PbO_2 in an alkaline solution" Electrochem. Acta 1965, **10**, (7), 651-656.
35) J Burbank: "Anodic oxides of lead" J. Electrochem. Soc. 1959, **106**, (5), 369-376.
36) S J Bone and M Fleischmann: "Electrolytic behaviour of PbO_2" Direct Current 1961, **6**, (2), 53-55.
37) H Bode: "Chemical processes on the electrodes of galvanic sources of current" Angew. Chem. 1961, **73**, (16), 553-560.
38) A I Zaslavsky, Yu D Kondrashov and S S Tolkachev: "A new modification of PbO_2 and the texture of anode deposits" Dokl. An. Akad. Nauk SSSR 1950, 75, (4), 559-561.
39) K Vetter: "Electro-chemical kinetics" Khimiya 1967, 856 pp.
40) H J Engel: "The dissolution of oxides in dilute acids" Z. für Phys. Chem. 1956, 7, (3/4), 158-181.
41) I A Aguf: "Some problems of the thermodynamics of a PbO_2 electrode" Zh. Fiz. Khimiya 1965, **39**, (5), 1127-1134.
42) G A Kokorev, N G Bakhchisaraytsyan and V V Panteleyeva: "Research on the process of electrolytic separation of oxygen taking into account the changes in the surface of a PbO_2 anode" Works of the Mendeleyev M. Kh. T. I. 1967, **54**, 161-169.

Chapter 3

1) O S Ksenzhek: "Porous electrodes in electrolysis" Khimiya Technologiya Vol. 8 Kharkov 1967, 21-27.
2) V S Daniel-Beck: "The problem of polarisation of porous electrodes. The distribution of current and potential inside the electrode" Zhur. Fiz. Khim. 1948, **22**, (6), 693-710.
3) I A Aguf: "Some problems of the theory of the porous electrode and processes occurring in a lead acid battery" Collection of works on Chemical sources of Current Vol. 3 Energiya 1968, 87-100.
4) O S Ksenzhek: "Diffusion regime of the work of porous electrodes" Zhur. Fiz. Khimiya 1962, **36**, (2), 243-248.
5) K Micki: "The theory of porous electrodes. 1 The basis of the equation" Collection - Czechoslovok Cem. Commun. 1964, **29**, (9), 1998-2007.
6) E A Grins: "The assumptions forming the basis of theoretical models of porous electrodes" Electrochem. Acta 1970, **15**, (6), 1047-1057.
7) V A Yanchenko and I A Selitsky: "The influence of the branching of the leads of the grid on the work of the plates of a lead acid battery" Elektrotekhnika 1964, (5), 42-44.
8) A N Frumkin, V S Bagotsky, Z A Iofa and B N Kabanov: "The kinetics of electrode processes" Moscow State Univ. 1952, pp319.
9) V S Daniel-Beck: "The work of a porous electrode in the sphere of low values of polarisation" Elektrokhimiya 1965, **1**, (11), 1319-1324.
10) V S Daniel-Beck: "The influence of the resistance of the solid phase on the distribution of potential and current in the electrode" Elektrokhimiya 1966, **2**, (6), 672-677.
11) O S Ksenzhek and V V Stender: "Current distribution in a porous electrode"

Dokl. an Akad. Nauk SSSR 1956, **107**, (2), 280-283.
12) L S Sergeyeva and I A Selitsky: "Current distribution in a porous electrode of a lead acid battery" Zhur. Fiz. Khimiya 1965, **39**, (1), 204-206.
13) Yu D Dunayev, G Z Kiryakov and Z N Chernyshev: "Heterogeneity of the surface and electrode processes on a porous Pb anode" Works of the Trudy Inst. Khim. Nauk an Kazakh SSR 1962, **9**, 18-41.
14) O S Ksenzhek: "Polarisation of thin porous electrodes" Zhur. Fiz. Khimiya 1962, **36**, (3), 633-637.
15) T M Bessonovo, N V Bolshakova and P B Zhivotinsky: "Changes in the structure of porous plates of a lead acid battery in operation" Collection of papers on Chemical sources of Current Vol. 6 Energiya 1971, 28-34.
16) I A Aguf: "The distribution of polarisation along the thickness of a porous electrode" Elektrotekhnika 1968, (11), 38-39.
17) G M Shepherd: "An equation characterising the discharge of a battery" J. Electrochem. Soc. 1965, **112**, (7), 657-664.
18) A Winzel: "Current distribution in porous electrodes" J. Electrochem. Soc. 1962, **66**, (4), 287-304.
19) I A Selitsky and V S Yanchenko: "Limit values of potential and current density in the depth of a porous electrode" Elektrokhimiya 1965, **1**, (6), 701-702.
20) I A Aguf: "The distribution of potential along the thickness of the negative elctrode of a lead acid battery in the presence of surface-active additives" Collection of works on Chemical sources of Current Vol. 5 Energiya 1970, 17-20.
21) I A Aguf: "The influence of surface-active additives on the distribution of polarisation along the thickness of a porous electrode" Elektrotekhnika 1971, (2), 55-56.
22) M I Yershova, I I Astakhov and B N Kabanov: "The influence of surface-active substances on the structure of the passivating layer of $PbSO_4$" Elektrokhimiya 1966, **2**, (11), 1327-1330.
23) V A Yanchenko and I A Selitsky: "The dependence of the capacity of negative plates of a lead acid battery on thickness and current density" Elektrotekhnika 1968, (9), 49.
24) R C Alkire, E A Grens and C M Tobias: "The theory of porous electrodes suffering structural changes at anode polarisation in a solution" J. Electrochem. Soc. 1969, **116**, (10), 1328-1333.
25) L S Greenberg: "Determination of the capacity of batteries by the initial currents of the discharge graph" Collection of works on Chemical sources of Current Vol. 1 Energiya 1966, 222-226.
26) B V Belyayev: "Discharges of chemical sources of current at constant current strength" Elektrotekhnika 1968, (3), 35-38.
27) M I Gillibrand and G R Lomax: "Discharge characteristics of plates of a lead acid battery" Electrochem. Acta 1963, **8**, (9), 693-702.
28) I A Selitsky: "The influence of polarisation of internal resistance on the discharge tension of a lead acid battery" Proceedings of the Conference on electro-chemistry Academy of Sciences of the USSR 1953, 558-564.
29) S B Greene and N D Greene: "Theoretical analysis of the electro-chemical system of energy conversion" Electrochem. Technology 1963, **1**, (9-10), 276-282.
30) F Dolezalek: "The theory of the lead acid battery" ONTI 1934, 155.
31) P E Baikie, M I Gillibrand and K Peters: "The influence of temperature and current density on the capacity of plates of a lead acid battery" Electrochem. Acta 1972, **17**, (5), 839-844.
32) I A Selitsky: "The role of diffusion of acid in the work of a lead acid battery" Collection of works on batteries TsBTI Elektropr. 1958, 78-82.
33) H K Lening: "A mathematical description of the electro-chemical processes

in a lead acid battery" ETZ **9**, (2), 62-66.
34) C M Shepherd: "Calculation of galvanic cells and batteries. 1 The influence of polarisation and resistance on the characteristics of the cells" J. Electrochem. Soc. 1965, **112**, (3), 252-257.
35) V V Berend and V E Dmitrenko: "General laws of current distribution in electrodes of sources of current" Elektrotekhnika 1965, (2), 59-60.
36) V N Kosholkin and O S Ksenzhek: "Current distribution in batteries" Collection - Research in the field of chemical sources of current. Saratov University 1971, 43-47.
37) K J Euler and L Horn: "Current distribution along tubular elements of battery plates" Archiv. Electrotechn. 1965, **50**, (2), 85-90.
38) K J Euler: "Changes in current distribution in porous positive electrodes of batteries in the process of charge and discharge" Electrochem. Acta 1968, **13**, (7), 1533-1549.
39) H Bode and J Euler: "Automatic radiographic investigation of current distribution in the plates of a lead acid battery" Electrochem. Acta 1966, **11**, (9), 1211-1230.
40) H Bode, H Panesar and E Voss: "The use of the mass and current distribution in a porous PbO_2 electrode" Chem. Eng. Techn. 1969, **41**, (15), 878-879.
41) H Haebler, H Panesar and E Voss: "Electrolyte current and the use of the mass of a porous PbO_2 electrode" Electrochem. Acta 1970, **15**, (8), 1421-1425.
42) D Simonsson: "Current distribution in a porous PbO_2 electrode" J. Electrochem. Soc. 1973, **120**, (2), 151-157.

Chapter 4

1) A I Zaslavsky, Yu D Kondrashov and S S Tolkachev: "A new modification of PbO_2 and the texture of anode deposits" Dokl. Akad. Nauk an SSSR 1950, **75**, (4), 559-561.
2) A I Zaslavsky and S S Tolkachev: "The structure of α-PbO_2" Zh. Fiz. Khimiya 1952, **26**, (5), 743-752.
3) S S Tolkachev: "Lead oxides and their structure from the point of view of the theory of density of packing" Dissertation abstract Leningard State University 1958, 8.
4) I A Aguf: "Polymorphism of PbO_2 and its influence on the work of a lead acid battery" Elecktrotekhn. Prom. 1963, (2), 48-53.
5) H Bode and E Voss: "On the modifications of PbO_2 in a lead acid battery" Z. für Electrochem. 1956, **60**, (9/10), 1053-1056.
6) S J Bone and M Fleischmann: "Electrolytic behaviour of PbO_2" Direct Current 1961, **6**, (2), 53-55.
7) I G Kiseleva and B N Kabanov: "The formation and electro-chemical properties of crystalline modifications of PbO_2" Dokl. Akad. Nauk an SSSR 1958, **122**, (6), 1042-1045.
8) I I Astakhov, I G Kiseleva and B N Kabanov: "Polymorphism of lead dioxide and the formation of electrolytic deposits" Dokl. Akad. Nauk an SSSR 1959, **126**, (5), 1041-1043.
9) W Vietknecht: "Anode passivation and depassivation of Pb in H_2SO_4" Zh. Electrochem. 1958, **61**, (5-7), 795-803.
10) E A Dzhafarov: "Electrodeposition, properties and use of lead dioxide" Baku: Academy of Sciences of Azerbeigan SSR 1967, 102.
11) J Shibasaki: "The mechanical properties of electrodeposited lead dioxide" J. Chem. Soc. Jap. 1954, **57**, 611-613.
12) V H Dodson: "Some data on the composition of the positive active mass in a

lead acid battery" J. Electrochem. Soc. 1961, **108**, (5), 401-406.
13) N N Federova, I I Aguf, L M Levinzon and M A Dasoyan: "X-ray phase analysis of modifications of PbO_2" Zav. Labor. 1964, **30**, (6), 727-728.
14) N N Fedorova, I I Aguf, L M Levinson and M A Dasoyan: "Quantitative phase analysis of PbO_2 by the X-rav method" Collection of works on Chemical sources of Current Vol. 1 Energiya 1966, 252-259.
15) D Kordes: "Research on the positive active mass of a lead acid battery by the X-ray method" Chem. Ing. Techn. 1966, **38**, (6), 638-642.
16) W Fischer and H Rickert: "Thermodynamic research on a PbO_2 electrode" Bersch. Bungsengesellschaft - Phys. Chemische 1973, **77**, (10-11), 975-979.
17) U B Thomas: "The electrical conductivity of PbO_2" Trans. Electrochem. Soc. 1948, **94**, (2), 42-49.
18) A V Pamfilov, E G Ivancheva and P V Dragomiretsky: "Electrical properties of lead oxides" Zh. Fiz. Khimiya 1967, **41**, (5).
19) F Lappe: "Some physical properties of sprayed films of PbO_2" J. Phys. & Chem. Solids 1962, **23**, (11), 1563-1566.
20) W Mindt: "Electrical conductivity of electro-deposited films of PbO_2" J. Electrochem. Soc. 1968, **115**, (8), 227.
21) E K Cshe and I L Rosenfeld: "A new method of investigating surface oxides" Elektrokhimiya 1968, **4**, (10), 1200-1203.
22) I A Aguf, A I Rusin and M A Dasoyan: "The electrical conductivity of the crystalline modifications of PbO_2" Collection - The protection of metals and oxide coatings, the corrosion of metals and research in the field of electrochemistry, Nauka 1966, 328-333.
23) V S Yanchenko and I A Selitsky: "The influence of branching of leads of the grid on the work of the plates of a lead acid battery" Elektrotekhnika 1964, (5), 42-44.
24) M Yu Balshin: "Powder metallurgy" Metallurgizdat 1948, 332.
25) M Fleischmann and N Thirsk: "Research into electro-chemical kinetics at constant overvoltage; the behaviour of an electrode made of PbO_2" Trans. Faraday Soc. 1955, **51**, (1), 71-95.
26) B N Kabanov, I G Kiseleva and D I Leykis: "Determination of the zero charge potential on electrodes made of PbO_2" Report of the Academy of Sciences of the USSR 1954, **99**, (5), 805-808.
27) I G Kiseleva and B N Kabanov: "Adsorption of sulphuric acid on an electrode made of PbO_2" Dokl. Akad. Nauk an SSSR 1956, **108**, (5), 864-867.
28) B N Kabanov: "The mechanism of separation of O_2 on oxide electrodes" Proceedings of four conferences on electro-chemistry" Academy of Sciences of the USSR 1959, 252-256.
29) P Rüetschi, R T Angstadt and B D Cahan: "Oxygen overvoltage and the electrode potential of α and β-PbO_2" J. Electrochem. Soc. 1959, **106**, (7), 547-551.
30) A C Makrides: "The electro-chemistry of surface oxides" J. Electrochem. Soc. 1966, **113**, (11), 1158-1165.
31) D I Leykis and E K Venström: "Determination of zeta charge potential of electrodes of PbO_2" Dokl. Akad. Nauk an SSSR 1957, **112**, (1), 97-99.
32) I A Aguf and L M Levinson: "The positive electrode of a lead acid battery" VNIIEM 1965, 20pp.
33) P Rüetschi and P Delahaye: "The influence of the electrode material on the overvoltage of oxygen" J. Chem. Phys. 1955, **23**, (3), 556-560.
34) I A Aguf: "Some electrode properties of the tetragonal modification of PbO_2" Zh. Prikl. Khimiya 1970, **43**, (9), 1993-1999.
35) I A Aguf and M A Dasoyan: "Research into the electro-chemical properties of PbO_2" Collection of works on Chemical sources of Current Vol. 4

Energiya 1969, 93-107.
36) B B Damaskin: "The principles of current methods of studying electro-chemical reactions" Moscow State University 1965, 104pp.
37) G A Kokorev, N G Bakhchisaraytsyan, A N Smirnov and G I Medvedyev: "Interpretation of the results of impedance measurements of a lead dioxide electrode in H_2SO_4 solutions" Works of the Mendeleyev MKhTI 1967, **54**, 160-176.
38) G A Kokorev, N G Bakhchisaraytsyan and G I Medyedyev: "Research into the electro-chemical behaviour of PbO_2 by the alternating current method" Proc. of the 2nd All-Union Conference on Catalytic Reactions in the Liquid Phase, Alma-Ata Nauka 1967, 406-408.
39) N P Gnusin: "A new method of measuring polarisation capacity and resistance of the double layer" Zh. Fiz. Khimiya 1958, **32**, (3), 689-691.
40) N P Gnusin and A G Fomin: "The graph method of calculating the parameters of the impedance of the double layer by the frequency characteristics of its modulus" Siberian Sect. of Academy of Sciences of the USSR, Series of Chemical Sciences 1965, (3), Vol. 1 120-123.
41) I A Aguf: "The exchange current of equilibrium on a lead dioxide electrode" Elektrokhimiya 1968, **4**, (9), 1130-1132.
42) A P Okatov: "Chemical sources of current" Goskhimizdat 1948, 346pp.
43) L I Antropov: "Theoretical electro-chemistry" Visch. Skola 1969, 510pp.
44) S J Bone, M Fleischmann and W F K Wynne-Jones: "Exchange of β-PbO_2 with lead ions in the solution" Trans. Faraday Soc. 1959, **55**, (10), 1783-1791.
45) I V Vanyukova, M M Isayeva and B N Kabanov: "Solubility and the mechanism of dissolution of quadrivalent lead" Dokl. Akad. Nauk an SSSR 1962, **143**, (2), 377-379.
46) Yu D Dunayev, G Z Kiryakov and Z N Chernysheva: "Heterogeneity of the surface and the electrode processes on a porous lead anode" Trudy Inst. Khim. Akad. Nauk an Kazakh SSR 1962, **9**, 18-41.
47) N A Hampson, P C Jones and R F Phillips: "Electro-chemical reactions on a PbO_2 electrode" Canadian J. Chem. 1969, **47**, (12), 2171-2179.
48) K Thomson: "The mechanism of the reactions in a lead acid battery" Trans. Electrochem. Soc. 1939, **75**, (21), 253-255.
49) H Bode and E Voss: "Phosphate of quadrivalent lead; a contribution to the study of the reactions on a PbO_2 electrode" Electrochimia Acta 1962, **6**, (1/4), 11-16.
50) S Ikary and S Ioshizawa: "Thermal decomposition and electrode behaviour of PbO_2" J. Electrochem. Soc. (Japan) 1960, **28**, (7-9), 138-141.
51) S Ikary and S Ioshizawa: "A study of the positive active mass of a lead acid battery" J. Electrochem. Soc. (Japan) **29**, (3), 186-189.
52) A B Gansi: "Electro-deposition of PbO_2 from alkaline solutions" J. Electrochem. Soc. 1969, **116**, (11), 1496-1499.
53) B N Kabanov: "The electro-chemistry of metals and adsorption" Nauka 1966, 222pp.
54) L I Lyamina, N I Korolkova and K M Gorbunova: "Electro-crystallisation of Pb in the process of reduction of solid oxide" Electrochem. Acta 1970, **15**, (10), 1597-1608.
55) L I Lyamina, N I Korolkova and K M Gorbunova: "Cathodic reduction of PbO_2" Elektrokhimiya 1972, **8**, (5), 651-654.
56) D Bokris: "The kinetics of electrode processes" Collection - 'Some problems of current electro-chemistry' Foreign literature publishing house 1958, 209-321.
57) G V Malinin and Yu M Tolmachev: "Some peculiarities of the kinetics of

thermal decomposition of PbO_2 and Pb_3O_4" Zh. Neorg. Khimiya 1969, **14**, (11), 2889-3903.
58) H B Mark: "Discharge characteristics of α-PbO_2 in dilute H_2SO_4" J. Electrochem. Soc. 1962, **109**, (7), 634-638.
59) A I Rusin, M A Dasoyan and N V Merzlikina: "The problem of cathode passivation of α and β-PbO_2 in sulphuric acid" Collection - Research in the field of chemical sources of current, Novocherkassk 1966, 176-178.
60) P D Lukovtsev: "The role of protons in electro-chemical conversions of oxides" Elektrokhimiya 1968, **4**, (4), 379-383.
61) E Voss and J Freundlich: "Discharge capacities of α and β-PbO_2" in Batteries Pergamon Press, N.Y. (USA) 1963, 73-87.
62) P Rüetschi, J Sklarchuk and R T Angstadt: "Resistance and reactivity of PbO_2" Electrochem. Acta 1963, **8**, (5), 333-343.
63) S Ikari and S Ioshizawa: "Research on the behaviour of the anode material in a lead acid battery" J. Electrochem. Soc. (Japan) 1959, **27**, (10-12), 247-249.
64) B N Kabanov, D I Leykis and E I Krepanova: "The mechanism of cathode passivation of an electrode made of PbO_2" Dokl. Akad. Nauk an SSSR 1954, **98**, (6), 989-992.
65) E I Krepanova and B N Kabanov: "Research into the reasons causing deterioration of the active mass of positive plates of a lead acid battery" Collection of works on batteries TsBTI Elektropr. 1958, 58-64.
66) J F Dittman and G R Garner: "Barium sulphate as a deleterious admixture to the positive active mass" J. Electrochem. Soc. 1954, **101**, (11), 533-535.
67) V P Mashovets: "The testing of experimental samples of batteries with grids made of alloys containing admixtures" Zh. Prikl. Khimiya 1959, **31**, (9), 1355-1360.
68) U B Thomas, F F Forster and H E Haring: "Corrosion and deformation of the grid of storage batteries of Pb-Ca alloy depending on the Ca content" Trans. Electrochem. Soc. 1947, **97**, 313-317.
69) J Burbank: "The morphology of PbO_2 in positive plates of a lead acid battery" J. Electrochem. Soc. 1964, **111**, (7), 765-768.
70) N E Bogshaw and K P Wilson: "Microscopic study of the active materials of a lead acid battery" Electrochem. Acta 1965, **10**, (8), 867-873.
71) J Burbank: "Anodic oxidation of basic lead sulphates" J. Electrochem. Soc. 1966, **113**, (1), 10-14.
72) A C Simon: "Factors influencing the reduction of the active mass of the positive electrode of a lead acid battery" Batteries, Vol. 2, Pergamon Press, N. Y. (USA) 1965, 63-80.
73) S Tudor, A Weisstuch and S H Davant: "Batteries with lead-calcium grids and H_3PO_4 additive" Electrochemical Technology 1966, **4**, (7-8), 406-411.
74) N A Balashova, B N Kabanov and L D Kovba: "Transfer of lead in the positive electrode of a lead acid battery" Zh. Prikl. Khim. 1964, **37**, (4), 906-908.
75) N G Bakhchisaraytsyan, V A Oshchinsky, A A Grebenkina, E M Vasilyeva and D D Semenov: "An investigation of anode stability of electro-deposited PbO_2" Proceedings of the Mendeleyev MKhTI 1967, **54**, 149-156.
76) J J Lander: "Self-discharge of the positive electrode in a lead acid battery" J. Electrochem. Soc. 1952, **99**, (9), 339-342.
77) P Rüetschi and R T Angstadt: "Self-discharge reactions in a lead acid battery" J. Electrochem. Soc. 1958, **105**, (10), 555-563.
78) E V Krivolapova, E S Weissberg and B N Kabanov: "An investigation of a PbO_2 electrode by potential drop and separation on O_2" Proceedings of the 4th Conference on Electrochemistry, Academy of Sciences of the USSR 1959, 757-761.
79) S M Caudler, J S Murday and A C Simon: "Loss of hydrogen - the reason for

a lead acid battery becoming unserviceable" J. Electrochem. Soc. 1973, **120**, (11), 1515-1516.
80) E J Ritchie and J Burbank: "Cycling and overcharging of a battery with grids of pure and antimonal lead" J. Electrochem. Soc. 1970, **117**, (3), 299-305.
81) L I Antropov, S Ya Popov, T I Pochekayeva and N I Ramenskaya: "The influence of $CoSO_4$ on the work of a lead acid battery" Proceedings of the Conference on Electro-chemistry. Academy of Sciences of the USSR 1953, 549-557.
82) E V Krivolapova and B N Kabanov: "The influence of the addition of cobalt salt, temperature and other factors on the service life of the positive electrode of a lead acid battery: ibid. pp. 539-548.
83) J J Lander: "Silver, cobalt and the corrosion of the grid of a positive plate of a lead acid battery" J. Electrochem. Soc. 1958, **105**, (6), 289-292.
84) M A Dasoyan and I A Aguf: "The lead acid battery" TsINTIElektropr. 1960, 68pp.
85) J P Carr and N A Hampson: "Impedance of the PbO_2 on the work of the positive electrode of a lead acid battery" Cand. dissertation paper, Lensoviet LTI 1965, 14pp.
86) J P Carr and N A Hampson: "Impedance of the PbO_2/aqueous electrolyte interface; phosphate electrolytes" J. Electro-anal. Chem. 1970, 28, (1), 65-70.
87) A I Aguf: "The influence of phosphate ions on some electro-chemical properties of a PbO_2 electrode" Zh. Prikl. Khimiya 1972, **45**, (5), 984-988.
88) I I Koval and V I Barilenko: "The mechanism of the loss of working capacity of the active mass of the positive electrode of a lead acid battery" Proceedings of the 4th Conference on Electro-chemistry. Academy of Sciences of the USSR 1959, 748-756.
89) A F Nikolayev: "Synthetic polymers and plastics on which they are based" M-L Khimiya 1966, 768pp.
90) G Z Kiryakov: "Electrode processes in sulphuric acid solutions of zinc" Nauka, Alma-Ata 1964, 188pp.
91) J P Hoare: "The electrochemistry of oxygen" Interscience Publishers, New York (USA) 1968, 423pp.
92) I I Astakhov, E S Weissberg and B N Kabanov: "Anode corrosion of lead in sulphuric acid" Dokl. Akad. Nauk an SSSR 1964, **154**, (6), 1414-1416.
93) N F Razina, M T Kozlovsky and V V Stender: "The deterioration of lead anodes in electrolysis" Dokl. Akad. Nauk an SSSR 1956, **111**, (2), 404-406.
94) S O Izidinov: "Corrosion of the lead anode in H_2SO_4 at low temperatures" Zaschita Metallov 1968, **4**, (4), 456-458.
95) S O Izidinov and E Kh Rahmatulline: "The kinetics of electro-chemical processes of oxidation on a PbO_2 anode in sulphuric acid at low temperatures" Elektrokhimiya 1968, 4, (6), 647-655.
96) J J Lander: "Anode corrosion of lead in H_2SO_4 solutions" J. Electrochem. Soc. 1951, 97, (5), 213-219.
97) J J Lander: "New research into anode corrosion of lead in H_2SO_4 solutions" J. Electrochem. Soc. 1956, **103**, (1), 1-8.
98) I A Aguf and M A Dasoyan: "The influence of H_2SO_4 concentration on anode corrosion of lead and some of its alloys" Vestn. Elektropr. 1958, (11), 36-39.
99) J Burbank: "Anodic oxides of lead" J. Electrochem. Soc. 1959, **106**, (5), 369-376.
100) P Rüetschi and R T Angstadt: "Anodic oxidation of lead at constant potential" J. Electrochem. Soc. 1964, **111**, (12), 1323-1330.
101) D Pavlov: "The process of formation of oxide compounds of bivalent lead at anode oxidation in H_2SO_4" Electrochem. Soc. 1968, **13**, (10), 2051-2061.
102) P Rüetschi and B D Cahan: Discussion on Burbank's article "Anodic oxides of lead" J. Electrochem. Soc. 1959, **106**, (12), 1079-1081.

103) M A Dasoyan: "The influence of the structure of lead on the corrosion of it in sulphuric acid" Dokl. Akad. Nauk an SSSR 1956, **107**, (6), 863-866.
104) M A Dasoyan: "The use of low-quality lead and antimony in acid batteries" Zh. Prikl. Khimiya 1956, **29**, (12), 1827-1843.
105) S A Saltykov: "Stereometric metallography" Metallurgiya 1970, 375pp.
106) M A Dasoyan, G N Gordyakova, V S Smolkova and L A Valkova: "Dispersion hardening of lead-antimony alloy compounded with arsenic" Collection of papers on Chemical sources of Current Vol. 3 Energiya 1968, 136-141.
107) M A Dasoyan, G N Gordyakova and A Z Lyandres: "The influence of different factors on the quality of grids cast from arsenical alloy" Collection of papers on Chemical sources of Current Vol. 5 Energiya 1970, 11-16.
108) M A Dasoyan, G N Gordyakova, M L Ratner, G V Krivchenko and E I Smushkovich: "Corrosion-resistant alloys for lead acid batteries" Collection of papers on Chemical sources of Current Vol. 6 Energiya 1971, 3-9.
109) G W Mao and J G Larsen: "The influence of arsenic on the character of Pb-Sb alloy" Metallurgizdat 1968, **78**, (470), 236-245.
110) C G Fink and A J Dornblatt: "The influence of silver in battery grids" Trans. Electrochem. Soc. 1941, **79**, 269-305.
111) V P Mashovets and A Z Landres: "The influence of the additions to a Pb-Sb alloy on the work of the grids of lead acid batteries" Zh. Prikl. Khimiya 1948, **21**, (4), 347-361.
112) I A Aguf and M A Dasoyan: "The influence of silver on anode corrosion of Pb and Pb-Sb alloys in H_2SO_4" Vestn. Electropr. 1959, **10**, 62-67.
113) I A Aguf: "An investigation of the possibility of using some corrosion-resistant alloys with a lead base for the grids of the positive electrode of a lead acid battery, Cand. dissert. paper LTI 18pp.
114) D Pavlov, M Boton and M Stoyanova: "Anode corrosion of a Pb-Sb alloy with the addition of silver" Izv. Inst. Fiz. Khim. Bulgarian Akad. Nauk 1965, **5**, 55-59.
115) I A Aguf and M A Dasoyan: "Overvoltage of oxygen on anodically-oxidized lead some of its alloys in a concentrated solution of H_2SO_4" Collection - Technology of the Battery Industry TsINTI Electropr. 1960, 50-55.
116) J J Lander: "Silver, cobalt and the corrosion of the positive plates of a lead acid battery" J. Electrochem. Soc. 1958, 105, (6), 289-292.
117) G W Mao and P Rao: "The mechanism of the inhibition of the effect of the addition of silver on anode corrosion of the alloy Pb+4.5% Sb" Brit. Corr. J. 1971, **6**, (5), 122-128.
118) Yu D Dunayev, V G Bundzhe, L A Tskhe and G Z Kiryakov: "Methods of obtaining lead alloys compounded with cobalt and their anode properties" Trudy Inst. Organich. Kalaliza Electrokhimiya 1971, **2**, 84-97.
119) D Pavlov and T Rogatschev: "The influence of Ag and Tl on anode corrosion of lead alloys in H_2SO_4" Werkstoffe und Korr. 1968, **19**, (8), 677-679.
120) L M Levinzon, I A Aguf and M A Dasoyan: "An investigation of anode corrosion of lead alloys" Collection of papers on Chemical sources of Current Vol. 2 Energiya 1967, 11-20.
121) G Z Kiryakov and I A Korchmarek: "The role of the film of PbO_2 in the corrosion of a lead anode" Zh. Prikl. Khimiya 1953, **26**, (9), 921-924.
122) L M Levinzon, I A Aguf and M A Dasoyan: "A study of some characteristics of anode films forming on lead alloys" Collection of works on Chemical sources of Current Vol. 2 Energiya 1967, 21-27.
123) S S Popova and A F Fortunatov: "The anode behaviour of lead in alkaline solutions" Part 1 Elektrokhimiya 1966, 2, (4), 446-451.
124) D Pavlov, C N Paulleff, E Klaja and N Jordanov: "Dependence of the composition

of the anode layer on the oxidation of Pb in H_2SC_4 " J. Electrochem. Soc. 1969, **116**, (3), 316-319.
125) L M Levinzon, I A Aguf and M A Dasoyan: "Phase composition of the product of anode corrosion of lead and its alloys" Zh. Prikl. Khimiya 1966, **39**, (3), 556-561.
126) I A Aguf: "The thermodynamic stability of anodic films forming on the surface of lead and its alloys" Collection of works on Chemical sources of Current, Vol. 2 Energiya 1967, 5-10.
127) H Göhr: Two-phase coatings on metal electrodes" Electrochem. Acta 1965, **10**, (8), 747-760.
128) K Eckler: "The behaviour of a lead electrode in sulphuric acid" Canad. J. Chem. 1964, **42**, (66), 1355-1364.
129) R W Ose: "Oscillographic investigation of the formation of $PbO \cdot PbSO_4$ - an intermediate product in the system $Pb/PbSO_4/PbO_2$" Werstoffe und Korr. 1960, **11**, (4), 220-224.
130) P Rüetschi and B D Cahan: "Electro-chemical properties of PbO_2 and anode corrosion of lead and lead alloys" J. Electrochem. Soc. 1958, **105**, (7), 269-277.
131) J Burbank: "Anodic polarisation of lead in H_2SO_4" J. Electrochem. Soc. 1956, **103**, (2), 87-91.
132) E S Weissberg, E V Krivolapova and B N Kabanov: "An investigation of the influence of antimony on the character of the passivation of lead in sulphuric acid solutions" Zh. Prikl. Khimiya 1959, **32**, (10), 2354-2357.
133) L N Larikov: "The influence of alloying elements on the hardening of lead alloys" Collection - Questions of the physics of metals and of metallurgy, Academy of Sciences of the USSR, Kiev 1957, 128-144.
134) J J Lander: "The influence of corrosion and of growth of the grids on the service life of positive plates of a lead acid battery" J. Electrochem. Soc. 1952, **99**, (11), 467-473.
135) I A Aguf and L M Levinzon: "The theory of corrosion deformation of battery grids" Zaschita Metallov 1965, **1**, (5), 590-593.
136) I A Aguf and L M Levinzon: "Corrosion deformation of lead in the process of anodic polarisation" Zaschita Metallov 1966, **2**, (5), 592-594.
137) S P Timoshenko and S Voynovsky-Kriger: "Plates and jackets" Fizmatgiz 1963, 635pp.
138) P W Bridgman: "The influence of pressure on binary alloys" Acad. Arts and Sci. 1954, **83**, (5), 149-190.
139) M A Dasoyan, I A Aguf and A I Rusin: "Anode processes in a lead acid battery" Collection of works on Chemical sources of Current, Vol. 3, Energiya 1968, 47-86.
140) N K Mikhailova, I A Aguf and M A Dasoyan: "The influence of static load on the corrosion of anodes of lead and its alloys" Zaschita Metallov 1972, **8**, (4), 466-469.
141) F Garafalo: "The laws of creep and long-term strength of metals: Metallurgiya 1968, 304pp.
142) N K Mikhailova, I A Aguf and M A Dasoyan: "Investigations of the deformation of anode films on lead and its alloys by the potentiometric and impedance methods" Proceedings of the All-Union Conference on Electro-chemistry LTI 1971, 159-160.
143) N K Mikhailova, I A Aguf and M A Dasoyan: "An investigation of cathodic reduction of oxide films on lead and some of its alloys" Elektrokhimiya 1973, **9**, (4), 439-442.